Flowering Plants of Amazonian Ecuador - a checklist

S. S. Renner, H. Balslev & L. B. Holm-Nielsen

AAU REPORTS 24

Botanical Institute Aarhus University 1990
this issue in collaboration with
Pontificia Universidad Católica del Ecuador, Quito

Contents

Acknowledgments

Much of the background work for this checklist has been carried out as part of the long-standing collaboration between the Departamento de Ciencias Biológicas of the Pontificia Universidad Católica del Ecuador (PUCE) and the Botanical Institute of Aarhus University. We are especially indebted to the directors of this department, Dra. Laura Arcos Terán, Dr. Tjitte de Vries, and Dr. Fernando Ortiz Crespo, who constantly supported the research and training activities that made it possible for us to gather the information about the Ecuadorean flora essential for the production of this publication. We also thank Dra. Eugenia del Pino for supporting the establishment of the herbarium in Quito and for continued encouragement of its botanical activities. We are most grateful for the help we received from friends and colleagues at the herbarium at PUCE (Herbario QCA).

Those who identified material of various plant families or made changes and additions to the taxonomy are listed in Table 1 as well as under the family headings in the checklist. Thanks are due to the curators of the herbaria of Göteborg, Stockholm, the Marie Selby Botanical Gardens, the Pontifícia Universidad Católica, the Field Museum of Natural History, The New York Botanical Garden, the U.S. National Herbarium, and the Missouri Botanical Garden. Special thanks are due to David Neill who already in mid-1988 provided a computer print-out listing the collections made by him and his collaborators.

Financial support for the preparation of this checklist came from the Danish Natural Science Research Council. The collaboration between P. Universidad Católica and Aarhus University has been generously supported by DANIDA. A Visiting Scientist position at the Marie Selby Botanical Gardens provided the first author the opportunity to revise part of this checklist.

Authors

Susanne Sabine Renner. Born 1954. Master's degree 1980 and Doctorate in biology 1982 at Hamburg University. 1984–1987 Postdoctoral Fellow at the Smithsonian Institution, Washington D.C., USA. Since 1987 associate professor, Botanical Institute, Aarhus University, Nordlandsvej 68, DK-8240 Risskov, Denmark.

Henrik Balslev. Born 1951. Cand. scient. Aarhus University 1978. Ph.D. City University of New York and New York Botanical Garden 1982. 1981–1984 director of the Herbario QCA, PUCE, Quito. Since 1984 associate professor and curator of the herbarium, Botanical Institute, Aarhus University, Bygn. 137, Universitetsparken, DK-8000 Aarhus C., Denmark.

Lauritz B. Holm-Nielsen. Born 1946. Mag. scient. Aarhus University 1971. 1971–1989 associate professor at the Botanical Institute, Aarhus University. 1976–1979 Dean of the Faculty of Sciences, Aarhus University. 1979-1981 director of the Herbario QCA, PUCE, Quito. Since 1989 Rector of the Danish Research Academy, Palludan Müllersvej 17, DK-8000 Aarhus C., Denmark.

Flowering Plants of Amazonian Ecuador

Renner, Balslev & Holm-Nielsen

1. INTRODUCTION

Like other parts of the Amazon region, Amazonian Ecuador has great natural resources, including petroleum reserves and a flora rich in species. This natural wealth is currently threatened; the population of the area is increasing, mainly due to immigration from Andean and coastal Ecuador, and the changes experienced in the Amazon Basin over recent years, rather than fostering economic growth, have accelerated environmental degradation. Much of the rain forest of Amazonian Ecuador grows on poor soils with easily depleted nutritional supplies that cannot for long withstand careless land use. Soil compaction, destruction of the nutrient cycle, flooding and erosion, once started, may form a vicious circle. To achieve a viable and sustainable productivity from such land requires extremely careful resource management.

The biological diversity, especially the richness in plant species of Amazonian Ecuador in our opinion constitutes its most important resource. For example, in the United States about 25% of all prescriptions dispensed from pharmacies in 1980 contained plant extracts or active principles prepared from higher plants (Marles *et al.*, 1988), and wild genetic resources are of growing importance in plant breeding. In both respects, the Amazonian lowland flora is almost untapped. Reducing the biological diversity and thereby eroding the genetic base for future plant breeding may actually diminish the region's long-term economic viability.

This checklist of flowering plants is intended as a step towards the assessment of the biological diversity of Amazonian Ecuador. We hope it will be useful not only for botanists and others working on, for example, floristic inventories, but also for those concerned with land use planning. Over the last ten years taxonomic work has been stimulated by flora projects encompassing eastern Ecuador and neighboring regions, such as the *Flora of Ecuador*, the *Flora Neotropica*, the *Flora de Colombia*, and the *Flora of Peru*; in addition, several vegetation-analytical studies have been carried out. We therefore feel that, although our knowledge of the vegetation is still very far from complete, an overview of the plant cover of Amazonian Ecuador can now be attempted.

2. DESCRIPTION OF THE REGION

Geography

Ecuador spans the equator from 1°30' N to 5° S latitude. It is traversed by the Andean cordilleras, dividing the country into three natural regions: the coastal plain, the "Sierra," and the eastern Amazonian lowlands. The latter are locally called *Oriente* and form a flat terrain comprising most of the provinces Sucumbíos[1], Napo, Pastaza, and Morona-Santiago. They comprise an area of around 71,000 square km below 600 meters elevation (Fig. 1). The belt between 600 and 900 m is the natural distributional limit of many flowering plant species, which tend to be confined either to the montane forest above this zone or to the lowland forest below. Fluvial transport stops at about 300 m altitude.

To the north, Amazonian Ecuador is limited by the border with Colombia. To the west, the 600 m elevation line forms a winding but generally north/south oriented border. To the south and east, the area covered by this checklist is limited by the Línea del Protocolo de Rio de Janeiro of 1942, which Peru claims as its border with Ecuador, a claim Ecuador disputes.

Climate

The climate in Amazonian Ecuador is perpetually wet with an annual precipitation between 2500 mm and 6000 mm, the parts receiving most rain being those closest to the Andean foothills. The precipitation is distributed evenly throughout the year, with no month receiving less than 100 mm rain on average. May through July are the wettest months and December through February are the least wet months. Clouds are abundant, but hours of clear sky are frequent and cause rather abrupt changes in the temperature and relative humidity immediately above the canopy. In the Amazonian plain away from the Andean foot hills

---

[1]In January 1989, the Province of Napo was subdivided, with the southern portion retaining the name Napo. The northern part, comprising the Cantones Gonzalo Pizarro, Lago Agrio, Shushufindi, Putumayo, and Sucumbíos, now forms the Province Sucumbíos, with Lago Agrio as its capital. Most of this checklist was prepared before that change, and all references to Napo refer to the province in its former boundaries.

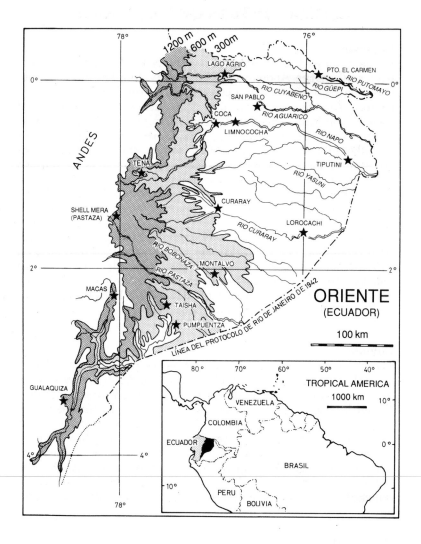

Figure 1. Map of tropical America indicating the position of the area covered by the present checklist. Amazonian Ecuador is bordered by Colombia to the north and by the Andean cordillera to the west. The eastern and southern limits of the study area is the Línea del protocolo de Rio de Janeiro de 1942. Towns are indicated by stars. The shaded areas are the altitudinal zones between 300–600 m and 600–1200 m, respectively.

the average yearly temperature is about 25°C; for example, in Tiputini at 219 m altitude it is 25.2°C. On the Andean foot hills the temperature decreases; thus, Tena at 665 m altitude has a mean temperature of 23.4°C and Pastaza at 1036 m has an average temperature of 20.3°C. Precipitation, on the other hand, increases in the foot hills: whereas Tiputini receives about 2400 mm per year, Tena receives about 4500 mm, and Pastaza (at 1036 m) about 5100 mm (Fig. 2). These altitudinal changes in temperature and precipitation create climatic limits to plant distributions in the 600–900 m belt (Grubb *et al.*, 1963; Grubb and Whitmore, 1966; Neill and Palacios, 1989). Data on the climatic changes in Amazonian Ecuador during the Holocene and on the history of human occupation may be found in, *e.g.*, Bush and Colinvaux (1988) and Bush *et al.* (1991).

Geomorphology and Soils

The soils of Amazonian Ecuador have been described and their distributions mapped by a MAG-ORSTOM team of soil scientists (Sourdat and Custode, 1980) who distinguish the following five main geomorphological types (Fig. 3):

1. dissected tables of old parent rock
2. old peniplanized sedimentary rocks
3. swampy plains and alluvial terraces
4. plains with poor sandy soils
5. plains with highly fertile, often volcanic, soils

The soils of the area constitute a mixture of old weathered and more recently deposited fluvial sediments; the surface rocks are insufficiently known. Sourdat and Custode's soil map, based on aereal photos and field reconnaisance, shows that the soils are generally poor. A few areas, for instance the plains around Shushufindi and the alluvial floodplains adjacent to large rivers, have agricultural potential.

There are no peat swamps or podsols, and no areas of white sand such as are found in other parts of the Amazon basin have been reported for Amazonian Ecuador.

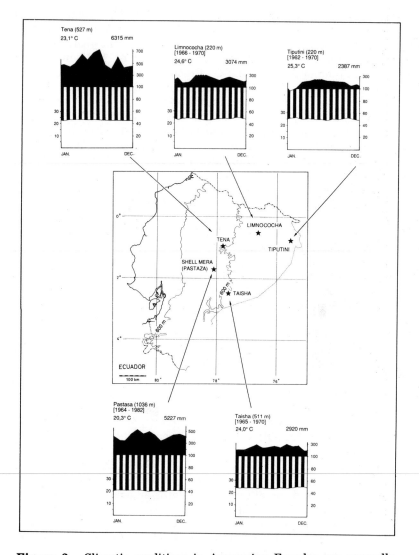

Figure 2. Climatic conditions in Amazonian Ecuador are generally characterized by stable temperatures around 25°C throughout the year and continuously high rainfall with annual precipitation varying from 2400 mm to over 6000 mm. Stations close to the Andean cordillera generally have higher rainfall and lower temperatures than stations further out on the Amazonian plain.

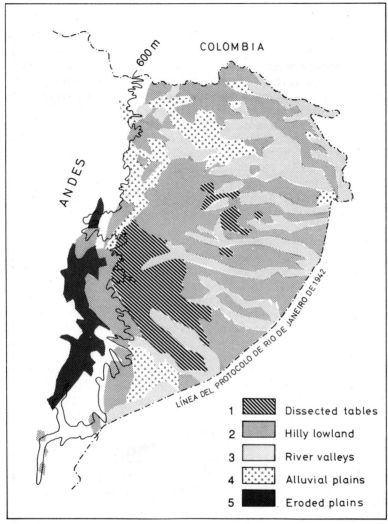

Figure 3.   Amazonian Ecuador is characterized by the following geomorphological types.   1. Dissected tables with good drainage and brown soils with low fertility. 2. Hilly lowland with good drainage on red soils with very low fertility. 3. River valleys with bad drainage on brown soils, occasionally with good fertility. 4. Alluvial plains with relatively good drainage on brownish soils with good fertility. 5. Eroded plains with relatively good drainage on fragile, poor soils. (Based on Sourdat and Custode, 1980).

Rivers

The San Miguel, Putumayo, Coca, Napo, Pastaza, Cangaime, and Santiago are the major rivers draining the eastern slopes of the Andes and flowing through Amazonian Ecuador. The rivers are generally white water rivers with a large load of clay particles that become suspended when the waters descend the Andean slopes at high velocity and with enormous eroding capacity. Water levels in the white water rivers that originate in the Andean Cordillera do not follow a seasonal pattern. Instead, they may be high or low at any time of the year and changes from one extreme to the other may occur overnight, for example, after a rain storm in a river's catchment area. For this reason, the floodplain forests associated with the white water rivers in Ecuadorean Amazonia are not subject to a seasonal regime of changes in the water table as in the lower Amazon basin (*cf.* Prance, 1979).

Between the large white water rivers there is a system of smaller rivers with black, oligotrophic water draining the flat Amazonian plain and in some places, black water lakes have formed. In contrast with the white water rivers, the water level in black water rivers and lakes is entirely dependant on the precipitation within Amazonian Ecuador itself. Local seasonal changes in rainfall are sometimes just large enough for evapo-transpiration to exceed precipitation so that some lakes, for example, those of the Cuyabeno area, dry up from December through March. The forests along their margins are therefore exposed to seasonal changes in water level and correspond to the black water flooded *igapó* forests of the lower Amazon basin (Prance, 1979).

3. HUMAN RESOURCES AND PRODUCTIVE ACTIVITIES

Population

The population of Ecuador is estimated at about 10 million people with an annual growth of 2.5–3%; that of Amazonian Ecuador at 350,000 people with an annual growth of close to 5%. Amazonian Ecuador has a population density of 2–3 inhabitants per km^2. There are six major indigeneous groups, the Siona-Secoya, the Waorani, the Cofán, the Quichua, the Shuar, and the Achuar, the last two belonging to the Jivaroan dialect group (Fig. 4). The recognition and protection of the lands traditionally occupied by these groups has created and still creates tension between the central administration and native communities. The laws governing rights to land are often ambiguous and agencies such as IERAC (Instituto Ecuatoriano de Reforma Agraria y Colonización) have been more eager to construct roads and facilitate immigration and settlement by people from outside the Amazonian region than to protect native interests. In the Río Napo region only 24 of 78 Quichua communities have received titles to their lands and among the Shuar only 83 of 265 "centros" have had their lands fully adjudicated (Fundación Natura, 1988).

The Siona-Secoya speak a western Tukano language and number about 700 people. In Ecuador there are four main Siona-Secoya communities; one of them lives on the border of the Cuyabeno Faunal Reserve, the other near San Pablo and along the Aguarico river. The latter is highly threatened by oil exploration and spontaneous settlement by "colonos." The Waorani, who comprise about 700 individuals speaking a language related to Zaparo, live mostly within the Yasuní National Park and their situation is similarly critical, being threatened by the same factors. The Cofán, who belong to the Chibcha language group and comprise about 500 members, live partly within the Cayambe-Coca Biological Reserve and are the indigenous group most affected by recent oil exploration and land settlement activities. The Jivaroan tribes dwell chiefly in the Río Upano and Río Zamora valleys and along some affluents of the Río Pastaza (in Morona-Santiago and southern Pastaza) and may number 20,000 individuals.

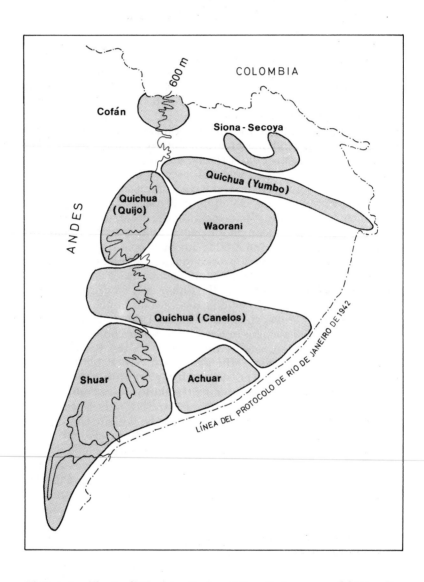

Figure 4. The traditional territories of the ethnic groups of Amazonian Ecuador.

Finally the Quichua groups, *i.e.,* the Quijo, Canelos, and Yumbo numbering perhaps 25,000 individuals, are more acculturated and depend less on the exploitation of wild animals and plants than the Waorani, Siona-Secoya, Cofán, Shuar, and Achuar.

With constant growth at the current annual rate of 2.5–3% the population of Ecuador would reach 20 million in 25–30 years which would create an immense pressure on the Amazonian part of the country. If Amazonian Ecuador were to absorb a proportion of the national population corresponding to its proportion of the national territory its population would reach 4 million (up from 350,000 at present) which is far beyond the area's carrying capacity (Hicks *et al.,* 1990).

Petroleum Industry
Oil exploration in eastern Ecuador started in the 1940s and led to the gradual establishment of airstrips, roads, and other installations during the 1950s and early 1960s. Oil was discovered in Lago Agrio some 38 km from the Colombian border on the third of March 1967 and large-scale exploration began in the early 1970s. Subsequently, this non-renewable resource became the most important source of economic growth in Ecuador and contributed more foreign exchange earnings than any other export item. Although the Amazon region provides by far the largest share of the resources for Ecuador's petroleum earnings, most of the economic benefits are going to other parts of the country. Even worse, drainage from oil pools and emulsion processes often contaminates surrounding aquatic systems, and during transport leakages or spills are frequent due to poor maintenance of the pipelines or natural disasters like earthquakes and landslides. Such ecological costs need to be considered when evaluating the economic benefits resulting from petroleum production and export. For Amazonian Ecuador, the impact of the petroleum industry so far has been negative (Hicks *et al.,* 1990).

Agriculture and Cattle Production
The improved accessibility of Amazonian Ecuador and the growing population have led to a strong increase in the area cleared for agricultural purposes. From 1983 to 1986 the area under production in Amazonian Ecuador doubled from 53,000

hectares to 106,000 hectares with the strongest increase in Napo (Fundación Natura, 1988). Agriculture is practised as traditional subsistence systems, corporate plantations, and mixed systems.

Traditional subsistence systems are practised by the indigenous groups and are characterized by hunting, fishing, food collection, and itinerant farming. This form of land use is becoming less common and is being replaced by cattle ranching and sedentary agriculture due to the influence of the immigrants settling in Amazonian Ecuador.

Corporate plantations are found in Napo and are primarily monoculture plantations of oil palms and tea, the latter on the Andean slopes above 600 m elevation. The plantations depend on the use of pesticides and fertilizers.

Mixed systems are practised on small family farms owned by settlers who produce subsistence crops and some cash crops like coffee, cocoa, and naranjilla or papaya. These family farms often include some pasture for cattle.

There are 500,000 hectares of pasture land in Amazonian Ecuador and the number of cattle is 340,000 (Hicks *et al.*, 1990). The conversion of tropical rain forest to pasture has been furthered by the land tenure legislation requiring land to be developed. Significant ecologic costs are associated with cattle production, including deforestation, soil compaction, and erosion; these costs are generally much higher than those of rotational agriculture.

Forestry and Deforestation
All forest resources in Amazonian Ecuador are natural, there being no plantation forestry. A report from the United Nations Environment Program (1986, cited in Hicks *et al.*, 1990) estimated that 7% of Ecuador's forest industry wood supply originated in the Amazonian region; however, another report prepared for the U.S. Agency for International Development (Cabarle, 1989, cited in Hicks *et al.*, 1990) estimated this proportion to be 40%.

Deforestation in Amazonian Ecuador is considerable, possibly as much as 75,000 hectares per year (Hicks *et al.*, 1990). Nevertheless, deforestation is primarily due to settlers and not commercial timber exploitation (Fig. 5). Whatever the causes, current deforestation represents a waste of natural resources without forseeable long-term economic benefits.

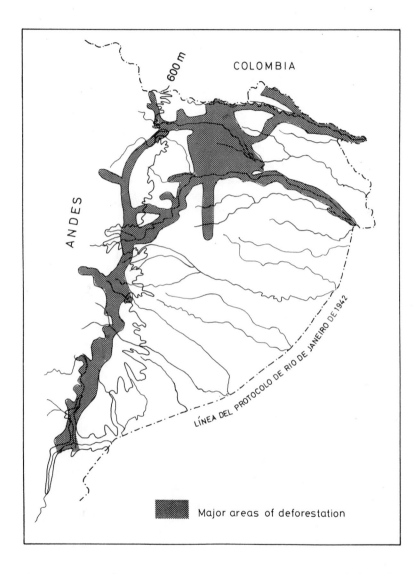

Figure 5. Deforestation in Amazonian Ecuador is concentrated along the large rivers and along the access roads to the oil exploration sites.

4. THE VEGETATION

A brief description of the vegetation types of Ecuador is given by Harling (1979) and Cañadas Cruz (1983) published a map of the bioclimatic zones of the country. Both authors treat the Amazonian part of Ecuador as a single category. Nevertheless, several vegetation units may be recognized within the area and the following section gives a brief introduction to the most important ones.

Vegetation Types

Upland Forests on Terra Firme. — Upland forests are never reached by the waters of the rivers even at their maximum flooding. Terra firme forests cover extensive areas throughout Amazonian Ecuador. Their canopy layer is some 30–35 m above the ground with emergents attaining heights of 60–70 m. The density of trees over 10 cm dbh is 700–800 stems per hectare and the basal area in one such forest was calculated to be 33.7 m^2 (Balslev *et al.*, 1987). The upland terra firme forests are species-rich; at Añangu 52 families and 228 species of trees with a dbh over 10 cm were found in one hectare *(loc. cit.)*. At Cuyabeno the number of trees above 10 cm dbh is similar, but there are as many as 400 species when all woody species with a dbh over 1 cm are included. As is typical of species-rich tropical forests, many species are rare while a few are common; at Añangu the palm *Iriartea deltoidea* accounted for 13% of the individuals and 8% of the basal area, whereas almost 120 species of trees (>10 cm dbh) were represented by a single individual in one hectare.

Black Water Forests. — The system of black water rivers and lakes in Amazonian Ecuador is fed entirely by local precipitation and the water level therefore closely follows the annual rainfall cycle. Although there is no pronounced dry season, the months of December through March have less rainfall than the rest of the year. During this period the level of the black water lakes is low, the floodplains are dry, and some lakes dry up. On sloping terrain along river margins and especially along lake shores, a zonation is created in the vegetation by the variation in the duration of flooding. The trees tolerating the longest flooding are *Macrolobium acaciifolium* and a species of *Bactris*. The *Bactris-Macrolobium* forests have an open canopy and during the dry season appear like savannas due to a grass cover on the dried-out lake beds. Areas subjected to slightly shorter flooding are dominated by the shrub *Myrciaria dubia* and the tree *Genipa americana* that may form an impenetrable tangle. The upper limit of regular inundation corresponds to an often very distinct zone dominated by *Astrocaryum jauari*, a palm often growing in dense stands with as many as 270 mature trees, 820 juveniles, and 26,400 seedlings per hectare (Borgtoft Pedersen and Balslev, 1990).

White Water Forests. — The system of white water rivers in Amazonian Ecuador is mostly fed by precipitation falling on the east Andean slopes and the inter-Andean catchment areas draining into the Amazon. In these areas rainfall is irregular and thunder storms or downpours are frequent. Following a rainstorm in the Andes the white water rivers in Amazonian Ecuador may rise several meters overnight and inundate the floodplain, only to retreat and leave a wet but not inundated floodplain the next night. The white waters carry a heavy sediment load and they are alkaline. Forests on white water floodplains are species-rich and tall with high wood volumes. One such forest was analyzed in detail at Añangu (Balslev *et al.,* 1987).

Mauritia flexuosa Swamps. — Swampy ground is often covered by a vegetation dominated by *Mauritia flexuosa.* This palm may reach 40 m height and attain a trunk diameter of up to 60 cm; its fan-shaped leaves may measure up to 2 m across. *Mauritia flexuosa* is adapted to water-logged soils; its very extensive but superficial root system has pneumatophores growing up through the muddy ground. Because of this adaptation it out-competes most other species in such habitats and often forms large monospecific stands called "moretales" from the palm's common name "morete." Moretales are found in black as well as white water inundated areas.

Lakes and Open Swamps. — Lakes and open swamps are common in Amazonian Ecuador. Besides small ponds and lakes on low ground, there are two characteristic geomorphological forms, sicle-shaped old riverbends and extensive landscape depressions. The lake water is often transparent and dark; it is rich in organic acids and acidic with pH around 5. Lake shores are often dominated by *Montrichardia linifera* that forms large stands towards the open water. In more shallow waters *Cyperus, Echinodorus, Saggitaria, Limnocharis,* and *Ludwigia* are common elements. Further into the lake, there may be individuals of *Nymphaea* and free-floating plants such as *Cabomba* and *Pontederia* or submerged ones such as *Utricularia* and *Ceratophyllum.* Floating meadows may be formed by *Cyperus, Eichornea, Pontederia, Heteranthera, Mimosa, Ludwigia,* and *Justicia* among others.

Riverside Vegetation. — The riverside vegetation along the large meandering white water rivers on the outer curve of the meander is a transect of the forest growing on the land being eroded, often a terra firme forest. The inner curve of the meander is slowly filled-up with sediment and there a sucessional vegetation develops. The outermost zone on the newly deposited sand- and mud-banks is covered by *Tessaria integrifolia,* followed by a zone dominated by *Gynerium saggitatum.* Beyond this there is a belt with *Cecropia,* and then a more diverse woody vegetation where certain *Ficus* species are very common and often dominant.

Secondary Vegetation. — Around the settlements as well as along the roads and major rivers the natural vegetation is altered, often quite extensively. In many cases the natural forests have been completely cleared and/or burned. After a few years of corn, cassava, or banana growing, agriculture is often given up, permitting the growth of a secondary forest dominated by pioneers such as *Cecropia.* Other areas used for cattle raising are covered by the grass *Axonopus scopamus* in an open, park-like landscape. Some large trees such as *Ceiba* and several palms, for instance *Astrocaryum* and *Iriartea,* are left for shade. In the vicinity of the oil wells the roads are paved with surplus crude oil which permits the growth of only scattered individuals of the most persistent species such as *Cecropia* and *Adropogon bicornis* and seedlings are not seen.

Distribution Patterns of Species

Of the species occurring in Amazonian Ecuador below 900 m, 43% are widespread in the neotropical region, 17% are distributed in the northwestern part of South America on both sides of the Andes, and 40% are distributed only in the Amazon Basin[2]. Of the species in Amazonian Ecuador, 3% are endemic to the area and 18% are restricted to the western part of the Amazon Basin (Balslev, 1988). The flora of Amazonian Ecuador has a large proportion of widespread species and is poor in endemics because there are no barriers preventing species from migrating in and out of the area. The fact that 40% of the Ecuadorean species are restricted to the Amazonian lowlands indicates that their flora diversified enormously following the Andean uplift starting some 20 million years ago.

The three dimensional distribution of species and individuals contributes greatly to the diversity of tropical vegetation; different life forms dominating different strata. The same species may compete with one set of competitors for minerals and water in the root zone and with another for light in the canopy; and they may depend on yet another set of species of plants and animals for their reproduction through pollination, seed dispersal, *etc.* The biological complexity of tropical ecosystems is high and their diversity and maintenance depends on this complexity. Unfortunately, few detailed descriptions of these complex interactions are available; this is true for tropical rain forests in general and certainly for the forests of Amazonian Ecuador.

Life Forms

Trees. — The tree is the most conspicuous life form in Amazonian Ecuador as in other tropical rain forests. The tallest trees reach 65–70 m or more, but most attain no more than 35 m in height; their stems are usually straight and unbranched for most of their length and may reach 2 m or more in diameter, but such large individuals are rare. In a sample of a floodplain forest only 2.2% of the trees with diameters over 10 cm had diameters over 85 cm; in a terra firme forest that percentage was 0.6% (Balslev *et al.*, 1987). In the same sample, 1 in 20 dicotyledon trees had stilt roots, and these were especially common in the genera *Cecropia, Pourouma, Inga, Coccoloba,* and *Bauhinia;* buttresses were found in 14–17% of the trees. The leaves were of

---

[2]This paragraph is based on an analysis of the Ecuadorean flora in three elevational intervals: 0–900 m, 900–3000 m, 3000 m and upwards (Balslev, 1988). The lower zone includes a slightly larger area than the area covered by the present checklist (0–600 m).

moderate or large size with 61–72% of the trees having mesophyllous leaves (20–180 cm^2) and 24–37% having macrophyllous ones (180–1640 cm^2). The most important tree families were Moraceae, Leguminosae, Cecropiaceae, Euphorbiaceae, Lauraceae, Lecythidaceae, Meliaceae, Myristicaceae, Rubiaceae, Bombacaceae, and Violaceae. Some families, for example Lauraceae, are important because they are represented by a high number of species, others because they have enormous individuals (*e.g.,* Bombacaceae). The Moraceae and the Leguminosae have many species, many individuals, and large basal areas.

Shrubs. — Shrubs and shrubby treelets are the most common life form in tropical rain forests but, of course, not as conspicuous as the trees. Shrubs in the rain forests often have rather slender branches and small hard leaves with driptips. Flowers are often small, greenish, and inconspicuous. Common shrubs belong to Melastomataceae, Rubiaceae, Solanaceae, and Malvaceae.

Ground Herbs. — Ground herbs in tropical rain forests are often inconspicuous. Generally there is a continuous layer of brown litter with small herbs only in light gaps or rock outcrops. Most ground herbs belong to the Araceae, ferns, Marantaceae, Cyperaceae, Poaceae, Costaceae, Heliconiaceae, Zingiberaceae, Commelinaceae, Gesneriaceae, Rubiaceae, and Melastomataceae (Poulsen and Balslev, 1991). In temporarily flooded forests Alismataceae are frequent (Haynes and Holm-Nielsen, 1989). Plants growing from bulbs, corms, or rhizomes such as Haemodoraceae, Amaryllidaceae, and Orchidaceae are rare. In light gaps or clearings and along rivers, lakes, or swampy areas giant herbs such as *Heliconia, Costus, Carludovica, Calathea,* and species of the aroid family are common.

Epiphytes. — Epiphytes grow on other plants without parasitising them. Herbaceous climbers may grow epiphytically without being rooted in the ground; hemi-epiphytes grow epiphytically during part of their life cycle and are rooted in the ground during other parts. Nest and bracket epiphytes collect litter and humus around their roots and leaf bases and tank epiphytes store water between their leaf bases. The most prominent epiphytic groups in Amazonian Ecuador are the Orchidaceae, Araceae, Bromeliaceae, Cactaceae, and ferns.

Vines and Lianas. — Vines and lianas are rooted in the ground and ascend to the canopy using other plants for support. Lianas are woody with very large vessels, whereas vines are herbaceous. Many lianas are cauliflorous which makes their reproduction dependent on the animal life of the interior of the forests, whereas their primary production depends on the light and microclimate in the canopy. In terms of numbers of species and individuals the most important families among vines and lianas are Bignoniaceae, Leguminosae, Araceae, Celastraceae, Olacaceae, Sapindaceae, Menispermaceae, Malpighiaceae, and Combretaceae (Paz y Miño, 1990). Although less numerous such families as Cucurbitaceae, Convolvulaceae, Apocynaceae, and Passifloraceae are quite conspicuous among the vines and lianas because of their showy flowers. Vines are especially abundant along riversides and in light gaps, often forming a dense tangle in the vegetation. Typically they depend on the fauna of open areas in the forests or its margins for their pollination, their seeds often being dispersed by wind. Leaf-shedding trees like *Ceiba* are often densely covered by lianas and vines.

Stranglers. — In Amazonian Ecuador stranglers are repre-sented by two groups; one is Clusiaceae, the other consists of certain species of Moraceae including *Ficus* and others. Stranglers germinate on tree branches in the canopy growing into epiphytic shrubs. Aereal roots then connect to the ground and eventually grow into stem- and trunk-like structures that finally close around the host tree. The host dies and rots while the typical reticulate trunk of the strangling figs or *Clusia* species remains.

Saprophytes. — Phanerogamic saprophytes are usually inconspicuous plants growing in the litter layer on the forest floor. Being saprophtic their stems and leaves are devoid of chlorophyll and have a whitish or translucent color. Their flowers, however, may be brightly colored as, for example, the yellow flowers of *Voyria*. Rain forest saprophytes may belong to typically saprophytic families such as Burmanniaceae *(Burmannia, Gymnosiphon, Apteria, Dictyostegia, Thismia)*, to families otherwise mostly epiphtic such as Orchidaceae *(Wullschlae-gelia)*, or to terrestrial families such as Gentianaceae *(Voyria)*. The Ecuadorean phanerogamic saprophytes were reviewed by Maas and Maas (1987) who list the following species for

Amazonian Ecuador: *Burmannia tenella, Gymnosiphon minutus, G. brachycephalus, G. suaveolens, Apteria aphylla, Dictyostega orobanchoides, Thismia panamensis, T. singeri, T. melanomitra, Wullschlaegelia calcarata, Voyria aphylla, V. aurantiaca, V. flavescens, V. spruceana,* and *V. tenella.*

Parasites. — Holo-parasitic phanerogams recorded from our study area belong to the Balanophoraceae and Rafflesiaceae. Balanophoraceae are obligate root parasites and three species have been recorded for Amazonian Ecuador below 600 m: *Lophophytum mirabile, Ombrophytum peruvianum,* and *O. violaceum.* The only Rafflesiaceae, *Apodanthes caseariae,* grows on the branches of trees and shrubs and only its small flowers protrude through the bark.   Hemi-parasitic phanerogams include species of Viscaceae and Loranthaceae (Kuijt, 1986). Species of both these families are shrubs with green leaves growing parasitically on the branches of trees and shrubs. Loranthaceae are represented by 11 species and Viscaceae by six species in our area.

Nature Reserves

In 1979 Ecuador established an extensive net of nature reserves covering a total of 2.8 million hectares.   Within lowland Amazonian Ecuador there are three nature reserves (Fig. 6). The largest one is the Yasuní National Park covering 678,000 hectares south of the Río Napo and east of Coca. The Cuyabeno Faunal Reserve is located north of the Río Aguarico and covers an area of 255,000 hectares. The smallest protected area is the Limoncocha Biological Reserve covering 5,261 hectares north of the Río Napo and east of Coca.

The Cayambe-Coca Ecological Reserve (403,000 ha), the Sangay National Park (271,000 ha), and the Podocarpus National Park (146,000 ha) are located on the Andean slopes bordering the eastern lowlands.

For all of these nature reserves the operational budgets for protection are as low as US$ 0.10 per hectare (Hicks *et al.,* 1990). This effectively limits true protection to areas far away from human settlements. The petroleum industry is controlled by the Ministry of Mines and Industry whereas the nature reserves are administered by the Ministry of Agriculture (MAG). Consequently, conflicts of interest between petroleum exploration

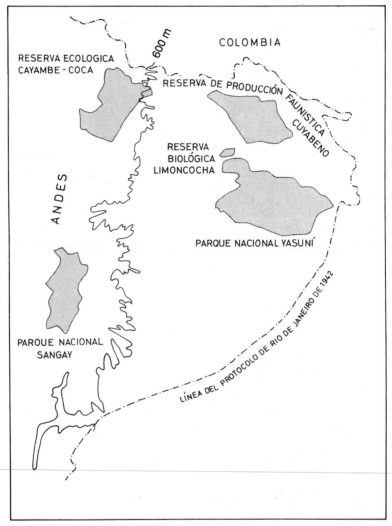

Figure 6. The nature reserves in Amazonian Ecuador and adjacent Andean slopes. The largest reserve is Parque Nacional Yasuní covering 678,000 ha, second is Reserva de Producción Faunistica Cuyabeno (255,000 ha), and the smallest is Reserva Biológica Limoncocha (5261 hectares). The Andean nature reserves are Reserva Ecologica Cayambe-Coca (403,000 ha), Parque Nacional Sangay (271,000 ha) and Parque Nacional Podocarpus (146,000 ha, located south of the area shown on map).

and preservation of renewable resources are resolved with difficulty and more often than not oil exploration overrules protection.

5. FLORISTIC INVENTORY

Botanical Exploration

A complex geological history with much volcanic activity and tectonic movements has contributed to the high diversity of soils and habitats found in Ecuador. This setting created excellent opportunities for the diversification of the flora and despite its restricted size of only 270,000 km^2, Ecuador has one of the richest floras among tropical countries. This botanical wealth has long attracted naturalists. The early explorers' attention, however, remained more or less confined to the coastal area and the Andes, access to the eastern lowlands being rather difficult. A history of the botanical exploration of Amazonian Ecuador, including an index to botanical collecting localities is being published elsewhere (Renner, in press).

The first naturalists to visit the lowlands east of the Andes were the French botanist Joseph de Jussieu (1704–1779) and the geographer and naturalist Charles Marie de la Condamine (1701–1774). La Condamine descended the Río Chinchipe in June 1743 and from there went down the Marañón to the mouth of the Amazon; La Condamine made no botanical collections. His compatriot Jussieu, however, during a visit to Loja in 1739, collected extensively and though most of Jussieu's plants are from higher elevations at least some seem to come from the lower slopes of the Río Zamora valley. In August 1802 Humboldt and Bonpland also reached the Río Chinchipe near its junction with the Marañón, and during their 17-day stay at Rentema, at the border beween Peru and Ecuador, Bonpland collected plants at around 300 m altitude.

The next to reach Ecuadorean Amazonia were Manuel Villavicencio, Gaetano Osculati, William Jameson, Richard Spruce, and Juan Isern y Battló. Osculati followed the Río Napo from its sources to its junction with the Amazon and down to Belém. In 1847 he collected mosses near Puerto Napo where he stayed at the house of another naturalist and collector, Manuel Villavicencio. Jameson, professor of Chemistry and Botany at the Universidad Central in Quito, in 1857 travelled to Tena, Archidona, Puerto Napo, Ahuano, Santa Rosa and back but made few collections during that trip. In the same year Richard Spruce, coming up the Río Bobonaza from Peru, reached Canelos from where he continued over land to Baños. Though Spruce collected a large number of mosses and hepatics near Pucayacu, just south of Canelos, he gathered no flowering plants until Baños (Renner, in press, for details). In 1865 the Spaniard Juan Isern y Battló visited Archidona, Puerto Napo, and the slopes of Volcán Sumaco, then continuing down the Río Napo to Coca.

Several professional plant hunters came to Ecuador at about the same time. Richard Pearce collected in the Cuenca vicinity in 1862, Gustav Wallis and Hugo Poortman along the banks of the Río Zamora in 1876 and 1882, respectively. It is unclear if one of them penetrated into the eastern lowlands. A professor at the university in Cuenca, August Rimbach, was the last of the 19th century collectors. In 1894 he descended the Río Bobonaza, but made only few collections during that trip.

In terms of botanical collecting, the 20th century in eastern Ecuador began with Carlo Crespi and Raymond Bénoist. Crespi, an Italian Salesian missionary, worked mainly in the vicinity of Indanza in 1924 and Raymond Bénoist, a French botanist, collected around Puerto Napo in 1931. Arnold and Hertha Schultze-Rhonhof also came to Ecuador during the 1930s and collected in the environs of Mera, Puyo, and Canelos. In 1935 Ynés Mexía visited Canelos on the Río Bobonaza and Puerto Napo, Tena, and Archidona in the Napo valley. During the same year Erica Heinrichs collected near Archidona, Tena, and Nuevo Rocafuerte as well as near Canelos and Sarayacu and in the vicinity of Méndez and Macas in Morona-Santiago. Erik Asplund worked in the vicinity of Tena and Archidona in 1939, but relatively few of his collections were made below 600 m altitude. As his assistant Asplund employed Manuel Lugo, a citizen of Mera, who had already worked for the Schultze-Rhonhofs. Subsequently, Manuel Lugo also worked for Gunnar Harling and he and his son Hólguer Lugo have collected a total of over 6000 numbers, mostly trees.

Gunnar Harling first came to eastern Ecuador towards the end of 1946 as a member of a Finnish-Swedish ethnographical expedition; he returned in 1958–59 and on seven subsequent expeditions, most recently in 1985. Other early Swedish collectors were Folke Fagerlind and his student Per-Göran Wibom from the University of Stockholm who visited Puyo, Mera, and the lower Río Napo between Tiputini and Lagartococha in 1952–53.

Concomittant with the large-scale exploration of oil from the late 1960s on, the accessibility and infrastructure of eastern Ecuador improved and scientific exploration increased. From 1739 to 1968 some 30 people botanized in Amazonian Ecuador, but since 1968 over 160 collectors have worked in the area (Renner, in press; this figure includes main and secondary collectors). In 1968 L. B. Holm-Nielsen and S. Jeppesen from the Botanical Institute of Aarhus University conducted the first expedition to Ecuador by Danish botanists, collecting extensively also in eastern Ecuador (Holm-Nielsen and Jeppesen, 1968). Holm-Nielsen returned to Ecuador in 1973 with S. Jeppesen, B. Løjtnant, and B. Øllgaard and was professor at the Pontificia Universidad Católica in Quito from 1979–1981. During that period he organized several expeditions to the eastern lowlands with his students J. Jaramillo, F. Coello, R. Alarcón, R. Andrade, E. Azanza, and J. Brandbyge. Holm-Nielsen was followed by H. Balslev (1981–84), S. Lægaard (1984–86), B. B. Larsen (1985–86), P. M. Jørgensen (1986–89), H. Borgtoft Petersen (1989–90), and B. Øllgaard (1990–) as professors of botany at the P. Universidad Católica, and numerous Ecuadorean and Danish students became involved in floristic and vegetation-analytical work in eastern Ecuador. At this writing the Aarhus University staff in collaboration with colleagues at PUCE have collected some 90,000 specimens from Ecuador of which 15–20,000 are from the eastern lowlands (Borchsenius, 1990; Jørgensen *et al.*, submitted).

A new type of floristic research work in Ecuador began in the 1960s, namely quantitative inventories that use sample plots where every tree is identified and measured. Such inventories allow estimations of local species diversity and give an impression of the dynamics of the forests. In eastern Ecuador this method was first used by P. J. R. Lloyd, T. D. Pennington, and T. C. Whitmore during an expedition of the Oxford University Exploration Club that collected about 3000 mostly sterile voucher specimens from a forest about 7 km east of Tena. Grubb and collaborators used a multidisciplinary approach, supplying forest transects of the kind commonly done by foresters with microclimatological measurements and soil analyses (Grubb *et al.*, 1963; Grubb and Whitmore, 1966, 1967).

In 1972 another ecological inventory was carried out by a University of Kansas team that set up a quadrat near Santa Cecilia, Napo, with the botanists B. MacBryde and J. D. Dwyer and the herpetologists J. E. Simmons and W. E. Duellman. Almost at the same time, in 1975 E. L. Little and collaborators carried out semi-quantitative surveys of the timber resources of northeastern and southeastern lowland Ecuador.

Two recent inventories, one at Añangu the other at Cuyabeno, are described in more detail below.

Collection Density
Between 1739–1988 about 61,000 herbarium specimens (excluding duplicates) have been collected in the eastern Ecuadorean lowlands below 600 m, *i.e.*, 52 per 100 km² (Renner, in press). The majority of these collections are deposited in the herbaria AAU, GB, MO, NY, QAME, QCA, QCNE, S, and US (acronyms following Holmgren *et al.*, 1990).

Collecting in different parts of Amazonian Ecuador is highly unequal (Fig. 7). Until the advent of petroleum exploration there were hardly 300 km of gravel roads reaching more or less far into the eastern lowlands and they were usually passable only during the dry season. The road from Quito ended at Baeza and the traditional collecting localities were along the mule trails from Baeza to Tena and Puerto Napo and from Tena to Puyo. Collections were, of course, also made along the margins of the Río Napo, especially near Ahuano, Santa Rosa, and Coca. Modern collecting localities in the Napo province include the oil road from Baeza to Lago Agrio, the road from there south to Coca, and the Auca oil fields. The black water lakes of Jatun-cocha, Lagartococha, and Cuyabeno have also been explored relatively recently, and D. Neill and his collaborators are now for the first time exploring the forests south of the Río Napo out of reach by fluvial and land transport with the help of helicopters from the oil companies.

In Pastaza the Río Bobonaza is the classic botanical collecting route. To reach Peru or, rather, the province of Maynas, one travelled from Baños to Canelos where a Dominican mission had been established in 1581 and from there one continued some 220 km down the Bobonaza. The latter was and is by far the most convenient fluvial route to the Pastaza and the Marañón, and eventually the Amazon. Naturally, most collecting has concentrated around Puyo; some has also been along the Río Curaray.

In Morona-Santiago activities have concentrated along the roads to and from Macas and near the military posts such as Taisha and Montalvo in the interior that may be reached by light aircrafts.

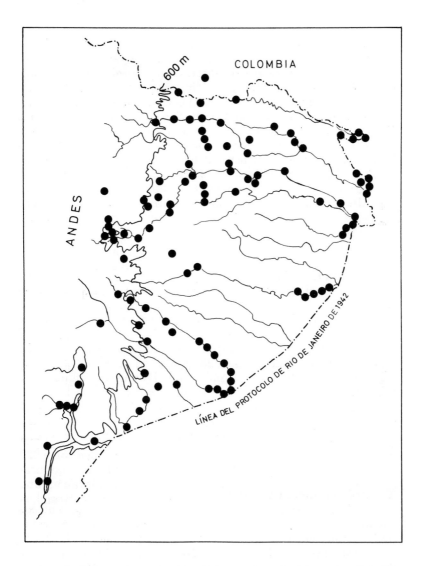

Figure 7. Map showing the collecting localities in Amazonian Ecuador. The map is based on the travel itineraries for all know collectors in the area between 1739 and 1988 (Renner, in press).

Over the three years (1987–1990) during which this checklist was compiled and revised, the initially rapid increase in recorded number of species leveled off and new records were balanced by the placing in synonymy of names by specialists. Still the quantitative inventories at Añangu and Cuyabeno (discussed below) continue to yield new species and records and it is clear from the above that there are immense patches of entirely uncollected vegetation between the rivers and roads. Using inventory data estimates of the relative contribution of different Ecuadorean biota to the country's total plant diversity and this checklist, Balslev and Renner (1989) estimated that the eastern lowlands of Ecuador harbour at least 4000 species of vascular plants. Neill and Palacios (1989) expect that the eventual number of tree species alone will be 3000, which is assuming an accordingly higher number of vascular plants. The current checklist contains 3100 species of flowering plants and two gymnosperms.

The Flora of Ecuador Project
In 1963 G. Harling from the University of Göteborg and B. Sparre from the Museum of Natural History in Stockholm began to make plans for a *Flora of Ecuador*. During a preparatory phase from 1968 on, collaborators were found and an international editorial board established; the first volume appeared in 1973 (Harling, 1973). Since volume 25, published in 1986, the editors have been G. Harling and L. Andersson. By now 51 families have been treated completely and three families (Polypodiaceae, Asteraceae, Orchidaceae) in part. Of the 149 families and 3100 species in this checklist, 40 and 552, respectively are treated in the *Flora of Ecuador*, giving a coverage of 18% of the species (Table 1).

Trees of Amazonian Ecuador
Since 1985 D. Neill of the Missouri Botanical Garden and his collaborators C. Cerón, W. Palacios, J. Zaruma, and F. Hurtado have carried out research on the trees of the eastern lowlands under contract with the Dirección Nacional Forestal and the U.S. Agency for International Development. Their *Arboles de la Amazonía Ecuatoriana* (Neill and Palacios, 1989) is a checklist of native tree species of Amazonian Ecuador below 600 m altitude

and includes 1069 species attaining at least 5 m in height. For each, information is included on the species' geographical distribution within Amazonian Ecuador, on habitat, on whether the tree reaches the canopy, and on its common and native names. D. Neill and A. Suárez also founded a biological reserve 8 km east of Puerto Misahualli, called "Jatun Sacha," that includes a series of permanent 1-hectare plots (Neill, 1988); a florula of Jatun Sacha is planned.

The Añangu Quantitative Inventory
From 1982–1984 the Pontificia Universidad Católica, The New York Botanical Garden, and the Botanical Institute of Aarhus University jointly carried out an inventory project at Añangu in the northwestern corner of the Yasuní National Park (Balslev *et al.*, 1987; Korning *et al.*, 1991). The comparative study of the tree species richness of a nonflooded forest and a white water floodplain forest showed that one hectare of nonflooded forest had 734 individuals and 153 species of trees (with a dbh over 10 cm) and that 728 trees collected along a nearby 4 km transect represented 244 species. In the floodplain forest, a 2 km transect with 420 trees comprised 149 species. In total, the two transects and the hectare plot, all located within an area of 3.5 x 0.5 km, included 394 species of trees with a dbh over 10 cm.

The Cuyabeno Quantitative Inventory
The Reserva de Producción Faunística Cuyabeno lies 70 km east of Lago Agrio. The Cuyabeno reserve includes a catchment area with black water lakes and rivers surrounded by low rolling hills that are never flooded. Here botanists from the P. Universidad Católica and the Aarhus University studied species richness of the vascular flora in a one hectare plot; data were collected from 1988–1990 and are still being processed. There are 96 species of ground herbs, 80 of lianas, 145 of epiphytes, 400 of trees and shrubs with a dbh below 5 cm, and more than 200 of trees with a dbh equal or over 5 cm (Poulsen and Balslev, 1991; Paz y Miño *et al.* 1991; Christensen, 1991).

Ethnobotany
Among the most interesting collections from Amazonian Ecuador are those made by anthrophologists who tend to work long

periods at remote places and to collect plant parts or life stages not usually collected such as roots, bark, saplings, *etc.* Because of their collaboration with local people and their different professional bias they also collect plants overlooked by regular botanists and their specimen labels are often unusually informative. On the other hand, ethnobotanical voucher material is often not widely distributed and it may be necessary to request it from the researcher's home institution.

Of the native groups living in Amazonian Ecuador, the largest are the lowland Quichua whose use of plants has been studied by Irvine (1987), Alarcón Gallegos (1988), Marles and Neill (Marles *et al.*, 1988), and Holm-Nielsen, Balslev, and students (Kvist and Holm-Nielsen, 1987). The use of plants by the Ashuar in Morona-Santiago has been studied by Baker, Lowell and Bradley Bennet of The New York Botanical Garden, and that of the Cofán living on the Colombian border by Pinkley (1973), and Cerón (1987, 1989). The Siona-Secoya have been studied ethnobotanically by Vickers and Plowman (Vickers and Plowman, 1984; Vickers, 1976, 1989; Paz y Miño *et al.*, 1991), Brandbyge and Azanza (1982), and Lescure, Balslev, and Alarcón (Lescure *et al.*, 1987), and finally the Waorani (Huaorani, Auca) by Davis and Yost (1983).

Useful Plants
Since 1986 the taxonomy and economic potential of Ecuadorean palms has been the focus of attention of botanists from the Universidad Católica in Quito and Aarhus University. This has resulted in the collection of hundreds of specimens of palms, otherwise often under-collected due to the practical problems in the preparation of specimens (*e.g.,* Borgtoft Pedersen and Balslev, 1990; Balslev and Barfod, 1987).

6. THE CHECKLIST

Format, Taxonomy and Difficult Taxa

The checklist of Flowering Plants of Amazonian Ecuador is based on the complete holdings of specimens from the eastern Ecuadorean lowlands in the herbaria of Aarhus University (AAU), Gothenburg University (GB), the Riksmuseet in Stockholm (S), the Marie Selby Botanical Gardens in Sarasota (SEL), and the P. Universidad Católica in Quito (QCA). For selected groups or collections the following herbaria were consulted: the Field Museum of Natural History in Chicago (F), The New York Botanical Garden (NY), the U.S. National Herbarium in Washington (US), and the Missouri Botanical Garden (MO). Families, genera, and species are arranged alphabetically. Families are those recognized by Cronquist (1988) except that Caesalpiniaceae, Fabaceae, and Mimosaceae are left together as Leguminosae.

The taxonomy is that of the most recent monographs, floristic treatments, or the relevant literature about species new to eastern Ecuador. The works we found most useful to determine the correct names of the plants listed are given under the family headings. Synonyms are only cited in a few cases where there have been recent taxonomic changes. Author abbreviations follow Meikle *et al.* (1980).

Most important Amazonian plant groups have specialists willing to do identifications. Table 1 presents a list of the families found in Amazonian Ecuador with the specialists or relevant floristic treatments if any. There are some conspicuous exceptions, however. These include the Araliaceae, Boraginaceae, Clusiaceae, Euphorbiaceae, Myrtaceae, and Rubiaceae. There are also numerous unidentified Annonaceae, Leguminosae, Orchidaceae, and Monimiaceae, but these families are currently being worked on. During the preparation of this checklist a number of undescribed species came to light and a few of them have been included as "sp. nov."

Biological Information

For each species the growth form (tree, shrub, herb, vine, or liana) is given as stated on the labels or in relevant literature; for parasites and saprophytes the life form is indicated. Information on altitudinal range is only given for species also collected above

600 m altitude. Because of the large number of species involved, no information on the species' total geographic distribution, total altitudinal range, or status (whether native, cultivated, introduced, *etc.*) has been included.

Specimens Cited

For each name included in the checklist the collector and collection number of at least one specimen are given. The standard herbarium acronyms (Holmgren *et al.*, 1990) after the cited collections indicate where a particular specimen was seen. Criteria for citing a specimen were how widely the collection was likely to be distributed, if it came from a poorly collected area, and if ethnobotanical information was associated with it. Information on the uses of plants by native people may be found in the publications of the collectors of ethnobotanical vouchers (compare the section on Ethnobotany above).

Abbreviations Used

Prov.   Province
N   Napo (including Sucumbíos)
P   Pastaza
M-S   Morona-Santiago
SEF   Studies of Ecuadorean Forests, a collecting programme
        of the Aarhus Botanical Institute (for details see Renner,
        in press).

Table 1.   Plant families in Amazonian Ecuador with their number of species in the checklist, together with the volume number of the relevant *Flora of Ecuador* (FE) or *Flora Neotropica* (FN) treatment and/or the name of the specialist who checked the respective part of the list.

1	Acanthaceae	35	Wasshausen, 1988
2	Actinidiaceae	3	FE 17, 1982
3	Agavaceae	1	
4	Alismataceae	6	FE 26, 1986
5	Amaranthaceae	13	FE 28, 1987
6	Amaryllidaceae	6	FE 41, 1990
7	Anacardiaceae	8	FE 30, 1987
8	Annonaceae	72	Maas, 1989
9	Apiaceae	1	FE 5, 1976
10	Apocynaceae	32	Zarucchi, 1989
11	Aquifoliaceae	2	
12	Araceae	92	Croat, 1989
13	Araliaceae	15	
14	Arecaceae	58	Balslev, 1990
15	Aristolochiaceae	1	
16	Asclepiadaceae	8	
17	Asteraceae	53	FE 8, 1978 p.p.; Robinson, 1988
18	Balanophoraceae	3	FE 19, 1983
19	Balsaminaceae	2	
20	Begoniaceae	8	FE 25, 1986
21	Bignoniaceae	55	FE 7, 1977; Gentry, 1989
22	Bixaceae	4	FE 20, 1983
23	Bombacaceae	23	Alverson, 1989
24	Boraginaceae	22	
25	Bromeliaceae	40	Luther, 1991
26	Brunelliaceae	1	FN 2, 1970 & suppl. 1985
27	Burmanniaceae	10	FN 42, 1986
28	Burseraceae	35	Daly, 1988
29	Buxaceae	1	
30	Cabombaceae	1	
31	Cactaceae	6	FE 35, 1989
32	Campanulaceae	8	FE 14, 1981; Stein, 1989
33	Cannaceae	2	FE 32, 1988
34	Capparidaceae	11	
35	Caprifoliaceae	1	
36	Caricaceae	6	FE 20, 1983
37	Caryocaraceae	4	FN 12, 1973
38	Cecropiaceae	32	FN 7, 1972; 51, 1990; Berg, 1990
39	Celastraceae	3	
40	Ceratophyllaceae	1	
41	Chenopodiaceae	1	
42	Chrysobalanaceae	20	FE 10, 1979
43	Clusiaceae	33	
44	Combretaceae	9	
45	Commelinaceae	11	Faden, 1988
46	Connaraceae	6	FN 63, 1983
47	Convolvulaceae	20	FE 15, 1982

48	Costaceae	14	FE 6, 1976; Maas, 1989
49	Crassulaceae	2	
50	Cucurbitaceae	31	
51	Cyclanthaceae	23	FE 1, 1973; Erikson, 1990
52	Cyperaceae	42	Goetghebeur, 1989
53	Dichapetalaceae	9	FE 12, 1980
54	Dilleniaceae	6	Kubitzki, 1988
55	Dioscoreaceae	2	
56	Ebenaceae	5	
57	Elaeocarpaceae	11	
58	Ericaceae	1	FN 35, 1983
59	Eriocaulaceae	1	
60	Erythroxylaceae	5	FE 36, 1989
61	Euphorbiaceae	70	
62	Flacourtiaceae	28	FN 22, 1980
63	Gentianaceae	7	FN 41, 1986; Maas, 1989
64	Gesneriaceae	60	Kvist, 1988
65	Gnetaceae	1	
66	Haemadoraceae	1	
67	Haloragaceae	1	
68	Heliconaceae	18	FE 22, 1985; Kress, 1989
69	Hernandiaceae	1	
70	Hippocastanaceae	1	
71	Hippocrateaceae	13	Mennega, Oct 1989
72	Humiriaceae	1	
73	Hydrocharitaceae	1	FE 26, 1986
74	Icacinaceae	8	Howard, 1989
75	Iridaceae	1	
76	Lacistemaceae	5	FN 22, 1980
77	Lamiaceae	9	
78	Lauraceae	63	Rohwer, 1990
79	Lecythidaceae	19	FN 21(I), 1979; 21(II), 1990
80	Leguminosae	176	Madsen (*Acacia*); Klitgaard (*Brownea*)
81	Liliaceae	1	
82	Limnocharitaceae	1	FE 26, 1986
83	Loganiaceae	11	
84	Loranthaceae	11	FE 24, 1986
85	Lythraceae	5	FE 37, 1989
86	Magnoliaceae	1	
87	Malpighiaceae	19	FN 30, 1982 p.p.
88	Malvaceae	21	Fryxell, 1991
89	Marantaceae	53	FE 32, 1988
90	Margraviaceae	5	
91	Melastomataceae	172	FE 13, 1980; Renner, 1990
92	Meliaceae	39	FN 28, 1981; Pennington, 1989
93	Menispermaceae	22	
94	Monimiaceae	14	Renner, 1991
95	Moraceae	77	FN 7, 1972 p.p.; Berg, 1990
96	Musaceae	3	FE 22, 1985
97	Myristicaceae	26	Rodrigues, 1991
98	Myrsinaceae	16	Pipoly, 1988
99	Myrtaceae	64	Landrum, 1989

100	Najadaceae	1	FE 26, 1986
101	Nyctaginaceae	9	
102	Ochnaceae	5	
103	Olacaceae	10	FN 38, 1984
104	Oleaceae	1	
105	Onagraceae	5	FE 3, 1974
106	Opiliaceae	1	
107	Orchidaceae	376	FE 9, 1978 p.p.; D. Christensen, 1991
108	Oxalidaceae	6	
109	Passifloraceae	18	FE 31, 1988
110	Phytolaccaceae	6	Eliasson, 1988
111	Piperaceae	63	Callejas, 1989
112	Poaceae	61	Lægaard, 1991; bamboos: Judziewicz
113	Podocarpaceae	1	
114	Polygalaceae	4	Eriksen, 1991
115	Polygonaceae	11	FE 38, 1989
116	Pontederiaceae	5	FE 29, 1987
117	Portulacaceae	3	
118	Proteaceae	3	
119	Quiinaceae	4	
120	Rafflesiaceae	1	
121	Ranunculaceae	1	
122	Rapateaceae	1	
123	Rhamnaceae	7	
124	Rosaceae	1	Romoleroux, 1990
125	Rubiaceae	175	Boom, 1989
126	Rutaceae	20	Kallunki, 1989
127	Sabiaceae	4	
128	Sapindaceae	64	Acevedo, 1991
129	Sapotaceae	38	FN 52, 1990
130	Scrophulariaceae	6	FE 21, 1984
131	Simaroubaceae	9	Thomas, 1989
132	Smilacaceae	1	
133	Solanaceae	71	
134	Staphyleaceae	2	
135	Sterculiaceae	21	Taylor, 1989 (*Sterculia*)
136	Styracaeae	2	
137	Symplocaceae	1	
138	Theaceae	1	
139	Theophrastaceae	5	FE 39, 1990
140	Thymelaeaceae	2	
141	Tiliaceae	6	
142	Ulmaceae	5	
143	Urticaceae	14	
144	Verbenaceae	22	
145	Violaceae	15	FN 46, 1988 p.p.
146	Viscaceae	6	FE 24, 1986
147	Vitaceae	5	
148	Vochysiaceae	8	
149	Zingiberaceae	11	FE 6, 1976; Maas, 1989

7. LITERATURE CITED[3]

Alarcón Gallegos, R. 1988. Etnobotánica de los Quichuas de la Amazonía ecuatoriana. Miscelánea Antropológica Ecuatoriana. Serie Monogr. 7. Banco Central del Ecuador, Guayaquil.

Balslev, H. 1988. Distribution patterns of Ecuadorean plant species. Taxon 37: 567–577.

Balslev, H. and A. Barfod. 1987. Ecuadorean palms — an overview. Opera Botanica 92: 17–35.

Balslev, H., J. Luteyn, B. Øllgaard and L. B. Holm-Nielsen. 1987. Composition and structure of adjacent unflooded and floodplain forest in Amazonian Ecuador. Opera Botanica 92: 37–57.

Balslev, H. and S. S. Renner. 1989. The diversity of the Ecuadorean forests east of the Andes. Pp. 287–295 *In:* L. B. Holm-Nielsen, I. Nielsen, and H. Balslev (eds.), Tropical Forests: Botanical Dynamics, Speciation and Diversity. Academic Press, London.

Borchsenius, F. 1990. The Aarhus University Ecuador project 1987–1989. *In:* S. Lægaard and F. Borchsenius (eds.), Nordic Botanical Research in the Andes and Western Amazonia. AAU Reports 25: 67–78.

Borgtoft Pedersen, H. and H. Balslev. 1990. Ecuadorean Palms for Agroforestry. AAU Reports 23: 1–122.

Brandbyge, J. and E. Azanza. 1982. Report on the 5th and 7th Danish-Ecuadorean Botanical Expeditions. Rep. Bot. Inst., University of Aarhus 5: 1–138.

Bush, M. B. and P. A. Colinvaux. 1988. A 7000-year pollen record from the Amazon lowlands, Ecuador. Vegetatio 76: 141–154.

Bush, M. B., P. A. Colinvaux, M. C. Weimann, D. Piperno and K.-B. Liu. 1991. Late Pleistocene temperature depression and vegetation change in Ecuadorian Amazonia. Quat. Res. 34: 330–345.

Cañadas Cruz, L. 1983. El mapa bioclimático y ecológico del Ecuador. Banco Central, Quito. 210 pp + map.

Cerón, C. 1987. Los Cofánes de Dureno. Rev. Geografica 24: 7–16.

Cerón, C. 1989. Etnobotánica de los Cofánes de Dureno,

---

[3]Taxonomic accounts published in *Flora of Peru, Flora of Ecuador,* or *Flora Neotropica* are cited under the relevant families in the checklist.

provincia del Napo. Tesis doctoral, Universidad Central del Ecuador, Quito.

Cronquist, A. 1988. An integrated system of classification of flowering plants. 2nd. ed. Columbia Univ. Press, New York.

Davis, E. W. and J. Yost. 1983. The ethnobotany of the Waorani of eastern Ecuador. Botanical Museum Leaflets 29: 159–217.

Fundación Natura. 1988. Development policy issues for Ecuador's Amazonia. Paper prepared for the World Bank, Quito. cited in Hicks *et al.*, 1990.

Grubb, P., J. R. Lloyd, T. D. Pennington and T. C. Whitmore. 1963. A comparison of montane and lowland rain forest in Ecuador. I. The forest structure, physiognomy, and floristics. J. Ecol. 51: 567–601.

Grubb, P. and T. C. Whitmore. 1966. A comparison of montane and lowland rain forest in Ecuador II. The climate and its effects on the distribution and physiognomy of the forest. J. Ecol. 54: 303–333.

Grubb, P. and T. C. Whitmore. 1967. A comparison of montane and lowland rain forest in Ecuador III. The light reaching the ground vegetation. J. Ecol. 55: 33–57.

Harling, G. 1973. Cyclanthaceae. Flora of Ecuador 1: 1–48.

Harling, G. 1979. The vegetation types of Ecuador - a brief survey. Pp. 165–174 *In:* K. Larsen and L. B. Holm-Nielsen (eds.), Tropical Botany. Academic Press, London.

Haynes, R. R. and L. B. Holm-Nielsen. 1989. Speciation of Alismatidae in the Neotropics. Pp. 211–219 *In:* L. B. Holm-Nielsen, I. Nielsen, and H. Balslev (eds.), Tropical Forests, Botanical Dynamics, Speciation and Diversity. Academic Press, London.

Hicks, J. F., H. E. Daly, S. H. Davis and M. de Lourdes de Freitas. 1990. Ecuador's Amazon Region, Development Issues and Options. World Bank Discussion Papers 75. The World Bank, Washington, D. C..

Holmgren, P. K., N. H. Holmgren and L. C. Barnett. (eds.) 1990. Index Herbariorum, Part I: The Herbaria of the World. 8th ed. New York Botanical Garden, New York.

Holm-Nielsen, L. B. and S. Jeppesen. 1968. Preliminary report on the expedition to Ecuador (April–August, 1968). Bot. Inst., University of Aarhus. Unnumbered publication.

Irvine, D. 1987. Resource management by the Runa Indians of the Ecuadorian Amazon. Ph.D. dissertation, Dept. of

Anthrophology, Stanford Univ.
Jørgensen, P. M., C. Ulloa U., H. B. Pedersen and J. L. Luteyn.
submitted. Herbarium QCA: 100,000 important collections
from Ecuador.
Korning, J., K. Thomsen and B. Øllgaard. 1991. Composition and
structure of a species rich Amazonian rain forest obtained by
two different sample methods. Nord. J. Bot. 11: 103–110.
Kuijt, J. 1986. Eremolepidaceae, Viscaceae, Loranthaceae. Flora
of Ecuador 24: 1–198.
Kvist, L. P. and L. B. Holm-Nielsen. 1987. Ethnobotanical
aspects of lowland Ecuador. Opera Botanica 92: 83–107.
Lescure, J.-P., H. Balslev and R. Alarcón. 1987. Plantas útiles de
la Amazonía ecuatoriana. Un inventario critico de los datos
disponibles en Quito. ORSTOM - P.U.C.E. - I.N.C.R.A.E. -
PRONAREG, Quito.
Maas, P. and H. Maas. 1987. Ecuadorean saprophytes, a
preliminary review. Opera Botanica 92: 131–145.
Marles, R. J., D. A. Neill and N. R. Farnsworth. 1988. A
contribution to the ethnopharmacology of the lowland
Quichua people of Amazonian Ecuador. Rev. Acad. Colomb.
Ci. Exact. 16: 111–120.
Meikle, R. D. and collaborators. 1980. Draft Index of Author
Abbreviations. The Herbarium, Royal Botanic Gardens, Kew.
Neill, D. A. 1988. Jatun Sacha Biological Station, Amazonian
Ecuador: An invitation to tropical biologists. Biotropica 20: 59.
Neill, D. A. and W. A. Palacios. 1989. Arboles de la Amazonia
ecuatoriana. Lista preliminar de especies. Ministerio de
Agricultura y Ganadería, Quito.
Paz y Miño C., G. 1990. Inventario cuantitativo de las lianas de
una hectarea de bosque tropical en la Reserva de Producción
Faunistica Cuyabeno, Amazonia del Ecuador. Thesis de
licenciatura, P. Universidad Católica del Ecuador, Quito.
Paz y Miño C., G, H. Balslev, R. Valencia R. and P. Mena V. 1991.
Lianas utilizadas por los indígenas Siona-Secoya de la
Amazonía del Ecuador. Ecociencia, Reportes Tecnicos 1:
1–40.
Pinkley, H. V. 1973. The ethno-ecology of the Kofán indians. Ph.
D. dissertation, Harvard University, Cambridge, Massa-
chusetts.
Poulsen, A. D. and H. Balslev. 1991. Abundance and cover of
ground herbs in an Amazonian rain forest. J. Veg. Science 2:
000–000.
Prance, G. T. 1979. Notes on the vegetation of Amazonia III. The

terminology of Amazon forest types subject to inundation. Brittonia 31: 26–38.

Renner, S. S.   in press. A history of botanical exploration in Amazonian Ecuador (1738–1988). 120 pp. ms.

Sourdat, M. and E. Custode. 1980. Problemática del Manejo Integral y Estudio Morfo-Pedológico de la Región Amazonica Ecuatoriana. MAG-ORSTOM, Quito.

Vickers, W. T. 1976. Cultural adaptation to Amazonian habitats: The Siona-Secoya of eastern Ecuador. Ph.D. dissertation, University of Florida, Gainesville.

Vickers, W. T. 1989. Los Sionas y Secoyas. Su adaptación al ambiente amazónico. Ediciones Abya-Yala, Quito.

Vickers, W. T. and T. Plowman. 1984. Useful plants of the Siona and Secoya Indians of eastern Ecuador. Fieldiana: Botany 15: 1–63.

8. CHEKLIST OF FLOWERING PLANTS[4]

Acanthaceae
E. C. Leonard, Fl. Costa Rica, Publ. Field Mus. Nat. Hist., Bot. Ser. 18: 1188–1263. 1938. Identifications mostly by D. Wasshausen, US.

Aphelandra attenuata **Wassh.**
  Prov.: N; shrub; *Holm-Nielsen & Jeppesen 743* (AAU); *Sparre 13119* (S)
Aphelandra aurantiaca **(Scheidw.) Lindley**
  Prov.: N; shrub; *Holm-Nielsen & Jeppesen 727* (AAU)
Aphelandra crenata **Leonard**
  Prov.: N; shrub; *Cerón 1289* (QAME n.v.)
Aphelandra crispata **Leonard emend. Wassh.**
  Prov.: N; shrub; *Arguello 578* (AAU)
Aphelandra dielsii **Mildbr.**
  Prov.: N, P; herb; *Holm-Nielsen & Jeppesen 935* (AAU)
Aphelandra flava **Nees**
  Prov.: N; shrub; *Neill 7612* (QAME n.v.)
Aphelandra hylaea **Leonard**
  Prov.: N, P; herb, shrub; *Neill et al. 6029* (QCA); *Jaramillo & Coello 3212* (QCA). Reaches 750 m alt. in Napo: *Asplund 8976* (S).
Aphelandra ochrolarynx **Leonard**
  Prov.: N; herb; *Asplund 9290* (S). Reaches 750 m alt.
Aphelandra tessmannii **Mildbr.**
  Prov.: N; herb; *Neill & Gómez 6426* (QCA); *Lawesson et al. 39795* (AAU, QCA)
Blechum **sp.**
  Prov.: P; herb; *Løjtnant & Molau 13403* (QCA)
Fittonia albivenis **(Lindley ex Veitch) Brummitt**
  Prov.: N, P; herb; *Luteyn et al. 8671* (AAU, NY); *Alarcón 19392* (QCA); *Balslev & Alarcón 2951* (QCA); *Vickers 213* (F). Syn. *Fittonia argyroneura* Coem.
Hygrophila guianensis **Nees**
  Prov.: N; shrub; *Holm-Nielsen et al. 20224* (AAU)
Jacobinia axiologa **Leonard**
  Prov.: N; shrub; *Neill 7065* (QAME n.v.)
Justicia appendiculata **(Ruíz & Pavón) Wassh.**
  Prov.: N; herb; *Holm-Nielsen & Jeppesen 907* (AAU, S)
Justicia chlorantha **Leonard**
  Prov.: N; herb, shrub; *Holm-Nielsen & Jeppesen 749* (AAU); *Gentry 9791* (AAU, GB, MO, QCA); *Harling 3598* (S); *Jaramillo & Coello 3718* (QCA)
Justicia comata **(L.) Lam.**
  Prov.: N, P; herb, shrub; *Holm-Nielsen 19283* (AAU); *Dwyer & MacBryde 9809* (QCA); *McElroy 179* (QCA)
Justicia idiogenes **Leonard**
  Prov.: P; shrub; *Neill 6718* (QAME n.v.)
Justicia sanchenioides **Leonard**
  Prov.: N; herb; *Harling 3574* (S)

---

[4]Only two species of gymnosperms are known to occur in the eastern Ecuadorean lowlands: ***Podocarpus rospigliosii* Pilger** (Prov. N; tree; *Neill 7202,* MO) and ***Gnetum nodiflorum* Brogn.** (Prov. N; liana; *Balslev et al. 84747,* AAU, QCA).

Acanthaceae (cont.)

Justicia struebelii Lindau
    Prov.: N; herb; *Holm-Nielsen & Jeppesen 774* (AAU)
Kalbreyeriella rostellata Lindau
    Prov.: N, P; herb, shrub; *Harling 3304* (S); *Korning & Thomsen 47402* (AAU);
    Oldeman & Arévalo 116 (QCA)
Mendoncia glabra (Poeppig & Endl.) Nees
    Prov.: N; shrub; *Irvine 521* (F)
Mendoncia orbicularis Turr.
    Prov.: N; shrub; *Zaruma et al. 521* (QAME n.v.)
Mendoncia sprucei Lindau
    Prov.: N, P; liana; *Holm-Nielsen et al. 21845* (AAU); *Neill & Gómez 6442*
    (QCA)
Ruellia chartacea (T. Anders.) Wassh.
    Prov.: N, P; shrub; *Holm-Nielsen & Jeppesen 742* (AAU); *Neill & Gómez 6435*
    (QCA). Syn. *Ruellia colorata* Baillon.
Ruellia humboldtiana (Nees) Lindau
    Prov.: N; shrub; *Korning & Thomsen 47201* (AAU)
Ruellia lasiostachya Leonard
    Prov.: N; shrub; *Korning & Thomsen 47138* (AAU)
Ruellia phyllocalyx Lindau
    Prov.: N, P; herb; *Balslev & Alarcón 2982* (QCA); *McElroy 270* (QCA)
Ruellia riopalenquensis Wassh.
    Prov.: N; shrub; *Alarcón 66* (QCA)
Ruellia terminale (Nees) Wassh.
    Prov.: N; herb; *Holm-Nielsen et al. 21646* (AAU)
Sanchezia longiflora (Hook.) Hook. f. ex Planchon
    Prov.: N; shrub or tree; *Korning & Thomsen 47184* (AAU)
Sanchezia oxysepala Mildbr.
    Prov.: N, P; herb, shrub; *Harling 3311* (S); *Balslev & Madsen 10586* (QCA);
    Holm-Nielsen & Jeppesen 387 (AAU, QCA)
Sanchezia sericea Leonard
    Prov.: N; tree; *Holm-Nielsen & Jeppesen 741* (AAU); *Gentry et al. 22104* (MO)
Sanchezia skutchii Leonard & Smith
    Prov.: N, P; shrub; *Gentry 12552* (AAU, MO); *Fagerlind & Wibom 1225* (S)
Sanchezia tigrina Leonard
    Prov.: N, P; herb, shrub; *Balslev 2311* (QCA). Reaches 900 m alt. in Napo:
    Sparre 17411 (S).
Teliostachya lanceolata Nees
    Prov.: N; herb; *Vickers 236* (F). Reaches 750 m alt. in Napo: *Asplund 9327* (S).

Actinidiaceae
D. D. Soejarto, Fl. Ecuador 17, 1982.

Saurauia aguaricana Soejarto
    Prov.: N; tree; *Løjtnant et al. 11933* (GB)
Saurauia herthae Sleumer
    Prov.: N, P; shrub, tree; *Harling & Andersson 17505* (GB); *Lugo 1723 (AAU);*
    MacBryde 1511 (QCA)

Actinidiaceae (cont.)

Saurauia prainiana Busc.
    Prov.: N, P; tree; *Neill 6997, 7091* (MO); *Mexía 7227* (US).   Reaches 3000 m alt.
    in Napo: *Boom et al. 1439* (AAU, NY).

Agavaceae

Cordyline terminalis (L.) Kunth
    Prov.: N, M-S; herb; *Vickers 151* (QCA); *Cerón 208* (QAME n.v.).   Possibly this
    is *C. fruticosa* (L.) A. Chev.

Alismataceae
L. B. Holm-Nielsen and R. R. Haynes, Fl. Ecuador 26, 1986.

Echinodorus bolivianus (Rusby) Holm-Nielsen
    Prov.: N; herb; *Øllgaard et al. 57661* (QCA), *57161* (AAU)
Echinodorus eglandulosus Holm-Nielsen & R. Haynes
    Prov.: N; herb; *Holm-Nielsen et al. 19996* (AAU, QCA)
Echinodorus grisebachii Small
    Prov.: N; herb; *Harling et al. 7441* (GB)
Echinodorus horizontalis Rataj
    Prov.: N, P; herb; *Holm-Nielsen et al. 22725* (AAU); *Jaramillo & Coello 3004*
    (AAU, QCA)
Echinodorus tunicatus Small
    Prov.: N, P; herb; *Holm-Nielsen et al. 21495* (AAU); *Jaramillo & Coello 4237*
    (AAU, QCA)
Sagittaria latifolia Willd.
    Prov.: N, P; herb; *Holm-Nielsen et al. 20012* (AAU)

Amaranthaceae
U. Eliasson, Fl. Ecuador 28, 1987.

Alternanthera bettzichiana (Regel) Voss
    Prov.: N; herb; *Lawesson et al. 39703* (AAU); *Alarcón 1* (QCA); *Vickers 20* (F);
Alternanthera mexicana (Schldl.) Hieron.
    Prov.: N, M-S; herb; *Harling 1140* (S); *Vickers 25* (F).   Reaches 2000 m alt. in
    Napo: *Balslev & Madsen 10337* (AAU).   Syn. *A. lanceolata* (Benth.) Schinz.
Alternanthera sessilis (L.) DC.
    Prov.: N, P; herb; *Molau & Öhman 1596* (GB); *Løjtnant & Molau 13412* (AAU,
    GB); *Fagerlind & Wibom 2259* (S)
Amaranthus cruentus L.
    Prov.: N; herb; *Vickers 7* (F).   Distributed as *A. caudatus* L.
Amaranthus hybridus L.
    Prov.: N, M-S; herb; *Lugo 3516* (GB); *Molau & Öhman 1566* (GB).   Reaches 980
    m alt. in M-S: *Holm-Nielsen et al. 4562* (AAU, S).

Amaranthaceae   (cont.)

Amaranthus spinosus L.
>   Prov.: N; herb; *Harling et al. 7276, 7316* (GB); *Molau & Öhman 1566* (GB)
>   Reaches 1000 m alt. in M-S: *Holm-Nielsen et al. 4426* (AAU)

Celosia argentea L.
>   Prov.: N; herb; *Vickers 1* (F); *Irvine 1058* (F, QCA).   Syn. *C. cristata* L.

Chamissoa acuminata C. Martius
>   Prov.: N; herb; *Lugo 2667* (GB); *Molau & Öhman 155* (GB).   Reaches 1000 m
>   alt. in Napo: *Asplund 9470* (S)

Chamissoa altissima (Jacq.) H.B.K.
>   Prov.: N, P, M-S; shrub; *Brandbyge & Azanza 31457* (AAU); *MacBryde 1534*
>   (MO, QCA).   Reaches 1700 m alt.

Cyathula achyranthoides (H.B.K.) Moquin
>   Prov.: N, P, M-S; herb, shrub; *Holm-Nielsen & Jeppesen 999* (AAU, S);
>   *Oldeman & Arévalo 70* (QCA).   Reaches 1000 m alt.

Cyathula prostrata (L.) Blume
>   Prov.: N, M-S; herb; *Holm-Nielsen et al. 20022* (AAU); *Brandbyge & Azanza*
>   *32287* (AAU, GB, QCA).

Iresine diffusa Humb. & Bonpl. ex Willd.
>   Prov.: N, P, M-S; herb; *Løjtnant & Molau 13375* (AAU); *Asdall 82-11* (QCA)
>   Reaches 1050 m alt. in Pastaza: *Holm-Nielsen & Jeppesen 359* (AAU)

Pfaffia paniculata (C. Martius) Kuntze
>   Prov.: N, M-S; scandent shrub; *Brandbyge et al. 33620* (AAU, QCA).   Reaches
>   1500 m alt. in M-S: *Harling & Andersson 24425* (GB)

Amaryllidaceae
A.W. Meerow, Fl. Ecuador 41, 1990.

Crinum erubescens Ait.
>   Prov.: N; herb; *Sparre 13261* (S)

Crinum × amabile Donn
>   Prov.: N; herb; *Azanza & Barfod 41198* (AAU)

Eucharis candida Planchon & Linden
>   Prov.: N, P, M-S; herb; *Madison et al. 5326* (F, SEL)

Eucharis formosa Meerow
>   Prov.: N, P; herb; *Holm-Nielsen et al. 20168* (AAU)

Eucharis moorei (Baker) Meerow
>   Prov.: M-S; herb; *Harling 1407* (S).   Mostly collected at higher altitudes.

Hippeastrum puniceum (Lam.) Kuntze
>   Prov.: N; herb; *Vickers 193* (F)

Anacardiaceae
A. Barfod, Fl. Ecuador 30, 1987.

Anacardium occidentale L.
>   Prov.: N; tree; *Harling et al. 7324* (AAU, GB); *Alarcón 726* (QCA)

Mangifera indica L.
>   Prov.: N; tree; *Brandbyge & Azanza 32857* (AAU); *Vickers 154* (QCA)

Anacardiaceae (cont.)

Mauria heterophylla Kunth
    Prov.: N; tree; *Palacios 1443* (QAME n.v.)
Mauria suaveolens Poeppig
    Prov.: M-S; tree; *Little et al. 85* (US)
Spondias mombin L.
    Prov.: N; tree; *Lugo 2525* (AAU, GB); *Alarcón 71* (QCA); *Neill 7160* (QCA);
    Vickers 111 (QCA). Syn. *S. venulosa* (Engl.) Engler.
Spondias purpurea L.
    Prov.: N; tree; *Korning & Thomsen 47494* (AAU); *Alarcón 71* (QCA)
Tapirira guianensis Aublet
    Prov.: N, P, M-S; tree; *Øllgaard 34980* (AAU); *Neill et al. 6364* (QCA). Reaches
    750 m alt. in Napo: *Asplund 8922* (S). Syn. *T. myriantha* Triana & Planchon.
Tapirira peckoltiana Engler
    Prov.: N; tree; *Brandbyge et al. 36015* (AAU); *Cerón 624* (QAME n.v.). Syn.
    T. marchandii Engler.

Annonaceae
R. E. Fries *in* J. F. Macbride, Fl. Peru 2(3), Publ. Field Mus. Nat. Hist.,
Bot. Ser. 13: 700–766. 1938. This listing checked by P. Maas, Jan 1989.

Anaxagorea brevipes Benth.
    Prov.: P; tree; *Holm-Nielsen et al. 22283* (AAU); *Øllgaard et al. 35282* (AAU)
Anaxagorea dolichocarpa Sprague & Sandw.
    Prov.: N; tree; *Holm-Nielsen et al. 19913* (AAU); *Foster 3707* (AAU, QCA)
Anaxagorea phaeocarpa C. Martius
    Prov.: N; tree; *Cerón 884* (QAME n.v.); *Neill 7233* (QAME n.v.)
Annona ambotay Aublet
    Prov.: N; tree; *Bloch & Valencia 68338* (AAU)
Annona duckei Diels
    Prov.: N; tree; *Neill et al. 6386* (QCA)
Annona hypoglauca C. Martius
    Prov.: N; tree; *Holm-Nielsen et al. 21429* (AAU)
Annona montana Macfad.
    Prov.: N; tree; *Korning & Thomsen 47485* (AAU)
Annona muricata L.
    Prov.: N; tree; *Balslev 4846* (QCA); *Pinkley 99* (S)
Annona purpurea Mociño & Sessé ex Dunal
    Prov.: N; tree; *Vickers 104* (QCA); *Irvine 720* (F, QCA)
Annona sp. 1
    Prov.: N; tree; *Brandbyge et al. 33568* (AAU)
Annona sp. 2
    Prov.: N; tree; *Korning & Thomsen 47499* (AAU)
Cremastosperma cauliflorum R. E. Fries
    Prov.: N, P, M-S; tree; *Brandbyge & Azanza 32225* (AAU, QCA)
Cremastosperma gracilipes R. E. Fries
    Prov.: N, P; shrub; *Øllgaard et al. 35223* (AAU, QCA); *Foster 3716* (QCA)
Cremastosperma megalophyllum R. E. Fries
    Prov.: N, P; tree; *Brandbyge & Azanza 30017* (AAU, QCA)
Cremastosperma monospermum (Rusby) R. E. Fries aff.
    Prov.: P; tree; *Holm-Nielsen & Jeppesen 903* (AAU, QCA)

Annonaceae   (cont.)

Cremastosperma sp.
　Prov.: N; tree; *Brandbyge et al. 32566* (AAU)
Cymbopetalum odoratissimum Barb. Rodr.
　Prov.: P; tree; *Holm-Nielsen & Jeppesen 958* (AAU)
Cymbopetalum sp.
　Prov.: N; tree; *Holm-Nielsen 22726* (AAU); *Balslev & Madsen 10651* (AAU)
Duguetia cf. argentea R. E. Fries
　Prov.: N; tree; *Korning & Thomsen 47816* (AAU)
Duguetia odorata (Diels) J. F. Macbr.
　Prov.: N; tree; *Neill & Palacios 6611* (QCA); *Nowak 90* (QCA)
Duguetia peruviana R. E. Fries
　Prov.:N; tree; *Palacios 875* (QAME n.v.)
Duguetia spixiana C. Martius
　Prov.: N; tree; *Øllgaard et al. 57148* (AAU); *Palacios 876* (QAME n.v.)
Duguetia tessmannii R. E. Fries
　Prov.: N; tree; *Chaguaro 11* (QCA)
Fusaea peruviana R. E. Fries
　Prov.: M-S; tree; *Brandbyge & Azanza 32184* (AAU); *Jaramillo 4077* (AAU)
Fusaea sp.
　Prov.: N; tree; *Bloch & Valencia 67440* (AAU)
　Probably = *F. longifolia* (Aublet) Saff.
Guatteria amazonica R. E. Fries
　Prov.: N; tree; *Bloch & Valencia 67887* (AAU)
Guatteria asplundiana R. E. Fries
　Prov.: N; tree; *Korning & Thomsen 47429* (AAU)
Guatteria brevicuspis R. E. Fries
　Prov.: N; tree; *Holm-Nielsen et al. 21632A* (AAU)
Guatteria chrysophylla Maas & van Setten
　Prov.: N; tree; *Davis & Yost 1011* (NY, QCA, U)
Guatteria discolor R. E. Fries
　Prov.: N; tree; *Korning & Thomsen 58668* (AAU)
Guatteria ecuadorensis R. E. Fries
　Prov.: N; tree; *Asplund 9400* (GB).   Reaches 750 m alt.
Guatteria excellens R. E. Fries
　Prov. N; tree; *Foster 3751* (AAU)
Guatteria megalophylla Diels
　Prov.: N, M-S; tree; *Øllgaard et al. 38999* (AAU); *Little et al. 546* (US)
Guatteria sp. 1
　Prov.: N; tree; *Holm-Nielsen 21632B* (AAU)
Guatteria sp. 2
　Prov.: N; tree; *Holm-Nielsen 818* (AAU)
Guatteria sp. 3
　Prov.: N; tree; *Jaramillo 3479* (AAU)
Guatteria sp. 4
　Prov.: N; tree; *Øllgaard et al. 58619* (AAU)
Guatteria sp. 5
　Prov.:N; tree; *Øllgaard et al. 57186* (AAU)
Guatteria sp. 6
　Prov.: N; tree; *SEF 10075* (AAU, QCA)

Annonaceae   (cont.)

Guatteria sp. 7
   Prov.: N; tree; *SEF 8573* (AAU, QCA)
Guatteria sp. 8
   Prov.: N; tree; *SEF 10109* (AAU)
Malmea depressa (Baillon) R. E. Fries
   Prov.: N; tree; *Neill 6402* (QAME n.v.)
Malmea lucida Diels
   Prov.: N; tree; *Zaruma 51* (QAME n.v.)
Malmea peruviana R. E. Fries aff.
   Prov.: N; tree; *SEF 8513* (AAU, QCA)
Malmea xanthochlora (Diels) R. E. Fries aff.
   Prov.: N; tree; *Brandbyge et al. 32968* (AAU); *Harling et al. 14790* (GB, QCA)
Malmea sp.
   Prov.: N; tree; *SEF 8919* (AAU, QCA)
Oxandra acuminata Diels
   Prov.: N; tree; *Øllgaard et al. 57185* (AAU); *SEF 9080* (AAU)
Oxandra euneura Diels aff.
   Prov.: N; tree; *Lawesson et al. 44366* (AAU)
Oxandra mediocris Diels
   Prov.: P; tree; *Neill 6647* (QAME n.v.)
Oxandra xylopioides Diels
   Prov.: N; tree; *Brandbyge et al. 36096* (AAU); *Little et al. 495* (US)
Porcelia nitidifolia Ruíz & Pavón
   Prov.: N; tree; *SEF 9117* (AAU)
Rollinia dolichopetala R. E. Fries
   Prov.: N; tree; *Neill 7298* (QAME n.v.)
Rollinia ecuadorensis R. E. Fries
   Prov.: N; tree; *Cerón 836* (QAME n.v.); *Neill et al. 6272* (QCA)
Rollinia edulis Triana & Planchon
   Prov.: N; tree; *Foster 3874* (AAU)
Rollinia glomerulifera Maas & Westra
   Prov.: N; tree; *Cerón 1463* (MO, U); *Jaramillo & Coello 3810* (AAU)
Rollinia helosioides Maas & Westra
   Prov.: N; tree; *Zaruma et al. 242* (MO, U); *Neill et al. 6184* (MO, U)
Rollinia hispida Maas & Westra
   Prov.: N; tree; *Palacios & Neill 751* (MO, U)
Rollina mucosa (Jacq.) Baillon
   Prov.: N, P; tree; *Neill et al. 6174* (QCA); *Palacios et al. 274* (AAU, QCA)
Rollinia pittieri Standley
   Prov.: M-S; tree; *Little et al. 733* (US); *Dodson et al. 14999* (MO, U)
Ruizodendron ovale (Ruíz & Pavón) R. E. Fries
   Prov.: N; tree; *Palacios et al. 1036* (AAU)
Tetrameranthus globuliferus Westra
   Prov.: N; tree; *Korning & Thomsen 47626* (AAU)
Trigynaea ecuadorensis R. E. Fries
   Prov.: N; shrub, tree; *Jaramillo & Coello 2801* (AAU, QCA)
Trigynaea sp.
   Prov.: N; tree; *Korning & Thomsen 47447* (AAU)
Unonopsis floribunda Diels
   Prov.: N; tree; *Palacios 495* (QAME n.v.)

Annonaceae (cont.)

Unonopsis veneficiorum (C. Martius) R. E. Fries
  Prov.: N, P; tree; *Øllgaard et al. 39177* (AAU); *Foster 3675* (AAU, F)
Xylopia cuspidata Diels
  Prov.: N; shrub, tree; *Lawesson et al. 39429* (AAU); *Foster 3816* (AAU)
Xylopia cuspidata Diels aff.
  Prov.: N; tree; *Bloch & Valencia 68699* (AAU)
Xylopia ligustrifolia Dunal
  Prov.: N; tree; *Foster 3677* (AAU, F)
Xylopia nitida Dunal
  Prov.: M-S; tree; *Little et al. 723* (US)
Xylopia parviflora Spruce
  Prov.: P; tree; *Neill 6745* (QAME n.v.)
Xylopia sericea A. St. Hil.
  Prov.: N; tree; *Korning & Thomsen 47607* (AAU)
Xylopia surinamensis R. E. Fries aff.
  Prov.: N; tree; *Bloch & Valencia 68634* (AAU)

Apiaceae
M. E. Mathias and L. Constance, Fl. Ecuador 5, 1976.

Eryngium foetidum L.
  Prov.: N, P, M-S; herb; *Holm-Nielsen & Jeppesen 718* (AAU, S); *Sparre 13007*
  (S); *Irvine 703* (F, QCA); *Balslev 4889* (QCA); *Pinkley 330* (S).   Reaches 1100 m.

Apocynaceae
J. F. Macbride, Fl. Peru 5(1), Publ. Field Mus. Nat. Hist., Bot. Ser. 13:
363–455. 1959. This listing checked by J. Zarucchi, Feb 1989.

Allamanda cathartica L.
  Prov.: N; shrub; *Pinkley 152* (ECON); *Lawesson et al. 39705* (AAU, QCA)
Aspidosperma inundatum Ducke
  Prov.: N; tree; *Foster 3749* (F, QCA)
Aspidosperma rigidum Rusby
  Prov.: N; tree; *SEF 8515* (AAU); *Pennington 10734* (MO)
Aspidosperma verruculosum Muell. Arg.
  Prov.: M-S; tree; *Little et al. 728* (US)
Aspidosperma sp.
  Prov.: N; tree; *SEF 8941, 9270* (AAU); *Holm-Nielsen et al. 20052B* (AAU)
Couma macrocarpa Barb. Rodr.
  Prov.: N; tree; *Alarcón 90* (QCA).   Same as *C. guianensis* Aublet ?
Fosteronia acouci (Ruíz & Pavón) R. E. Fries
  Prov.: N, tree; *Neill 7302* (QAME n.v.)
Himatanthus lancifolius (Muell. Arg.) Woodson
  Prov.: N; tree; *Jaramillo & Coello 4140* (AAU, QCA); *Davis & Yost 957* (QCA)
Himatanthus sucuuba (Spruce ex Muell. Arg.) Woodson
  Prov.: N; tree; *Neill et al. 6520* (MO, QCA)

Apocynaceae   (cont.)

Lacmellea floribunda (Poeppig) Benth.
    Prov.: N, tree; *Neill 6920* (QAME n.v.)
Lacmellea lactescens (Kuhlm.) Markgraf
    Prov.: N; tree; *Øllgaard et al. 39197* (AAU); *Balslev & Alarcón 2952* (QCA)
Lacmellea oblongata Markgraf
    Prov.: N; tree; *Korning & Thomsen 58729* (AAU); *Neill et al. 6499* (AAU, QCA)
Lacmellea speciosa Woodson aff.
    Prov.: M-S; tree; *Little et al. 715* (US)
Mandevilla callista Woodson
    Prov.: N, M-S; liana; *Azanza & Barfod 41186* (AAU, QCA). Reaches 1600 m
    alt. in M-S: *Gentry et al. 30842* (AAU).
Mandevilla hirsuta (Rich.) K. Schum.
    Prov.: N; shrub, liana; *Balslev & Madsen 10594* (AAU, QCA)
Mandevilla scabra (Roemer & Schultes) K. Schum.
    Prov.: N; shrub, liana; *Holm-Nielsen et al. 19907* (AAU)
Mandevilla trianae Woodson
    Prov.: N; shrub; *Cerón 773* (QAME n.v.)
Odontadenia cognata (Stadelm.) Woodson
    Prov.: N; liana; *Gentry 12547* (MO, QCA)
Odontadenia funigera Woodson
    Prov.: N; shrub; *Zaruma et al. 706* (QAME n.v.)
Odontadenia macrantha (Roemer & Schultes) Markgraf
    Prov.: N, P; shrub, liana; *Holm-Nielsen et al. 22141* (AAU); *Brandbyge &*
    Azanza 31488 (AAU, QCA); *Brandbyge et al. 33566* (AAU, QCA)
Prestonia acutifolia (Benth. ex Muell. Arg.) K. Schum.
    Prov.: N; shrub, liana; *Holm-Nielsen et al. 21159* (AAU)
Prestonia portobellensis (Beurl.) Woodson
    Prov.: N; liana; *Lawesson et al. 39366* (AAU, QCA)
Prestonia trifida (Poeppig) Woodson
    Prov.: N; liana; *Pennington 10637* (QCA)
Rauvolfia leptophylla A. S. Rao vel sp. aff.
    Prov.: N; tree; *Neill 6937* (QAME n.v.)
Rauvolfia praecox K. Schum. ex Markgraf
    Prov.: N; tree; *Neill & Palacios 7080* (AAU)
Tabernaemontana maxima Markgraf
    Prov.: P, M-S; tree, shrub; *Jaramillo et al. 31729* (QCA)
Tabernaemontana muelleriana C. Martius ex Muell. Arg.
    Prov.: P; liana, tree; *Holm-Nielsen et al. 22178* (AAU)
Tabernaemontana muricata Link aff.
    Prov.: N; tree; *Brandbyge & Azanza 30034* (AAU)
Tabernaemontana sananho Ruíz & Pavón
    Prov.: N, P; shrub, tree; *Holm-Nielsen et al. 21930* (AAU); *Foster 3738* (F, QCA);
    Alarcón 43 (QCA); *Vickers 46* (F); *MacBryde & Dwyer 1338* (MO, QCA);
    Irvine 369 (F, QCA)
Tabernaemontana siphilitica (L.f.) Leeuwenberg
    Prov.: N, P; shrub, tree; *Holm-Nielsen et al. 21636* (AAU)
Tabernaemontana submollis Muell. Arg. aff.
    Prov.: N; shrub, tree; *Holm-Nielsen et al. 21594* (AAU)
Tabernaemontana tetrastachya H.B.K
    Prov.: N; shrub, liana; *Pinkley 109, 499* (ECON, S)

Aquifoliaceae
J. F. Macbride, Fl. Peru 3A(1), Publ. Field Mus. Nat. Hist., Bot. Ser. 13: 270–288. 1951.

Ilex guayusa **Loes.**
　　Prov.: N, P; tree; *Balslev & Santos Dea 2824* (AAU); *Pinkley 199* (ECON); *Lawesson et al. 39636* (AAU, QCA); *Zarucchi 2351* (MO, S); *Little et al. 333* (COL, US); *Irvine 723* (F). Reaches 1000 m alt.
Ilex inundata **Poeppig ex Reiss.**
　　Prov.: N; tree; *Foster 3591* (F, S); *Lawesson et al. 43388, 44244* (AAU, QCA); *Jaramillo 6896* (AAU, QCA)

Araceae
J. F. Macbride, Fl. Peru 1(3), Publ. Field Mus. Nat. Hist., Bot. Ser. 13: 428–486. 1936. Identifications mostly by T. Croat, MO.

Anthurium acrobates **Sodiro**
　　Prov.: N, P, M-S; epiphytic herb; *Holm-Nielsen & Jeppesen 976* (AAU); *Balslev 2320* (QCA); *Palacios et al. 294* (QCA). Reaches 2000 m alt.
Anthurium alienatum **Schott**
　　Prov.: N; herb; *Holm-Nielsen et al. 21030* (AAU); *Balslev & Alarcón 3034* (QCA); *Madison et al. 5333* (QCA, SEL)
Anthurium apaporanum **R. E. Schultes**
　　Prov.: N; herb; *Cerón 972* (QAME n.v.)
Anthurium artropurpureum **Schultes & Maguire**
　　Prov.: N; herb; *Balslev & Madsen 10621* (AAU); *Brandbyge et al. 33207* (AAU)
Anthurium aureum **Engl.**
　　Prov.: N, P, M-S; terrestrial or epiphytic herb; *Brandbyge & Azanza 31050* (AAU, QCA); *McElroy 53* (QCA); *Balslev & Alarcón 2936* (QCA)
Anthurium bakeri **Hook. f.**
　　Prov.: N, P; herb; *Harling et al. 7556* (GB); *Lawesson et al. 43509* (AAU)
Anthurium brevipedunculatum **Madison**
　　Prov.: N; herb; *Lawesson et al. 39475* (AAU); *Harling et al. 7421* (GB)
Anthurium brevispadix **Madison**
　　Prov.: N; herb; *Poulsen 80529* (AAU, QCA)
Anthurium clavigerum **Poeppig & Endl.**
　　Prov.: N; epiphytic herb; *Øllgaard et al. 39236* (AAU); *Luteyn et al. 9083* (NY, QCA); *Neill et al. 6460* (QCA); *Alarcón 76* (QCA)
Anthurium croatii **Madison**
　　Prov.: N; herb; *Harling et al. 7197* (GB)
Anthurium decurrens **Poeppig**
　　Prov.: N, P; epiphytic herb; *Balslev 2296* (QCA); *Jaramillo & Coello 3521* (QCA)
Anthurium dolichostachyum **Sodiro**
　　Prov.: M-S; herb; *Brandbyge & Azanza 32304* (AAU). Reaches 1900 m alt.
Anthurium eminens **Engl.**
　　Prov.: N, P, M-S; epiphytic herb; *Holm-Nielsen & Jeppesen 921* (AAU); *Davis & Yost 962* (QCA); *Balslev 2334* (QCA)
Anthurium ernestii **Engl.**
　　Prov.: N, P, M-S; herb; *Holm-Nielsen et al. 21543* (AAU)

Araceae (cont.)

Anthurium formosum Schott
Prov.: P; herb; *Lugo 1131* (GB). Reaches 1050 m in Pastaza: *Holm-Nielsen & Jeppesen 506* (AAU).

Anthurium gracile (Rudge) Lindley
Prov.: N, P, M-S; epiphytic herb; *Holm-Nielsen & Jeppesen 815* (AAU); *Besse et al. 32* (QCA, SEL); *Alarcón 72* (QCA). Reaches 800 m alt. in M-S: *Holm-Nielsen et al. 4217* (AAU).

Anthurium cf. guayaguilense Engl.
Prov.: N; epiphytic herb; *Foster 3703 A* (QCA); prob. also *Vickers 254* (F)

Anthurium harlingianum Croat
Prov.: N; herb; *Cerón 1227* (QAME n.v.)

Anthurium interruptum Sodiro
Prov.: N; herb; *Cerón 865* (QAME n.v.)

Anthurium kunthii Poeppig
Prov.: N, M-S; epiphytic herb; *Lawesson et al. 44389* (AAU); *Madison et al. 5375* (QCA, SEL)

Anthurium loretense Croat
Prov.: N, herb; *Brandbyge et al. 33700* (AAU)

Anthurium margaricarpum Sodiro
Prov.: N; epiphytic herb; *Oldeman et al. 36* (QCA)

Anthurium cf. michelii Guill.
Prov.: N, P; herb; *Cerón 3124* (QAME n.v.). Reaches 900 m alt. in Pastaza: *Holm-Nielsen & Jeppesen 511* (AAU).

Anthurium mindense Sodiro
Prov.: N, P; terrestrial or epiphytic herb; *Jaramillo 97* (AAU, QCA); *Croat 49520* (MO, QCA). Reaches 1500 m alt.

Anthurium oxycarpum Poeppig
Prov.: N; epiphytic herb; *Holm-Nielsen et al. 21115* (AAU); *Lawesson et al. 44409* (AAU, QCA)

Anthurium pendulifolium N. E. Brown
Prov.: N; herb; *Brandbyge & Azanza 32892* (AAU); *Cerón 3000* (QAME n.v.)

Anthurium polyschistum Schultes & Idrobo
Prov.: N; terrestrial or epiphytic herb; *Holm-Nielsen et al. 19718* (AAU); *Asplund 9269* (S); *Madison et al. 5335* (QCA, SEL); *Alarcón 47a* (QCA)

Anthurium pseudoclavigerum Croat
Prov.: N, P; epiphytic herb; *Øllgaard et al. 34733* (AAU); *Balslev & Alarcón 2939* (QCA); *Croat 49653* (QCA)

Anthurium scandens (Aublet) Engl.
Prov.: N, P, M-S; epiphytic herb; *Øllgaard et al. 35147* (AAU, QCA). Reaches 1600 m alt. in M-S: *Øllgaard & Balslev 9041* (AAU).

Anthurium tessmannii Krause
Prov.: N; herb; *Palacios 448* (QAME n.v.)

Anthurium trinerve Miq.
Prov.: N, P; epiphytic herb; *Lawesson et al. 43350* (AAU); *Besse et al. 61* (QCA, SEL)

Anthurium triphyllum Brongn. ex Schott
Prov.: N, P, M-S; herb; *Harling 3330* (S). Reaches 1200 m alt.

Anthurium truncicolum Engl.
Prov.: N; terrestrial or scandent herb; *Besse et al. 54* (QCA, SEL); *Jaramillo & Coello 2711* (QCA); *Croat 58640* (AAU)

Araceae (cont.)

Anthurium cf. uleanum Engl.
    Prov.: N; epiphytic herb; *Vickers 220* (F); *Holm-Nielsen et al. 21120* (AAU)
Anthurium sp. nov.
    Prov.: N; herb; *Cerón 1336* (QAME n.v.). This new species will be described by
    T. Croat as *A. balslevii.*
Caladium bicolor (Aiton) Vent.
    Prov.: N, P; herb; *Jaramillo & Rivera 127* (QCA); *Balslev & Madsen 10614*
    (AAU). Reaches 1200 m alt. in Pastaza: *Holm-Nielsen et al. 19688* (AAU).
Chlorospatha longipoda (Krause) Madison
    Prov.: N; herb; *Cerón 1003* (QAME n.v.)
Colocasia esculenta (L.) Schott
    Prov.: N; herb; *Balslev & Azanza 4373* (QCA); *Vickers 26* (F); *Irvine 1112* (F)
Dieffenbachia seguine (L.) Schott
    Prov.: N; herb; *Luteyn et al. 9108* (QCA); *Palacios et al. 312* (QCA)
Dieffenbachia sp.
    Prov.: N; herb; *Alarcón 38, 67* (QCA); *Azanza & Barfod 41089* (QCA)
Dracontium loretense Krause
    Prov.: N; herb; *Neill 8160* (QAME n.v.)
Heteropsis sp.
    Prov.: N; climber; *Alarcón 99* (QCA); *Davis & Yost 951* (QCA)
    Probably *H. oblongifolia* Kunth
Homalomena crinipes Engl.
    Prov.: N; herb; *Cerón 2125* (QAME n.v.)
Homalomena sp.
    Prov.: N; herb; *Alarcón 54* (QCA)
Monstera adansonii Schott
    Prov.: N, P; epiphytic herb; *Andrade 33145* (AAU); *Vickers 251* (F)
Monstera aureum Engl.
    Prov.: P; epiphytic herb; *Holm-Nielsen et al. 22237* (AAU)
Monstera dilacerata C. Koch
    Prov.: N; epiphytic herb; *Balslev & Santos Dea 2845* (QCA)
Monstera dubia (H.B.K.) Engl. & K. Krause
    Prov.: N, P; epiphytic herb; *Jaramillo et al. 31517* (AAU)
Monstera lechleriana Schott
    Prov.: N; epiphytic herb; *Brandbyge et al. 32787* (AAU)
Monstera obliqua Miq.
    Prov.: N, P, M-S; epiphytic herb; *Øllgaard et al. 35434* (AAU); *Balslev 2409*
    (QCA); *Croat 50452* (MO, QCA)
Monstera spruceana (Schott) Engl.
    Prov.: P; epiphytic herb; *Jaramillo et al. 30704* (AAU)
Monstera subpinnata (Schott) Engl.
    Prov.: P; epiphytic herb; *Lugo 1603* (GB). Reaches 1200 m alt.
Montrichardia linifera Schott
    Prov.: N, P; terrestrial herb; *Øllgaard et al. 35078* (AAU); *Balslev 3008* (QCA)
Philodendron barrosoanum Bunting
    Prov.: N; epiphytic herb; *Luteyn et al. 8548* (AAU)
Philodendron cataniapoense Bunting
    Prov.: N; herb; *Cerón 2408* (QAME n.v.)
Philodendron colombianum Schultes
    Prov. N; herb; *Poulsen 78433* (AAU, QCA)

Araceae   (cont.)

Philodendron cuneatum Engl.
Prov.: N, P; epiphytic herb; *Jaramillo et al. 30706* (AAU)
Philodendron ernestii Engl.
Prov. N; herb; *Poulsen 78523* (AAU, QCA)
Philodendron fragrantissimum (H.B.K.) Kunth
Prov. N; herb; *Poulsen 78798* (AAU, QCA)
Philodendron hylaeae Bunting
Prov. N; herb; *Poulsen 76480* (AAU, QCA)
Philodendron krukovii Gleason
Prov.: N; herb; *Palacios 444* (QAME n.v.)
Philodendron linnaei Kunth
Prov. N, herb; *Poulsen 78222* (AAU, QCA)
Philodendron cf. maximum K. Krause
Prov.: N; epiphytic herb; *Sparre 13252* (GB)
Philodendron megalophyllum Schott
Prov.: N; herb; *Holm-Nielsen et al. 21446* (AAU); *Cerón 1021* (QAME n.v.)
Philodendron micranthum Schott
Prov.: N; herb; *Cerón 3318* (QAME n.v.)
Philodendron panduriforme (H.B.K.) Kunth
Prov.: N; epiphytic herb; *Luteyn et al. 8570* (QCA); *Poulsen 80715* (AAU, QCA)
Philodendron pedatum Kunth
Prov. N; herb; *Poulsen 79712* (AAU, QCA)
Philodendron pulchrum Barroso
Prov.: N; herb; *Cerón 2838* (QAME n.v.)
Philodendron cf. seguine Schott
Prov.: N; epiphytic herb; *Luteyn et al. 9077* (NY, QCA)
Philodendron sp. nov.
Prov.: N; herb; *Cerón 967, 1331* (QAME n.v.). This new species will be
described by T. Croat as *P. asplundii*
Pistia stratiotes L.
Prov.: N; floating herb; *Lawesson et al. 44430* (AAU, QCA)
Rhodospatha latifolia Poeppig & Endl.
Prov.: N; herb; *Cerón 3265* (QAME n.v.); *Poulsen 78541* (AAU, QCA)
Rhodospatha sp. 1
Prov.: N; epiphytic herb; *Harling & Andersson 11753, 11836, 19646* (GB)
Rhodospatha sp. 2
Prov.: N; epiphytic herb; *Miller et al. 2549* (MO n.v.)
Rhodospatha sp. 3
Prov.: N; epiphytic herb; *Brandbyge 32000, 31879* (AAU, MO)
Rhodospatha sp. 4
Prov.: N; epiphytic herb; *Gentry 6017* (MO); *Øllgaard et al. 39014* (AAU, MO)
Rhodospatha sp. 5
Prov.: N; epiphytic herb; *Croat 50760* (MO). Collected above 600 m alt.,
but also expected below that altitude.
Spathiphyllum cannaefolium (Dryander) Schott
Prov.: N, P; terrestrial herb; *Brandbyge & Azanza 32771* (AAU)
Spathiphyllum humboldtii Schott
Prov.: N; terrestrial herb; *Øllgaard et al. 38953* (AAU)
Stenospermation ammiticum Bunting
Prov.: N; herb; *Cerón 3369* (QAME n.v.)

Araceae   (cont.)

Stenospermation amomifolium (Poeppig) Schott
> Prov.: N; epiphytic herb; *Balslev & Alarcón 3057*(QCA)

Stenospermatum andreanum Engl.
> Prov.: N, M-S; herb; *Cerón 3134* (QAME n.v.). Reaches 900 m alt. in M-S: *Holm-Nielsen et al. 4376* (AAU)

Stenospermation sp.
> Prov.: N; epiphytic herb; *Jaramillo & Coello 2820, 2983* (QCA)

Syngonium podophyllum Schott
> Prov.: N; epiphytic herb; *Holm-Nielsen et al. 21517* (AAU); *Vickers 112* (F)

Syngonium yurimaguense Engl.
> Prov.: N; epiphytic herb; *Balslev & Santos Dea 2891* (QCA)

Urospatha friedrichsthalii Schott
> Prov.: N; herb; *Lugo 2624* (GB)

Urospatha saggittifolia (Rudge) Schott
> Prov.: N; terrestrial herb; *Lawesson et al. 39566* (AAU); *Croat 50318* (QCA)

Xanthosoma daguense Engl.
> Prov.: N; terrestrial herb; *Balslev 2338* (QCA)

Xanthosoma helleborifolium (Jacq.) Schott
> Prov.: N; terrestrial herb; *Balslev & Alarcón 2973* (QCA)

Xanthosoma trichophyllum K. Krause
> Prov.: N; terrestrial herb; *Neill et al. 6414* (QCA)

Xanthosoma viviparum Madison
> Prov.: N, P, M-S; terrestrial herb; *Lawesson et al. 39781* (AAU); *Madison et al. 5429* (QCA, SEL)

Zantedeschia aethiopica (L.) Sprengel
> Expected

Araliaceae

J. F. Macbride, Fl. Peru 5(1), Publ. Field Mus. Nat. Hist., Bot. Ser. 13: 8–44. 1959. M. J. Cannon and J. F. M. Cannon, Bull. Br. Mus. Nat. Hist. (Bot.) 19: 5–61. 1989.

Dendropanax arboreus (L.) Dcne. & Planchon
> Prov.: N; tree; *Korning & Thomsen 47404* (AAU)

Dendropanax sp.
> Prov.: N; tree; *Lawesson et al. 39508* (AAU, QCA); *Lescure 2035* (QCA)

Oreopanax sp.
> Prov.: N; shrub; *Oldeman & Arévalo 14* (QCA); *Jaramillo & Coello 3017* (QCA)

Schefflera diplodactyla Harms
> Prov.: N, P; tree; *Harling 3654* (S). Reaches 1200 m alt. in Pastaza: *Øllgaard & Balslev 9122* (AAU, S).

Schefflera morototoni (Aublet) Maguire, Steyerm. & Frodin
> Prov.: N, M-S; tree; *Korning & Thomsen 47764* (AAU); *Little et al. 578* (US); *Neill 7412* (QAME n.v.). Reaches 750 m alt. in Napo: *Asplund 9453* (S). The species was formerly placed in *Didymopanax*.

Schefflera cf. *planchoniana* (E. Marchal) Harms
> Prov.: N; tree; *Asplund 18267* (S)

Araliaceae   (cont.)

Schefflera stilpnophylla Harms
    Prov.: N; tree; *Harling 3814* (S)
Schefflera sp. 1
    Prov.: N; tree; *Brandbyge & Azanza 30434* (AAU)
Schefflera sp. 2
    Prov.: N; tree; *Holm-Nielsen 19221* (AAU)
Schefflera sp. 3
    Prov.: N; tree; *Holm-Nielsen et al. 22148* (AAU)
Araliaceae sp. 1
    Prov.: N; tree; *Øllgaard et al. 34825* (AAU)
Araliaceae sp. 2
    Prov.: N; tree; *Holm-Nielsen et al. 19704* (AAU)
Araliaceae sp. 3
    Prov.: N; tree; *Brandbyge & Azanza 30695* (AAU)
Araliaceae sp. 4
    Prov.: N; tree; *Brandbyge et al. 33185* (AAU)
Araliaceae sp. 5
    Prov.: N; tree; *Holm-Nielsen et al. 22310* (AAU)

Arecaceae

Aiphanes ulei   (Dammer)Burret
    Prov.: N, P, M-S; small tree; *Balslev et al. 62045* (AAU)
Aphandra natalia (Balslev & Henderson) Barfod
    Prov.: N, M-S; tree; *Balslev & Henderson 60651* (AAU holotype, BH, K, NY,
    QCA, QCNE isotypes).   Syn. *Ammandra natalia* Balslev & Henderson
Astrocaryum chambira Burret
    Prov.: N; tree; *Balslev & Alarcón 2907* (QCA)
Astrocaryum jauari C. Martius
    Prov.: N; tree; *Balslev 4313* (QCA)
Astrocaryum murumuru C. Martius
    Prov.: N; tree; *Balslev et al. 60702* (AAU, QCA, QCNE)
Bactris concinna C. Martius
    Prov.: N; shrub; *Balslev & Cox 4328* (QCA)
Bactris gasipaes H.B.K.
    Prov.: N; tree; *Balslev et al. 60747* (AAU, QCA)
Bactris setiflora Burret
    Prov.: P; shrub; *Schultze-Rhonhof 2233* (B holotype)
Bactris simplicifrons C. Martius
    Prov.: N; shrub; *Balslev 69044* (AAU)
Bactris sp. 1
    Prov. : N; tree; *Balslev & Azanza 4345* (AAU, K, NY, QCA, QCNE)
Bactris sp. 2
    Prov.: N; shrub; *Balslev et al. 60618*   (AAU)
Bactris sp. 3
    Prov.: N; shrub; *Balslev et al. 60039*   (AAU)
Bactris sp. 4
    Prov.: N; tree; *Balslev et al. 60038*   (AAU)

Arecaceae   (cont.)

Bactris sp. 5
   Prov.: N; shrub; *Balslev et al. 60062*   (AAU)
Bactris sp. 6
   Prov.: N; shrub; *Balslev et al. 69054*   (AAU)
Chamaedorea integrifolia (Trail) Dammer
   Prov.: N, P, M-S; shrub; *Balslev 4862* (AAU)
Chamaedorea pinnatifrons (Jacq.) Oerst.
   Prov.: N, P, M-S; shrub; *Balslev 4871* (AAU, QCA)
Chelyocarpus ulei Dammer
   Prov.: N, M-S; tree; *Balslev 62417* (AAU, QCA)
Cocos nucifera L.
   Tree; cultivated, but not collected in the area.
Desmoncus mitis C. Martius
   Prov.: N; liana; *Balslev 60633* (AAU, QCA)
Desmoncus orthacanthos C. Martius
   Prov.: N; liana; *Balslev 62042* (AAU, QCA)
Desmoncus sp.
   Prov.: N; liana; *Balslev et al. 60753* (AAU, QCA)
Elaeis guineensis Jacq.
   Prov. N; tree; cultivated, but not collected in the area.
Elaeis oleifera (H.B.K.) Cortés
   Prov.: M-S; tree; *Balslev 62401* (AAU, CEN, K, NY, QCA, QCNE)
Euterpe precatoria C. Martius
   Prov.: N; tree; *Balslev 4311* (QCA)
Geonoma acaulis C. Martius
   Prov.: N, M-S; shrub; *Balslev et al. 62061* (AAU)
Geonoma arundinacea C. Martius
   Prov.: N, P, M-S; shrub; *Skov et al. 64710* (AAU)
Geonoma brongniartii C. Martius
   Prov.: N, P; shrub; *Balslev 2335* (AAU, QCA)
Geonoma camana Trail
   Prov.: N, P, M-S; shrub; *Balslev & Irvine 4624* (AAU, QCA)
Geonoma deversa (Poit.) Kunth
   Prov.: N; shrub; *Balslev 4791* (AAU, QCA)
Geonoma euspatha Burret
   Prov.: N, P, M-S; shrub; *Balslev et al. 4303* (QCA)
Geonoma interrupta(Ruiz & Pavón) C. Martius
   Prov.: N, P, M-S; shrub; *Balslev et al. 60692* (AAU)
Geonoma laxiflora C. Martius
   Prov.: N; shrub; *Holm-Nielsen et al. 19928* (AAU)
Geonoma macrostachys C. Martius
   Prov.: N, P, M-S; shrub; *Balslev 2391* (AAU, QCA)
Geonoma maxima (Poit.) C. Martius
   Prov.: N, P; shrub; *Balslev et al. 4306* (QCA)
Geonoma piscicauda Dammer
   Prov.: N; shrub; *Balslev & Brako 4320* (AAU, QCA)
Geonoma pycnostachys C. Martius
   Prov.: N, P, M-S; shrub; *Balslev et al. 62410* (AAU)
Geonoma stricta (Poit.) Kunth
   Prov.: N; Shrub; *Balslev et al. 4302* (AAU, GB, QCA)

Arecaceae   (cont.)

Geonoma triglochin Burret
Prov.: N, M-S; shrub; *Balslev et al. 4303* (QCA)
Geonoma sp.
Prov.: N; shrub; *Balslev 60739* (AAU)
Hyospathe elegans C. Martius
Prov.: N, P, M-S; shrub; *Balslev 60682* (AAU)
Iriartea deltoidea Ruíz & Pavón
Prov.: N, P, M-S; tree; *Balslev & Brako 4278* (QCA)
Jessenia bataua (C. Martius) Burret
Prov.: N; tree; *Balslev 4309* (QCA)
Mauritia flexuosa L.f.
Prov.: N; M-S; tree; *Balslev et al. 60749* (AAU, QCA)
Mauritiella aculeata (H.B.K.) Burret
Prov.: N; tree; *Balslev et al. 84632* (AAU)
Maximiliana maripa (Aublet) Drude
Prov.: N; tree; *Balslev 4789* (AAU, QCA)
Oenocarpus mapora Karsten
Prov.: N; tree; *Balslev 4310* (QCA)
Pholidostachys synanthera (C. Martius) H. E. Moore
Prov.: P, M-S; tree; *Balslev 4423* (QCA, NY, AAU, QCNE)
Phytelephas dasyneura Burret
Prov.: N; tree; *Balslev et al. 62070* (AAU, NY, QCA, QCNE)
Phytelephas macrocarpa Ruíz & Pavón
Prov.: N, P; tree; *Balslev et al. 60557* (AAU, NY, QCA, QCNE)
Prestoea asplundii H. E. Moore
Prov.: N, P, M-S; tree; *Asplund 19477* (S holotype)
Prestoea schultzeana (Burret) H. E. Moore
Prov.: P; tree; *Schultze-Rhonhof 2433* (B holotype)
Scheelea attaleoides Karsten
Prov.: N; shrub; *Lawesson et al. 44408* (AAU)
Scheelea brachyclada Burret
Prov.: N; tree; *Balslev 4339* (AAU, QCA, NY)
Socratea exorrhiza (C. Martius) Wendl.
Prov.: N; tree; *Balslev & Henderson 60672* (AAU, NY, QCA)
Syagrus sancona Karsten
Prov.: P; tree; seen but not collected in the area.
Syagrus sp.
Prov.: M-S; tree; *Balslev 62414* (AAU, QCA)
Wettinia maynensis Spruce
Prov.: N, P, M-S; tree; *Balslev et al. 62065* (AAU, QCA)

Aristolochiaceae
J. F. Macbride, Fl. Peru 2(2), Publ. Field Mus. Nat. Hist., Bot. Ser. 13: 431–443. 1937.

Aristolochia sp.
Prov.: N; liana; *Jaramillo & Coello 2679, 2826, 4270, 4514* (QCA); *Balslev & Irvine 4629* (AAU, QCA); *Vickers 242* (F)

Asclepiadaceae
Identifications mostly by G. Morillo, VEN.

***Asclepias curassavica* L.**
Prov.: N, P; herb, shrub; *Brandbyge et al. 33313* (AAU, QCA); *McElroy 411* (QCA); *Palacios et al. 275* (QCA); *Lescure 2203* (QCA)

***Marsdenia asplundii* Morillo & Spellman**
Prov.: N; epiphytic herb; *Asplund 9455* (S). Reaches 750 m alt.

***Matelea rivularis* Woodson**
Prov.: N; shrub; *Holm-Nielsen 19226* (AAU)

***Metalepis* sp.**
Prov.: N, P; vine; *Øllgaard et al. 34609* (AAU); *Pennington 10629* (QCA)

***Sarcostemma clausum* (Jacq.) Roemer & Schultes**
Prov.: N; liana; *Jaramillo & Coello 4446* (AAU, QCA)

***Asclepiadaceae* sp. 1**
Prov.: N; shrub; *Azanza & Barfod 41151* (AAU, QCA)

***Asclepiadaceae* sp. 2**
Prov.: N; liana; *Azanza & Barfod 41189* (AAU)

***Asclepiadaceae* sp. 3**
Prov.: N; liana; *Azanza & Barfod 41215* (AAU, QCA)

Asteraceae
Identifications mostly by H. Robinson, US, who already treated the Liabeae in Fl. Ecuador 8, 1978.

***Acmella alba* (L'Hér.) R. U. Jansen**
Prov.: N; herb; *Vickers 183* (F). Syn. *Spilanthes alba* L.'Hér.

***Acmella brachyglossa* Cass.**
Prov.: M-S; herb; *Brandbyge et al. 32262* (AAU, QCA)

***Acmella ciliata* (H.B.K.) Cass.**
Prov.: N; herb; *Andrade 33114* (AAU). Reaches 1000 m alt.

***Adenostemma fosbergii* R. King & H. Robinson**
Prov.: N, P; herb; *Brandbyge & Azanza 32780* (AAU, QCA)

***Adenostemma lavenia* (L.) Kuntze**
Prov.: N; herb; *Jaramillo & Coello 3016* (QCA)

***Ageratum conyzoides* L.**
Prov.: N; herb; *Brandbyge et al. 30271* (AAU). Reaches 1800 m alt.

***Aspilia pastazensis* H. Robinson**
Prov.: P; shrub; *Brandbyge & Azanza 31088* (QCA)

***Ayapana ecuadorensis* R. King & H. Robinson**
Prov.: P; herb; *Øllgaard et al. 34617* (AAU)

***Bidens cynapifolia* H.B.K.**
Prov.: N; herb; *Alarcón 19383* (QCA)

***Bidens pilosa* L.**
Prov.: P, M-S; herb; *Brandbyge & Azanza 32252* (AAU, QCA)

***Clibadium eggersii* Hieron.**
Prov.: N; shrub; *Lugo 3094* (QCA); *Oldeman et al. 770* (QCA)

***Clibadium mexiae* Blake**
Prov.: N; herb; *Mexía 6946* (US)

***Clibadium microcephalum* Blake**
Prov.: P; shrub; *Lugo 4554* (US). Usually at higher altitudes.

Asteraceae (cont.)

Clibadium surinamense L.
Prov.: N, P, M-S; shrub; *Andrade 33147* (AAU); *Irvine 104* (QCA); *Vickers 210* (F); *Pinkley 3* (ECON, S). Syn. *C. asperum* (Aublet) DC.

Clibadium sylvestre (Aublet) Baillon
Prov.: N, M-S; shrub; *Brandbyge & Azanza 32290* (AAU, QCA); *Irvine 363* (F, QCA); *Alarcón 13* (QCA)

Critoniopsis tungurahuae (Benoist) H. Robinson
Prov.: P; tree; *Jaramillo et al. 30962* (AAU)

Eclipta prostrata (L.) L.
Prov.: N; herb; *Alarcón 19395* (QCA). Syn. *E. alba* (L.) Hassk.

Erato polymnioides DC.
Prov.: P; herb; *Mexía 6957* (US)

Erechites valerianaefolia (Wolf) DC.
Prov.: N; herb; *Lawesson et al. 39712* (AAU, QCA)

Eriocentrodea corazonensis (Hieron.) Blake & Sherff
Prov.: N; climber; *Jaramillo & Coello 3989* (AAU)

Fleischmannia microstemon (Cass.) R. King & H. Robinson
Prov.: N, M-S; herb; *Brandbyge & Azanza 32296* (AAU, QCA)

Fleischmannia sideritidis (Benth.) King & Robinson
Prov.: N; shrub; *Humbles 6207* (US)

Hebeclinium macrophyllum (L.) DC.
Prov.: N; shrub; *Andrade 33025* (QCA); *Alarcón 19549* (QCA); *Irvine 154* (QCA); *Balslev & Santos Dea 2881* (QCA)

Jaegeria hirta (Lag.) Less.
Prov.: N, P; herb; *Alarcón 19174* (QCA); *Lugo 4582* (QCA)

Liabum amplexicaule Poeppig & Endl.
Prov.: N; herb; *Harling & Andersson 11879* (GB)

Melanthera aspera (Jacq.) Small
Prov.: N; herb; *Andrade 33139* (AAU)

Melanthera decora Poeppig
Prov.: N; herb; *Mexía 6947* (US)

Mikania banisteriae DC.
Prov.: N; shrub; *Mexía 7317* (US). Syn. *M. ruiziana* Poeppig.

Mikania cordifolia (L.f.) Willd.
Prov.: N, P; shrub or liana; *Løjtnant & Molau 1332* (GB); *Dwyer 9647* (QCA)

Mikania guaco H.B.K.
Prov.: N, P; climber; *Villegas & Meneses 41* (QCA). A likely synonym is *M. napensis* Blake, described from *Mexía 7259* (US)

Mikania hookeriana DC.
Prov.: N, P; vine; *Øllgaard et al. 35445* (AAU). Reaches 1500 m alt.: *Balslev & Madsen 10456* (AAU).

Mikania klugii B. L. Robinson
Prov.: N; scandent; *Brandbyge et al. 33499* (AAU)

Mikania leiostachya Benth.
Prov.: N; scandent; *Brandbyge et al. 33446* (AAU)

Mikania lindleyana DC.
Prov.: P; vine; *Øllgaard et al. 35007* (AAU)

Mikania micrantha H.B.K.
Prov.: N; climber; *Holm-Nielsen et al. 19695* (AAU); *Alarcón 19370* (QCA)

Asteraceae (cont.)

Mikania nigropunctulata Hieron.
Prov.: N; liana; *Mexía 6941* (US)
Mikania psilostachya DC.
Prov.: N, P; vine; *Brandbyge et al. 30207* (AAU). Reaches 1000 m alt.
Mikania vitifolia DC.
Prov.: N; liana; *Lugo 2231* (GB, US)
Neomirandea homogama (Hieron.) Robinson & Brettell
Prov.: N; herb; *Skutch 4554* (US). Collected at 750–1000 m alt.
Neurolanea lobata (L.) R. Brown
Prov.: N; shrub; *Vickers 180* (F)
Otopappus australis Blake
Prov.: N; herb; *Lugo 2254* (GB, QCA)
Piptocarpha lechleri (Schultz-Bip.) Baker
Prov.: P; climber; *Øllgaard et al. 35492* (AAU)
Pollalesta discolor (H.B.K.) Aristeg.
Prov.: P, M-S; shrub; *McElroy 374* (QCA); *Jaramillo & Coello 3518* (QCA)
Schistocarpha eupatorioides (Fenzl) Kuntze
Prov.: N, M-S; herb; *Brandbyge & Azanza 32295* (AAU, QCA)
Sciadocephala amazonica R. King & H. Robinson
Prov.: P; shrub; *Jaramillo et al. 31711* (QCA)
Spilanthes cf. paniculata Jacq.
Prov.: N; herb; *Alarcón 19175, 19554* (QCA); *Vickers 183* (F) as "*S. alba L'Hér.*"
Synedrella nodiflora (L.) Gaertner
Prov.: M-S; herb; *Brandbyge & Azanza 32238* (AAU, QCA)
Tagetes erecta L.
Prov.: N; herb; *Vickers 3, 4* (F)
Tessaria integrifolia Ruíz & Pavón
Prov.: N; treelet; *Pennington 12312* (K)
Vernonia patens H.B.K.
Prov.: N, P, M-S; shrub; *Holm-Nielsen et al. 19132* (AAU, QCA); *Alarcón 19376* (QCA). Reaches 800 m alt. Syn. *V. baccharoides* H.B.K.
Wulffia baccata (L.f.) Kuntze
Prov.: N, P, M-S; herb or vine; *Irvine 222* (F, QCA); *Alarcón 19385* (QCA)
Wulffia macrocephala H. Robinson
Prov.: N, P; shrub; *Jaramillo et al. 31746* (AAU, US)
Zinnia peruviana (L.) L.
Prov.: N; herb; *Vickers 2* (F); *Navarrete 28* (QCA). Syn. *Z. elegans* Jacq.

Balanophoraceae
B. Hansen, Fl. Ecuador 19, 1983.

Lophophytum mirabile Schott & Endl.
Prov.: N; root parasite; *Luteyn et al. 8508* (AAU, NY)
Ombrophytum peruvianum Poeppig & Endl.
Prov.: N, P; root parasite; *Løjtnant & Molau 13573* (AAU); *Davis & Yost 1034* (QCA)
Ombrophytum violaceum B. Hansen
Prov.: N; root parasite; *Sparre 13049* (S); *Brandbyge et al. 32498* (AAU)

Balsaminaceae

Impatiens balsaminea L.
Prov.: N, P; herb; *Lawesson et al. 39643* (AAU, QCA); *Vickers 8* (F)
Impatiens wallerana Hook. f.
Prov.: N, P, M-S; herb; *Pinkley 447* (ECON); *Alarcón 19379* (QCA). Reaches 1050 m alt. in Pastaza: *Holm-Nielsen & Jeppesen 501* (AAU).

Begoniaceae
L. B. Smith and D. C. Wasshausen, Fl. Ecuador 25, 1986.

Begonia brandbygeana L. B. Smith & Wassh.
Prov.: M-S; herb; *Brandbyge & Azanza 31965* (AAU, QCA)
Begonia glabra Aublet
Prov.: N, P; epiphytic herb; *Holm-Nielsen 19320* (AAU); *Balslev & Irvine 4628* (QCA); *Foster 3560* (AAU, QCA). Reaches 1900 m alt.
Begonia humilis Aiton
Prov.: N, M-S; herb; *Holm-Nielsen et al. 20548* (AAU)
Begonia maynensis A. DC.
Prov.: N, P, M-S; herb; *Holm-Nielsen 19199* (AAU); *Harling et al. 7750* (GB, QCA)
Begonia oellgaardii L. B. Smith & Wassh.
Prov.: N; herb; *Øllgaard et al. 39192* (AAU)
Begonia rossmanniae A. DC.
Prov.: N, P, M-S; epiphytic herb; *Holm-Nielsen & Jeppesen 826* (AAU); *Brandbyge & Azanza 31899* (AAU, QCA). Reaches 700 m alt.
Begonia semiovata Liebm.
Prov.: N, P; herb; *Brandbyge & Azanza 31661* (AAU)
Begonia sparreana L. B. Smith & Wassh.
Prov.: N, M-S; herb; *Lawesson et al. 39595* (AAU, QCA). Reaches 800 m alt. in M-S: *Sparre 19025* (S).

Bignoniaceae
A. Gentry, Fl. Ecuador 7, 1977. This listing checked by A. Gentry, Apr 1989.

Adenocalymma impressum (Rusby) Sandw.
Prov.: N; shrub, also creeping; *Harling & Andersson 16552* (GB, QCA)
Adenocalymma inundatum C. Martius ex DC.
Prov.: P; shrub; *Jaramillo et al. 31364* (AAU)
Adenocalymma purpurascens Rusby
Prov.: N; liana; *Gentry 12486* (MO)
Amphilophium aschersonii Ule
Prov.: N; liana; *Gentry 12486* (MO)
Amphilophium paniculatum (L.) H.B.K.
Prov.: N; liana; *Gentry 9796, 12480* (MO)

Bignoniaceae   (cont.)

Anemopaegma chrysoleucum (H.B.K.) Sandw.
Prov.: N; liana; *Holm-Nielsen et al. 21452* (AAU)

Anemopaegma patelliforme A. Gentry
Prov.: P; liana; *Brandbyge & Azanza 30678* (AAU)

Arrabidaea candicans (L. Rich.) DC.
Prov.: N; liana; *Gentry 12545* (MO)

Arrabidaea chica (Humb. & Bonpl.) Verlot
Prov.: N; vine; *Vickers 106, 108* (F); *Pinkley 175* (ECON); *Balslev 4884* (QCA)

Arrabidaea corallina (Jacq.) Sandw.
Prov.: N; *Palacios 2378* (QAME n.v.)

Arrabidaea egensis Burret & K. Schum.
Prov.: N; liana; *Gentry 12538* (MO)

Arrabidaea florida DC.
Prov.: N, P; liana; *Gentry 12424, 12452* (MO).   Reaches 1000 m alt. in Pastaza: *Asplund 19080* (S).

Arrabidaea japurensis (DC.) Burret & K. Schum.
Prov.: N, P; *Neill 7279* (QAME n.v.)

Arrabidaea patellifera (Schlecht.) Sandw.
Prov.: N, P, M-S; liana; *Jaramillo et al. 31562* (AAU); *Lugo 2702* (AAU, QCA)
Reaches 1000 m alt. in M-S: *Harling & Andersson 12805* (GB)

Arrabidaea pearcei (Rusby) K. Schum. ex Urban aff.
Prov.: N, M-S; liana; *Neill & Palacios 7124* (AAU, QCA).   Reaches 900 m alt. in
M-S: *Harling & Andersson 13052* (AAU, GB, MO)

Arrabidaea spicata Burret & K. Schum.
Prov.: N, P; liana; *Øllgaard et al. 35069* (AAU); *Neill & Palacios 6644* (QCA)

Arrabidaea verrucosa (Standley) A. Gentry
Prov.: P; liana; *Neill & Palacios 6805* (AAU); *Gentry 9805* (MO, QCA)

Arrabidaea sp. nov.
Prov.: N; vine; *Brandbyge & Azanza 30393* (AAU, MO); *Zaruma et al. 108*
(QAME n.v.).   This new species will be described by A. Gentry as *A. affinis*

Callichlamys latifolia (L. Rich.) K. Schum.
Prov.: N; liana; *Brandbyge & Azanza 32913* (AAU); *Balslev & Alarcón 3003*
(QCA)

Ceratophytum tetragonolobum (Jacq.) Sprague & Sandw.
Prov.: N; liana; *Gentry 12506* (MO)

Clytostoma binatum (Thunb.) Sandw.
Prov.: N, P; liana; *Holm-Nielsen et al. 22131* (AAU); *Foster 3859* (QCA); *Lugo 2882* (GB)

Clytostoma sciuripabulum Burret & K. Schum.
Prov.: N; liana; *Gentry 12513* (MO, S)

Crescentia cujete L.
Prov.: N, P; tree; *Vickers 130* (QCA); *Davis & Yost 1037* (QCA); *Pinkley 227*
(S); *Balslev 2805* (QCA). Reaches 1100 m alt. in Pastaza: *Asplund 19542* (S)

Cydista aequinoctialis (L.) Miers
Prov.: N, P; liana; *Holm-Nielsen et al. 21304* (AAU); *Lawesson et al. 43463*
(AAU, QCA); *Gentry 9744* (MO)

Distictella magnoliifolia (H.B.K.) Sandw.
Prov.: N; liana; *Balslev & E. Madsen 10598* (AAU); *Harling & Andersson
11947* (GB)

Distictis cf. steyermarkii A. Gentry
Prov.: N; liana; *Brandbyge et al. 30541* (AAU)

Bignoniaceae   (cont.)

Jacaranda copaia (Aublet) D. Don
ssp. *spectabilis* (C. Martius ex Berg) A. Gentry
Prov.: N, M-S; tree; *Korning & Thomsen 47741* (AAU); *Irvine 115* (F, QCA)
Reaches 650 m alt. in Napo: *Mexía 7295* (F).
Jacaranda glabra (DC.) Burret & K. Schum.
Prov.: N, P, M-S; tree; *Øllgaard et al. 34832* (AAU); *Balslev & Alarcón 3037*
(QCA); *Gentry 9837* (MO, QCA); *Irvine 198* (F)
Lundia corymbifera (Vahl) Sandw.
Prov.: N, P; liana; *Brandbyge et al. 30286* (AAU); *Mexía 9601* (US)
Lundia puberula Pittier
Prov.: N, P; liana; *Lugo 4560* (AAU); *Neill 8175* (QAME n.v.)
Lundia spruceana Burret
Prov.: N, P; liana; *Holm-Nielsen et al. 21134* (AAU); *Neill 7159* (AAU, QCA);
McElroy 412 (QCA).   Reaches 750 m alt. in Napo: *Asplund 9436* (S)
Macfadyena uncata (Andr.) Sprague & Sandw.
Prov.: N, P; liana; *Harling & Andersson 17728* (AAU, QCA)
Macfadyena unguis-cati (L.) A. Gentry
Prov.: N; liana; *Gentry 9725* (GB, MO, QCA)
Mansoa alliacea (Lam.) A. Gentry
Prov.: N; liana; *Lugo 2831* (AAU); *Vargas 75* (QCA)
Mansoa hymenaea (DC.) A. Gentry
Prov.: N; liana; *Harling & Andersson 11938* (AAU); *Lugo 2867, 2831* (GB)
Mansoa kerere (Aublet) A. Gentry
Prov.: N; shrub; *Holm-Nielsen et al. 21654* (AAU)
Mansoa parvifolia (A. Gentry) A. Gentry
Prov.: P; vine; *Løjtnant & Molau 13345* (AAU); *Fagerlind & Wibom 2218* (S)
Mansoa standleyi (Steyerm.) A. Gentry
Prov.: N; liana; *Lawesson et al. 39686* (AAU, QCA); *Alarcón 7* (QCA)
Mansoa verrucifera (Schlecht.) A. Gentry
Prov.: N, P; liana; *Holm-Nielsen et al. 22521* (AAU); *Gentry 9757* (QCA)
Memora cladotricha Sandw.
Prov.: N, P; tree; *Holm-Nielsen et al. 22523* (AAU); *Balslev & Santos Dea 2858*
(QCA); *Irvine 461* (F)
Parabignonia steyermarkii Sandw.
Prov.: N; liana; *Cerón 1478* (QAME n.v.)
Paragonia pyramidata (L. Rich.) Burret
Prov.: N, P; liana; *Holm-Nielsen et al. 21125* (AAU).   Reaches 1000 m alt. in
Pastaza: *Asplund 18904* (S)
Pithecoctenium crucigerum (L.) A. Gentry
Prov.: N; liana; *Gentry 12523* (MO).   Reaches 1000 m alt.
Pryganocydia corymbosa (Vent.) Burret ex K. Schum.
Prov.: N; liana; *Gentry 9733* (MO)
Roentgenia bracteomana (Schum. ex Sprague) Urban
Prov.: N, P, M-S; liana; *Holm-Nielsen et al. 21432* (AAU); *Lugo 2557* (GB,
QCA); *Cazalet & Pennington 7558* (US)
Schlegelia parviflora (Oerst.) Monach.
Prov.: N; treelet; *Azanza & Barfod 41095* (AAU); *Palacios 1318* (QAME n.v.)
Spathicalyx xanthophylla (DC.) A. Gentry
Prov.: N, P; liana; *Lugo 2695* (GB, QCA).   Syn. *Arrabidaea xanthophylla* DC.

Bignoniaceae (cont.)

Spathodea campanulata Beauv.
> Prov.: M-S; tree; *Zaruma et al. 494* (QAME n.v.). Cultivated.

Stizophyllum inaequilaterum Burret & K. Schum.
> Prov.: N, M-S; liana; *Harling & Andersson 11681* (AAU, GB); *MacBryde & Dwyer 1358* (QCA); *Camp E-1432* (NY)

Stizophyllum riparium (H.B.K.) Sandw.
> Prov.: N; liana; *Lugo 2623* (AAU, GB); *2687* (GB, QCA)

Tabebuia chrysantha (Jacq.) Nichols.
> Prov.: N, M-S; tree; *Pennington & Tenorio 10788* (QCA); *Zaruma 365* (AAU)

Tabebuia serratifolia (Vahl) Nicols.
> Prov.: N; treelet; *Neill 9096* (QAME n.v.)

Tanaecium jaroba Sw.
> Prov.: N; liana; *Lawesson et al. 44326* (AAU, QCA)

Tourretia lappacea (L'Hér.) Willd.
> Prov.: N; climber; *Holm-Nielsen et al. 26410* (AAU)

Tynanthus polyanthus (Burret) Sandw.
> Prov.: N; liana; *Neill 7151* (QCA); *Gentry 9836* (MO)

Bixaceae
U. Molau, Fl. Ecuador 20, 1983.

Bixa arborea Huber
> Prov.: N, M-S; tree; *Neill 6931* (QCA); *Lugo 1014* (GB, QCA)

Bixa orellana L.
> Prov.: N, P; shrub, tree; *Balslev 4856* (QCA); *Irvine 472* (F, QCA); *Alarcón 17* (QCA); *Davis & Yost 1013* (QCA); *Vickers 240* (F). Reaches 1400 m alt.

Bixa platycarpa Ruíz & Pavón ex G.Don
> Prov.: N; tree; *Lugo 1014* (AAU); *Cerón 2190* (QAME n.v.)

Bixa urucurana Willd.
> Prov.: N, P; tree; *Holm-Nielsen et al. 22536* (AAU); *Andrade 33132* (AAU)

Bombacaceae
J. F. Macbride, Fl. Peru 3A(2), Publ. Field Mus. Nat. Hist., Bot. Ser. 13: 593–622. 1956. This listing checked by W. S. Alverson, May 1989.

Ceiba pentandra (L.) Gaertner
> Prov.: N, P; tree; *Neill 6860* (QAME n.v.); *Vickers 60* (QCA). Reaches 1050 m alt. in Pastaza: *Asplund 20523* (S).

Ceiba samauma (C. Martius) K. Schum.
> Prov.: N; tree; *SEF 10018* (AAU, QCA); *Neill 7138* (AAU, QCA)

Ceiba sp. 1
> Prov.: N; tree; *Holm-Nielsen et al. 22068* (AAU)

Ceiba sp. 2
> Prov.: N; tree; *Lawesson et al. 43547* (AAU)

Chorisia insignis H.B.K. aff.
> Prov.: N; tree; *Neill 6279* (QAME n.v.); *Bravo & Gómez 192* (QCA)

Matisia cf. alata Little
> Prov.: N; tree; *SEF 8795* (AAU, NY, QCA); *Lawesson et al. 39676* (QCA)

Matisia alchornaefolia Triana & Planchon
> Prov.: N; tree; *Brandbyge et al. 33829* (AAU)

Bombacaceae   (cont.)

Matisia bracteolosa Ducke
   Prov.: N; tree; *Øllgaard et al. 39188* (AAU); *Neill & Palacios 6764* (MO, QCA)
Matisia cordata Humb. & Bonpl.
   Prov.: N; tree; *Balslev 4349* (QCA); *Brandbyge et al. 32954* (AAU)
Matisia malacocalyx (Robyns & Nilsson) Alverson
   Prov.: N, P; tree; *SEF 8882* (AAU, QCA); *Neill & Palacios 6694* (QCA)
Matisia obliquifolia Standley
   Prov.: N; tree; *SEF 9157* (AAU, QCA); *Vickers 85* (F); *Lescure 2097* (QCA)
Matisia ochrocalyx K. Schum.
   Prov.: N, P; tree; *Brandbyge & Azanza 31276* (AAU); *Irvine 668* (F)
Ochroma pyramidale (Cav.) Urban
   Prov.: N, P, M-S; tree; *Balslev & E. Madsen 10618* (AAU, QCA); *Alarcón 24*
   (QCA); *Vickers 158* (F)
Pachira aquatica Aublet
   Prov.: P, M-S; tree; *Brandbyge & Azanza 31791* (AAU, QCA)
Pachira insignis (Sw.) Sav.
   Prov.: N; tree; *Palacios 464* (QAME n.v.)
Patinoa sp.
   Prov.: N; tree; *Øllgaard et al. 39681* (AAU); *Korning & Thomsen 47435* (AAU)
Phragmotheca ecuadorensis Alverson
   Prov.: N; tree; *Neill & Cerón 7577* (MO, QAME, QCNE, WIS)
Phragmotheca leucoflora D. Simpson
   Prov.: P; tree; *Zak & Espinosa 4532* (QCNE)
Phragmotheca mammosa Alverson
   Prov.: N; tree; *Neill et al. 6371* (MO, QAME , WIS)
Pseudobombax septenatum (Jacq.) Dugand
   Prov.: M-S; tree; *Neill 7476* (QAME n.v.); *Little et al. 368* (US)
Quararibea amazonica Ulbr.
   Prov.: N; tree; *Neill 7773* (QAME n.v.); *Pennington 10568* (K)
Quararibea guianensis Aublet
   Prov.: N; tree; *Brandbyge et al. 30539* (AAU)
Quararibea wittii K. Schum. & Ulbr.
   Prov.: N; tree; *Palacios 1206* (QAME n.v.)

Boraginaceae
J. F. Macbride, Fl. Peru 5(2), Publ. Field Mus. Nat. Hist., Bot. Ser. 13:
539–609. 1960.

Cordia alliodora (Ruíz & Pavón) Oken
   Prov.: N, P, M-S; tree; *Brandbyge et al. 33471* (AAU); *Irvine 161* (QCA).
   Reaches ca. 1000 m alt. in Pastaza: *Asplund 20002* (S)
Cordia bifurcata Roemer & Schultes
   Prov.: N; shrub; *Jaramillo & Rivera 176* (AAU, QCA); *Alarcón 19536* (QCA)
Cordia corymbosa (L.) Don
   Prov.: N; shrub; *Jaramillo & Rivera 176* (AAU, QCA, S).   Reaches ca. 750 m
   alt.: *Asplund 8959* (S).
Cordia eriostigma Pittier
   Prov.: N; tree; *Luteyn et al. 9044* (AAU, NY, QCA); *SEF 10144* (AAU, QCA)

Boraginaceae   (cont.)

Cordia cf. *hebeclada* I. M. Johnston
    Prov.: N; tree; *SEF 10185* (AAU, QCA)
Cordia lomatoloba I. M. Johnston
    Prov.: N; tree; *Zaruma 140* (QAME n.v.)
Cordia nodosa Lam.
    Prov.: N, P, M-S; tree; *Holm-Nielsen et al. 21278* (AAU); *Alarcón 92* (QCA)
Cordia cf. *poeppigii* DC.
    Prov.: N; tree; *SEF 10203* (AAU, QCA); *Cerón 1298* (QAME n.v.)
Cordia sericicalyx A. DC.
    Prov.: N; tree; *Korning & Thomsen 47792* (AAU); *Nowak 136* (QCA)
Cordia spinescens L.
    Prov.: N, P; liana; *Luteyn et al. 8627* (AAU, NY, QCA); *Neill & Palacios 6567* (QCA); *Gentry 9821* (S)
Cordia ucayaliensis I. M. Johnston
    Prov.: P; tree; *Holm-Nielsen et al. 21874* (AAU)
Cordia sp. 1
    Prov.: N; tree; *Øllgaard et al. 35016* (AAU). =*C. ripicola* I. M. Johnston?
Cordia sp. 2
    Prov.: N; tree; *Holm-Nielsen et al. 21979* (AAU). =*C. panamensis* Ridley?
Tournefortia angustiflora Ruíz & Pavón
    Prov.: N; shrub; *Vickers 107* (F).   Reaches 750 m alt.: *Asplund 8962* (S)
Tournefortia bicolor Sw.
    Prov.: N; tree; *Harling 3830* (S).   Reaches 1700 m alt.
Tournefortia glabra L.
    Prov.: N; tree; *Lawesson et al. 39825* (AAU); *Alarcón 19529* (QCA); *Asdall 81-7* (QCA).   Reaches 700 m alt. in Napo: *Harling 3850* (GB)
Tournefortia sp. 1
    Prov.: N; tree; *Brandbyge et al. 33536* (AAU)
Tournefortia sp. 2
    Prov.: N; tree; *Brandbyge et al. 30199* (AAU)
Tournefortia sp. 3
    Prov.: N; tree; *Brandbyge & Azanza 30673* (AAU)
Tournefortia sp. 4
    Prov.: N; tree; *Jaramillo & Coello 3273* (AAU)
Tournefortia sp. 5
    Prov.: N; tree; *Brandbyge et al. 33432* (AAU)
Tournefortia sp. 6
    Prov.: N; tree; *Løjtnant & Molau 15954* (AAU)

Bromeliaceae
L. B. Smith and R. J. Downs, Fl. Neotropica 14 (1–3), 1974, 1977, 1979. H. Luther, Phytologia 67(4): 312–330, 1989: A provisional checklist of the Bromeliaceae of Ecuador. This listing checked by H. Luther, Jan 1991.

Aechmea abbreviata L. B. Smith
    Prov.: N, P; epiphytic herb; *Lawesson et al. 43333* (AAU)
Aechmea chantinii (Carr.) Baker
    Prov.: P; epiphytic herb; *Øllgaard et al. 34701* (AAU)

Bromeliaceae (cont.)

Aechmea corymbosa (Martius ex Schultes f.) Baker
Prov.: N; epiphytic herb; *Lawesson et al. 44443* (AAU, QCA)
Aechmea hoppii (Harms) L. B. Smith
Prov.: N, P; epiphytic herb; *Luteyn et al. 8660* (NY, QCA); *Øllgaard et al. 35297* (AAU)
Aechmea mertensii (Meyer) Schultes f.
Prov.: N; epiphytic herb; *Harling et al. 7240* (GB); *Andrade 33107* (AAU)
Aechmea nidularioides L. B. Smith
Prov.: N; epiphytic herb; *Lugo 2066* (GB); *Brandbyge & Azanza 31021* (AAU)
Aechmea cf. nivea L. B. Smith
Prov.: N; terrestrial herb; *Holm-Nielsen et al. 19949* (AAU)
Aechmea penduliflora André
Prov.: N; epiphytic herb; *Luteyn et al. 8595* (AAU, QCA); *Asplund 9364* (S)
Aechmea retusa L. B. Smith
Prov.: N; epiphytic herb; *Harling et al. 7110* (GB). Reaches 900 m alt. in Napo: *Besse et al. 74* (QCA, SEL)
Aechmea romeroi L. B. Smith
Prov.: N; epiphytic herb; *Holm-Nielsen et al. 21514* (AAU); *Jaramillo & Coello 4416* (QCA)
Aechmea setigera Martius ex Schultes f.
Prov.: N; epiphytic herb; *Cerón 6019* (MO, QAME, SEL)
Aechmea tessmannii Harms
Prov.: P; epiphytic herb; *Øllgaard et al. 35132* (AAU)
Aechmea tillandsioides (C. Martius ex Schultes f.) Baker
Prov.: N, P; epiphytic herb; *Holm-Nielsen et al. 22574* (AAU)
Aechmea woronowii Harms
Prov.: P; epiphytic herb; *Foster 3603* (AAU, QCA)
Aechmea zebrina L. B. Smith
Prov.: N, P; epiphytic herb; *Holm-Nielsen & Jeppesen 966* (AAU, S); *Alarcón 68* (QCA)
Ananas comosus (L.) Merrill
Prov.: N; terrestrial herb; *Vickers 174, 175, 176* (QCA)
Billbergia decora Poeppig & Endl.
Prov.: N; epiphytic herb; *Brandbyge et al. 36044* (AAU)
Billbergia stenopetala Harms
Prov.: N; epiphytic herb; *Luther et al. 1282* (SEL, QCNE n.v.)
Bromelia plumieri (E. Morren) L. B. Smith
Prov.: N; terrestrial herb; *Poulsen 79917* (AAU, QCA)
Guzmania lingulata (L.) Mez
Prov.: N, P; epiphytic herb; *Holm-Nielsen & Jeppesen 820* (AAU)
Guzmania melinonis Regel
Prov.: N, P; epiphytic herb; *Jaramillo & Coello 3560* (QCA)
Guzmania monostachia (L.) Rusby ex Mez
Prov.: N; epiphytic herb; *Luther et al. 1289* (SEL)
Guzmania tarapotina Ule
Prov.: N, P; epiphytic herb; *Brandbyge & Azanza 31000* (AAU)
Neoregelia eleutheropetala (Ule) L. B. Smith
Prov.: P; epiphytic herb; *Holm-Nielsen et al. 22342* (AAU)
Neoregelia myrmecophila (Ule) L. B. Smith
Prov.: P; epiphytic herb; *Holm-Nielsen et al. 22342* (AAU)

Bromeliaceae   (cont.)

Neoregelia peruviana L. B. Smith
Prov.: P; epiphytic herb; *Zak 4115* (MO, QAME, SEL)
Neoregelia stolonifera L. B. Smith
Prov.: N; epiphytic herb; *Lawesson et al. 44320* (AAU, QCA)
Streptocalyx longifolius (Rudge) Baker
Prov.: N, P; epiphytic herb; *Brandbyge & Azanza 32157* (AAU); *Palacios et al. 646* (MO, SEL n.v.); *Foster 3670* (AAU)
Streptocalyx lugoi Gilmartin & Luther
Prov.: P; epiphytic herb; *Lugo 308* (MO, S)
Streptocalyx pallidus Luther
Prov.: N, P; epiphytic herb; *Øllgaard et al. 35348* (AAU), *Luther et al. 1278A* (SEL)
Streptocalyx williamsii L. B. Smith
Prov.: P; epiphytic herb; *Brandbyge & Azanza 30630* (AAU)
Tillandsia adpressiflora Mez
Prov.: N, P; epiphytic herb; *Brandbyge & Azanza 33993* (AAU)
Tillandsia barthlottii Rauh
Prov.: M-S; epiphytic herb; *Luther et al. 696* (SEL)
Tillandsia paraensis Mez
Prov.: N; epiphytic herb; *Hirtz 4706* (SEL)
Vriesea albo-rubrobracteata Rauh
Prov.: N; epiphytic herb; *Øllgaard et al. 39083* (AAU)
Vriesea heliconioides (Kunth in H.B.K.) Hook. ex Walpers
Prov.: N; epiphytic herb; *Holm-Nielsen et al. 19942* (AAU)

Additional species seen by H. Luther, but not vouchered:
Tillandsia fendleri Grisebach
Tillandsia rhomboidea André
Vriesea gladioliflora (Wend.) Antoine
Vriesea sanguinolenta Cogn. & March.

Brunelliaceae
J. Cuatrecasas, Fl. Neotropica 2, 1970 and supplement, 1985.

Brunelliaceae sp.
Prov.: N, P, M-S; shrub, tree; *Brandbyge & Azanza 32089* (AAU); *Palacios 58* (QAME n.v.)

Burmanniaceae
P. J. M. Maas et al., Fl. Neotropica 21, 1986.

Apteria aphylla (Nutt.) Barnhart ex Small
Prov.: M-S; saprophytic herb; *MacBryde 955* (MO).   Reaches 2000 m alt.
Burmannia kalbreyeri Oliver
Prov.: P; herb, usually epiphytic; *Asplund 18764* (S).   Reaches 2300 m alt.
Burmannia tenella Benth.
Prov.: M-S; saprophytic herb; *Brandbyge 36069* (AAU).   Reaches 1400 m alt.

Burmanniaceae   (cont.)

Dictyostega orobanchoides (Hook.) Miers
    Prov.: M-S, Z-C; saprophytic herb; *MacBryde 980* (MO); *Steyermark 54574* (F)
    Reaches 2600 m alt.
Gymnosiphon minutus Snelders & Maas
    Prov.: N; saprophytic herb; *Lawesson et al. 39612* (AAU)
Gymnosiphon suaveolens (Karsten) Urban
    Prov.: N, P; saprophytic herb; *Harling et al. 16300* (GB).   Reaches 2300 m alt.
Thismia melanomitra Maas & Maas
    Prov.: P; saprophytic herb; *Læssøe 59947* (holotype AAU)
Thismia panamensis (Standley) Jonker
    Prov.: N; saprophytic herb; *Balslev 60635* (AAU)
Thismia singeri (de la Sota) Maas & Maas
    Prov.: N; saprophytic herb; *Balslev 60638* (AAU)

Burseraceae
J. F. Macbride, Fl. Peru 3(2), Publ. Field Mus. Nat. Hist., Bot. Ser. 13:
703–717. 1949. This listing checked by D. Daly, Dec 1988.

Crepidospermum goudotianum (Tul.) Triana & Planchon
    Prov.: P; tree; *Øllgaard et al. 34995* (AAU)
Crepidospermum rhoifolium (Benth.) Triana & Planchon
    Prov.: N; tree; *Brandbyge et al. 33689B* (AAU); *Palacios et al. 891* (AAU)
    Syn.   *Hemicrepidospermum rhoifolium* (Benth.) Swart.
Dacryodes cf. kukachkana L. O. Williams
    Prov.: N; tree; *Vickers 55* (F)
Dacryodes cf. olivifera Cuatrec.
    Prov.: N; tree; *Palacios 2320* (NY)
Dacryodes peruviana (Loes.) Lam aff.
    Prov.: N, P, M-S; tree; *Neill et al. 6106* (QCA); *Pennington & Tenorio 10761*
    (QCA).   Reaches 1050 m alt. in M-S: *Gentry et al. 30929* (AAU, MO)
Dacryodes cf. sclerophylla Cuatrec.
    Prov.: N; tree; *Lawesson et al. 44401* (AAU, QCA)
Dacryodes sp.
    Prov.: N; tree; *Palacios 1172* (NY)
Protium aracouchini (Aublet) March.
    Prov.: N; tree; *Palacios 1009* (MO)
Protium divaricatum Engl.
    Prov.: N; tree; *Korning & Thomsen 47089* (AAU)
Protium ecuadorense Benoist
    Prov.: N; tree; *Brandbyge & Azanza 32718* (AAU)
Protium ferrugineum (Engl.) Engl.
    Prov.: N; tree; *Palacios 1966* (QAME n.v.)
Protium fimbriatum Swart
    Prov.: N, P; tree; *Brandbye et al. 33900* (AAU); *Jaramillo & Coello 3531* (QCA)
    Syn. *Paraprotium amazonicum* Cuatrec.
Protium glabrescens Swart aff.
    Prov.: N, tree; *SEF 10367* (AAU)
Protium insigne (Triana & Planchon) Engl.
    Prov.: N; tree; *Foster 3646* (AAU, F, QCA); *SEF 8595* (AAU, QCA).   This may
    be a synonym of *P. sagotianum* (Daly, pers. comm.).

Burseraceae   (cont.)

Protium macrocarpum Cuatrec. aff.
Prov.: N, M-S; tree; *Davis & Yost 1021* (AAU, QCA); *Little et al. 726* (US)
Protium macrophyllum (H.B.K.) Engl.
Prov.: N, M-S; tree; *Little et al. 712* (US); *Pinkley 478* (ECON, F)
Protium nodulosum Swart
Prov.: N; tree; *Korning & Thomsen 47446* (AAU); *Little et al. 515* (US)
Protium opacum Swart
Prov.: N; tree; *Neill 7423* (QAME n.v.)
Protium pedicellatum Swart
Prov.: N; tree; *Brandbyge et al. 33968* (AAU); *Foster 3647* (AAU, F, QCA)
Protium puncticulatum J. F. Macbr.
Prov.: N; tree; *Palacios 1359* (QAME n.v.)
Protium robustum (Swart) Porter
Prov.: N, P; tree; *Lawesson et al. 44336* (AAU); *Korning & Thomsen 47469*
(AAU); *Neill & Palacios 6603* (QCA)
Protium cf. sagotianum March.
Prov.: N; tree; *Chaguaro 12* (QCA); *Neill 7324* (QAME n.v.)
Protium subserratum (Engl.) Engl.
Prov.: N; tree; *Brandbyge et al. 33896* (AAU); *Jaramillo 8486* (QCA)
Protium tenuifolium Engl.
Prov.: M-S; tree; *Palacios 689* (QAME n.v.); *Little et al. 785* (US)
Protium trifoliolatum Engl.
Prov.: P; tree; *Neill & Palacios 6722* (QCA)
Protium unifoliolatum Engl.
Prov.: N; shrub; *Brandbyge et al. 33795* (AAU); *Palacios & Neill 768* (AAU)
Syn. *Tetragastris unifoliolata* (Engl.) Cuatrec.
Protium vestitum (Cuatrec.) Daly
Prov.: N; tree; *Palacios et al. 1017* (AAU)
Protium sp. 1
Prov.: N; tree; *Barfod & Azanza 32809* (AAU)
Protium sp. 2
Prov.: N; tree; *Korning & Thomsen 58747* (AAU)
Tetragastris altissima (Aublet) Swart
Prov.: N; tree; *SEF 8701* (AAU)
Tetragastris panamensis (Engl.) Kuntze
Prov.: N; tree; *Korning & Thomsen 47743* (AAU)
Trattinnickia burserifolia C. Martius
Prov.: N; tree; *Øllgaard et al. 39274* (AAU)
Trattinnickia glaziovii Swart
Prov.: N; tree; *Palacios 2377* (QAME n.v.)
Trattinnickia peruviana Loes.
Prov.: M-S; tree; *Neill 7405* (QAME n.v.).   Reaches 900 m alt.: *Zaruma et al.
367* (QAME n.v.).
Trattinnickia rhoifolia Willd.
Prov.: N; tree; *SEF 8581* (AAU, QCA)

Buxaceae
J. F. Macbride, Fl. Peru 3A(1), Publ. Field Mus. Nat. Hist., Bot. Ser. 13: 220–221. 1951.

Styloceras brokawii Gentry & Foster
Prov.: N; tree; *Zarucchi 2375* (MO, QCA)

Cabombaceae
M. Ørgaard, Nord. J. Bot. 11: 179–203. 1991.

Cabomba furcata Schultes & Schultes f.
Prov.: N; aquatic herb; *Jaramillo 6906* (AAU, QCA)

Cactaceae
J. E. Madsen, Fl. Ecuador 35, 1989.

Disocactus amazonicus (Schum.) D. Hunt
Prov.: N; epiphytic herb; *Brandbye et al. 33266* (AAU, QCA). Syn. *Wittia amazonica* Schum.
Disocactus ramulosus (Salm-Dyck) Kimnach
Prov.: M-S; herb; *Sparre 19140* (S). Collected at 700–800 m alt.
Epiphyllum phyllanthus (L.) Haw.
Prov.: N; epiphytic herb; *Azanza & Barfod 41139* (AAU); *Alarcón 70* (QCA)
Rhipsalis baccifera (J. S. Muell.) Stearn
Prov.: N; herb; *Lawesson et al. 39363* (AAU, QCA)
Rhipsalis occidentalis Barthlott & Rauh
Prov.: N; herb; *Heinrichs 295* (G). Collected et 700 m alt.
Selenicereus megalanthus (Schum. ex F. Vaupel) Moran
Prov.: N; herb; *Lawesson et al. 43387* (AAU, QCA)

Caesalpiniaceae   (see Leguminosae)

Campanulaceae (incl. Lobeliaceae)
S. Jeppesen, Fl. Ecuador 14, 1981. This listing checked by B. Stein, Apr 1989.

Centropogon alsophilus Wimmer
Prov.: P, M-S; herb; *Øllgaard et al. 35063* (AAU). Reaches 1100 m alt.
Centropogon capitatus Drake
Prov.: N, P, M-S; herb; *Brandbyge & Azanza 32187* (AAU)
Centropogon cornutus (L.) Druce
Prov.: N, P; shrub; *Holm-Nielsen & Jeppesen 633* (AAU, S); *Foster 3733* (AAU, QCA). Reaches 700 m alt. in Napo: *Asplund 9466* (S).
Centropogon eurystomus Wimmer
Prov.: P; herb; *Øllgaard et al. 34544* (AAU)

Campanulaceae   (cont.)

Centropogon gamosepalus Zahlbr.
Prov.: N, P, M-S; shrub; *Harling & Andersson 12749* (GB); *Holm-Nielsen et al. 20433* (AAU, NY); *Besse et al. 1661* (SEL). Reaches 1200 m alt. in Napo.

Centropogon loretensis Wimmer
Prov.: N, P, M-S; shrub; *Holm-Nielsen et al.* 21702 (AAU); *Foster 3829* (AAU, F, NY); *Irvine 1076* (F, QCA). Reaches 1200 m alt. Formerly often erroneously treated as *C. colombiensis* Wimmer

Centropogon tessmannii Wimmer
Prov.:N, P, M-S; herb; *Brandbyge & Azanza 32017* (AAU, QCA); *Neill 6911* (QCA); *Harling et al. 7145* (GB)

Hippobroma longiflora (L.) G. Don
Prov.: N, P; herb, shrub; *Lægaard 51474* (AAU, QCA). Reaches 900 m alt. in Pastaza: *Asplund 19642* (S). Syn. *Isotoma longiflora* (L.) Presl.

Cannaceae
L. Andersson, Fl. Ecuador 32, 1988. This listing checked by P. Maas, Jan 1989.

Canna indica L.
Prov.: N, M-S; herb; *Holm-Nielsen et al. 19108* (AAU, QCA); *Vickers 152* (FLAS); *Pinkley 255* (ECON)

Canna jaegeriana Urban
Prov.: N, P, M-S; herb; *Brandbyge & Azanza 32068* (AAU); *Asdall 81-4* (QCA). Reaches 2000 m alt. Syn. *C. leucocarpa* Bouché.

Capparidaceae
J. F. Macbride, Fl. Peru 2(3), Publ. Field Mus. Nat. Hist., Bot. Ser. 13: 984–1006. 1938. Identifications mostly by H. Iltis, WIS.

Capparis baducca L.
Prov.: N; tree; *Pennington 10587* (QCA)

Capparis detonsa Triana & Planchon
Prov.: N; tree; *Palacios 517* (QAME n.v.)

Capparis macrophylla H.B.K.
Prov.: N, P; tree; *Brandbyge & Azanza 31632* (AAU)

Capparis magnifica Gilg ex Ule
Prov.: N; tree; *Brandbyge et al. 33310* (AAU, QCA); *Vickers 82* (F)

Capparis schunkei J. F. Macbr.
Prov.: N; tree; *Korning & Thomsen 47594* (AAU)

Capparis sola J. F. Macbr.
Prov.: N; tree; *Holm-Nielsen et al. 21262* (AAU); *Irvine 984* (F)

Cleome hassleriana Chodat
Prov.: P, M-S; shrub; *Holm-Nielsen et al. 20557* (AAU)

Capparidaceae sp. 1
Prov.: N; shrub; *Holm-Nielsen et al. 21054* (AAU)

Capparidaceae sp. 2
Prov.: N; tree; *Jaramillo & Coello 3626* (QCA)

Capparidaceae sp. 3
Prov.: N; tree; *Balslev & Alarcón 2992* (QCA); *Jaramillo & Coello 2694* (QCA)

Capparidaceae   (cont.)

Capparidaceae sp. 4
Prov.: N; tree; *Jaramillo & Coello 3783* (QCA)

Caprifoliaceae   (incl. Sambucaceae)
E. P. Killip *in* J. F. Macbride, Fl. Peru 6(2), Publ. Field Mus. Nat. Hist.,
Bot. Ser. 13: 281–287. 1937.

Sambucus mexicanus Presl ex DC.
Prov.: N; shrub; *Pinkley 401* (ECON n.v.).   Reaches 2800 m alt.(=*S. peruviana*
H.B.K. ?)

Caricaceae
V. M. Badillo, Fl. Ecuador 20, 1983.

Carica microcarpa Jacq.
Prov.: N, P; tree; *Balslev 2406* (QCA); *Lugo 4841* (AAU).   Reaches 1400 m alt.
Carica monoica Desf.
Prov.: N, P; herb or shrub; *Harling et al. 7044* (GB).   Reaches 1000 m alt. in
Pastaza: *Asplund 18503* (S)
Carica papaya L.
Prov.: N, M-S; tree; *Balslev & Azanza 4371* (QCA).   Reaches 950 m alt. in M-S:
Harling & Andersson 14029 (GB).
Jacaratia digitata (Poeppig & Endl.) Solms-Laub.
Prov.: N, M-S; tree; *Brandbyge et al. 36239* (AAU); *Little et al. 762* (US);
Lescure 2051 (QCA).   Reaches 700 m alt.
Jacaratia dolichaula (Donn. Smith) Woodson aff.
Prov.: N; tree; *Neill & Palacios 7093* (QCA)
Jacaratia spinosa (Aublet) A. DC.
Prov.: N, M-S; tree; *SEF 8572* (AAU, QCA); *Neill et al. 6854* (AAU, QCA)

Caryocaraceae
G. T. Prance and M. F. Silva, Fl. Neotropica 12. 1973.

Anthodiscus amazonicus (Gleason) A. C. Smith
Prov.: M-S; tree; *Cerón 435* (QAME n.v.)
Anthodiscus peruanus Baillon
Prov.: N; tree; *Cerón 885* (QAME n.v.)
Caryocar glabrum (Aublet) Pers.
Prov.: N; tree; *Brandbyge et al. 36183* (AAU); *Vickers 114* (QCA)
Caryocar villosum (Aublet) Pers.
Prov.: P; tree; *Neill & Palacios 6788* (QCA)

Cecropiaceae

C. C. Berg, Fl. Neotropica 7. 1972; C. C. Berg, R. W. A. P. Akkermans, and E. C. H. van Heusden, Fl. Neotropica 51. 1990. This listing checked by C. C. Berg, Nov 1990.

Cecropia distachya **Huber**
    Prov.: N; tree; *Cerón 3408* (BG, QAME); *Valenica et al. 375* (QCA)
Cecropia engleriana **Snethlage**
    Prov.: N; tree; *Berg & Akkermans 1104* (QCA)
Cecropia ficifolia **Warb. ex Snethlage**
    Prov.: N; tree; *Lawesson et al. 39398* (AAU, QCA); *Irvine 210* (QCA)
Cecropia herthae **Diels**
    Prov.: N; tree; *Palacios et al. 1774* (QAME n.v.)
Cecropia idroboi **Cuatrec. vel sp. aff.**
    Prov.: N; tree; *Cerón 712* (BG)
Cecropia latiloba **Miq.**
    Prov.: N; tree; *Balslev et al. 97162* (AAU, QCA)
Cecropia litoralis **Snethlage**
    Prov.: N; tree; *Balslev et al. 97160* (AAU, QCA)
Cecropia marginalis **Cuatrec.**
    Prov.: N, P, M-S; tree; *SEF 10108* (AAU, QCA); *Løjtnant et al. 13297* (AAU)
Cecropia membranacea **Trécul**
    Prov.: N; tree; *SEF 10099* (AAU, QCA); *Oldeman & Arévalo 90* (QCA)
Cecropia putumayonis **Cuatrec.**
    Prov.: N, P, M-S; tree; *SEF 10245* (AAU, QCA); Neill et al. 6003 (QAME n.v.)
Cecropia sciadophylla **C. Martius**
    Prov.: N; tree; *Jaramillo & Coello 3001* (AAU, QCA); *Irvine 103* (QCA)
Coussapoa asperifolia **Trécul**
    ssp. *magnifolia* (Trécul) Akkermans & C. C. Berg
    Prov.: N; tree; *Neill et al. 6247* (AAU, QAME n.v.)
Coussapoa asperifolia **Trécul**
    ssp. *rhamnoides* (Standley) Akkermans & C. C. Berg
    Prov.: N; tree; *Azanza et al. 41211* (QCA)
Coussapoa crassivenosa **Mildbr.**
    Prov.: N; tree; *Palacios 1361* (BG). Most collections are from above 600 m alt.
Coussapoa longepedunculata **Akkermans & C. C. Berg**
    Prov.: N; tree; *Neill et al. 8289* (QAME n.v.); *Balslev et al. 97025* (AAU, QCA)
Coussapoa orthoneura **Standley**
    Prov.: N; tree; *Foster 3656* (F, QCA, S); *Korning & Thomsen 47558* (AAU)
Coussapoa ovalifolia **Trécul**
    Prov.: N, P, M-S; tree; *Holm-Nielsen et al. 22093* (AAU). Reaches 800 m alt. in M-S: *Berg 1220* (QCA). Including *Coussapoa nitida* Miq. and *C. napoensis* Akkermans & C. C. Berg.
Coussapoa parvifolia **Standley**
    Prov.: M-S; tree; *Palacios 1506* (QAME n.v.)
Coussapoa trinervia **Spruce ex Mildbr.**
    Prov.: N, P; tree or strangler; *Lawesson et al. 44357* (AAU); *Berg & Akkermans 1048* (QCA)
Coussapoa villosa **Poeppig & Endl.**
    Prov.: N; tree or strangler; Berg & *Akkermans 1040* (AAU). Reaches 1950 m alt.
Coussapoa sp.
    Prov.: N; tree; *Zaruma 386* (QAME n.v., QCA)
Pourouma acuminata **C. Martius ex Miq.**
    Prov.: N, P; tree; *Balslev et al. 97126* (AAU, BG, QCA)

Cecropiaceae   (cont.)

Pourouma bicolor C. Martius
> Prov.: N, M-S; tree; *Brandbyge et al. 30194* (AAU); *Korning & Thomsen 47640* (AAU); *Little et al. 350* (QAME n.v.). Including *Pourouma aspera* Trécul
Pourouma cecropiifolia C. Martius
> Prov.: N, M-S; tree; *Fagerlind & Wibom 2289* (S); *Lawesson et al. 39648* (AAU, QCA); *Vickers 123* (QCA); *Alarcón 135* (QCA); *Pinkley 108* (ECON, S)
Pourouma cucura Standley & Cuatrec.
> Prov.: N; tree; *Holm-Nielsen et al. 21364; Balslev et al. 97123* (AAU, QCA)
Pourouma cuspidata Mildbr.
> Prov.: N; tree; *SEF 8532* (AAU)
Pourouma guianensis Aublet
> Prov.: N; tree; *Christensen 72515* (AAU)
Pourouma melinonii Benoist
> Prov.: N; tree; *Cerón & Hurtado 40921* (BG)
Pourouma minor Benoist
> Prov.: N; tree; *Øllgaard et al. 57336* (AAU); *Irvine 180* (F)
Pourouma mollis Trécul
> Prov.: N; tree; *Pennington et al. 12300* (BG, K, QCA);   *Montesdeoca 05-31* (QAME n.v.).   Reaches altitudes above 600 m alt.
Pourouma napoensis C. C. Berg
> Prov.: N; tree; *Palacios 1874* (AAU, MO, NY, QAME)
Pourouma tomentosa Miq.
> Prov.: N; tree; *SEF 9266* (AAU); *Korning & Thomsen 47618* (AAU)
Pourouma sp.
> Prov.: N; tree; *SEF 10378* (AAU)

Celastraceae (excl. Hippocrateaceae)
J. F. Macbride, Fl. Peru 3A(1), Publ. Field Mus. Nat. Hist., Bot. Ser. 13: 259–270. 1951.

Maytenus ebenifolia Reisseck
> Prov.: N; shrub; *Brandbyge et al. 32501* (AAU, QCA); *Neill et al. 6500* (QCA)
Maytenus krukovii A. C. Smith
> Prov.: N; tree; *Neill 6957* (QAME n.v.)
Perrottetia sp.
> Prov.: N; tree; *Asplund 18452, 19341* (S)

Ceratophyllaceae

Ceratophyllum submersum L.
> Prov.: N; herb; *Azanza & Barfod 41240* (AAU, QCA)

Chenopodiaceae
Identifications by U. Eliasson, GB.

Chenopodium ambrosioides L.
> Prov.: N; herb; *Lawesson et al. 39637* (AAU); *Alarcón 68* (QCA); *Vickers 6* (F)

Chrysobalanaceae
G. T. Prance, Fl. Ecuador 10, 1979.

Couepia chrysocalyx (Poeppig & Endl.) Benth. ex Hook. f.
> Prov.: N, M-S; tree; *Brandbyge et al. 32659* (AAU); *Foster 3725* (AAU, QCA);
> *MacBryde & Dwyer 1376* (QCA).   Reaches 1000 m alt. in N.

Couepia ulei Pilger
> Prov.: N; shrub; *Holm-Nielsen et al. 20051* (AAU)

Hirtella bicornis C. Martius & Zucc.
> Prov.: M-S; tree; *Neill 7462* (QAME n.v.)

Hirtella elongata C. Martius & Zucc.
> Prov.: N; tree; *Brandbyge & Azanza 30575* (AAU)

Hirtella macrophylla Benth. ex Hook. f.
> Prov.: N, P; tree; *Lugo 4272* (AAU, GB, QCA); *Irvine 306* (QCA)

Hirtella pilosissima C. Martius & Zucc.
> Prov.: N; tree; *Brandbyge et al. 36119* (AAU)

Hirtella racemosa Lam.
> Prov.: N, P, M-S; shrub; *Holm-Nielsen et al. 19678* (AAU)

Hirtella triandra Sw. ssp. *triandra*
> Prov.: N; tree; *Brandbyge et al. 36177* (AAU); *SEF 8824, 10289* (AAU, QCA)
> Syn. *H. americana* auct. non L.

Licania apetala (E. Meyer) Fritsch
> Prov.: M-S; tree; *Ortega U. 76, 154* (NY)

Licania arborea Seem.
> Prov.: N; tree; *Neill 7217* (QAME n.v.)

Licania caudata Prance
> Prov.: N; tree; *Palacios 1122* (QAME n.v.)

Licania durifolia Cuatrec.
> Prov.: N, P; tree; *Oldeman & Arévalo 11* (QCA).   Reaches 1000 m alt. in
> Pastaza: *Lugo 44* (S).

Licania guianensis (Aublet) Griseb.
> Prov.: P; tree; *Øllgaard et al. 35032* (AAU); *SEF 10005* (AAU, QCA)

Licania harlingii Prance
> Prov.: N; tree; *Lugo 1054* (GB); *SEF 8901, 9217, 9296* (AAU, QCA)

Licania hypoleuca Benth.
> Prov.: M-S; tree; *Ortega U. 73, 74* (NY)

Licania longistyla (Hook. f.) Fritsch
> Prov.: N; tree; *SEF 10119* (AAU, QCA)

Licania macrocarpa Cuatrec.
> Prov.: N; tree; *SEF 8564* (AAU, QCA); *Jaramillo 6861* (QCA)

Licania reticulata Prance
> Prov.: N; tree; *SEF 9269* (AAU, QCA)

Licania sp.
> Prov.: N; tree; *SEF 8681* (AAU, QCA)

Parinari klugii Prance
> Prov.: N; tree; *SEF 10063* (AAU, QCA)

Clusiaceae

Calophyllum brasiliense **Cambess.**
Prov.: N; tree; *Neill 8972* (QAME n.v.)
Chrysochlamys macrophylla **Pax**
Prov.: N; tree; *Foster 3578* (QCA); *Irvine 1103* (QCA)
Chrysochlamys membranacea **Planchon & Triana**
Prov.: N, P; tree; *Holm-Nielsen et al. 21483* (AAU). Reaches 1050 m alt. in
Pastaza: *Holm-Nielsen & Jeppesen 345* (AAU). = *Tovomitopsis membranacea*
Chrysochlamys tenuifolia **Cuatrec.**
Prov.: N, P; shrub; *Brandbyge & Azanza 32901* (AAU)
Chrysochlamys weberbaueri **Engl.**
Prov.: N; tree; *Gentry 9738* (QCA). Reaches ca. 750 m alt in Napo: *Asplund 9051* (GB)
Clusia decussata **Ruíz & Pavón** vel sp. aff.
Prov.: N; epiphytic herb; *Gentry 9726* (MO, S)
Clusia lineata **(Benth.) Planchon & Triana**
Prov.: N; tree; *Zaruma et al. 273* (QAME n.v.)
Clusia mamillata **Cuatrec.**
Prov.: N; epiphytic herb; *Lawesson et al. 43427* (AAU, QCA)
Clusia cf. *palmicida* **L. C. Rich.**
Prov.: N; shrub; *Azanza & Barfod 41227* (AAU)
Clusia penduliflora **Engl.**
Prov.: N; tree; *Cerón 614* (MO)
Clusia sellowiana **Schlecht.** aff.
Prov.: N; epiphytic herb; *Korning & Thomsen 47160* (AAU)
Clusia **sp. 1**
Prov.: N; tree; *Lawesson et al. 39570* (AAU)
Clusia **sp. 2**
Prov.: N; tree; *Lawesson et al. 44315* (AAU)
Clusia **sp. 3**
Prov.: N; tree; *Lawesson et al. 43402* (AAU, QCA)
Clusia **sp. 4**
Prov.: N; epiphytic herb; *Luteyn et al. 9015* (AAU, NY)
Havetiopsis flexilis **Spruce ex Planchon & Triana**
Prov.: N; tree; *Sparre 13076* (S)
Marila cf. *cespedeziana* **Planchon & Triana**
Prov.: N, P; tree *Løjtnant & Molau 13591* (AAU, GB, QCA); *Øllgaard et al. 34671* (AAU); *Korning & Thomsen 58670* (AAU). Some specimens as *M.* cf.
pluricostata Standley & L. Williams, others as *M.* cf. *laxiflora* Rusby
Marila **sp.**
Prov.: N; tree; *SEF 9155* (AAU)
Quapoya peruviana **(Poepp. & Endl.) Kuntze**
Prov.: N, M-S; tree; *Neill 6907* (QAME n.v.); *Little et al. 354* (US)
Rheedia acuminata **(Ruíz & Pavón) Planchon & Triana**
Prov.: N; tree; *Irvine 761* (F, QCA); *Alarcón 121* (QCA); *Vickers 203, 303* (F)
Rheedia gardneriana **Miers ex Planchon & Triana**
Prov.: N; tree; *Korning & Thomsen 47749* (AAU)
Rheedia macrophylla **(C. Martius) Planchon & Triana**
Prov.: N; tree; *Korning & Thomsen 58692* (AAU); *SEF 8631* (AAU, QCA)
Rheedia madruno **Planchon & Triana**
Prov.: N; tree; *Villegas & Meneses 14* (QCA)

Clusiaceae   (cont.)

Rheedia sp.
   Prov.: N; shrub; *Azanza & Barfod 41112* (AAU)
Symphonia globulifera L. f.
   Prov.: P, M-S; tree; *Korning & Thomsen 47811* (AAU); *Neill & Palacios 6701* (AAU, QCA); *Little et al. 597* (US). Reaches 900 m alt.
Tovomita weddelliana Planchon & Triana
   Prov.: N; tree; *Neill 6773* (QAME n.v.)
Tovomitopsis sp.
   Prov.: N, M-S; tree; *Little et al. 401, 585* (US)
Vismia baccifera (L.) Planchon & Triana
   Prov.: N; tree; *SEF 8956* (AAU, QCA)
Vismia cayennensis (Jacq.) Pers.
   Prov.: P, M-S; tree; *Palacios et al. 5* (AAU); *Little et al. 658, 689, 718* (US)
Vismia confertiflora Spruce ex Reichb.
   Prov.: N, P; tree; *Irvine 616* (QCA); *Neill & Palacios 7100* (AAU, QCA)
Vismia floribunda Sprague
   Prov.: P, M-S; tree; *Brandbgye & Azanza 32202* (AAU, QCA)
Vismia macrophylla H.B.K.
   Prov.: N; tree; *Brandbyge et al. 30524* (AAU)
Vismia obtusa Spruce ex Reichb.
   Prov.: N; tree; *Luteyn et al. 8588* (AAU, NY)

Combretaceae
J. F. Macbride, Fl. Peru 4(1), Publ. Field Mus. Nat. Hist., Bot. Ser. 13: 221–229. 1941. Identifications mostly by C. A. Stace.

Buchenavia amazonica Alwan & Stace
   Prov.: N; shrub; *Brandbyge et al. 36154* (AAU)
Buchenavia sp.
   Prov.: M-S; tree; *Brandbyge & Azanza 31840* (AAU)
Combretum laurifolium C. Martius
   Prov.: N; tree; *Lawesson et al. 44233* (QCA)
Combretum laxum Jacq.
   Prov.: N; tree, liana; *Brandbyge et al. 33713* (AAU)
Combretum llewellynii J. F. Macbr.
   Prov.: N; liana; *Lawesson et al. 43470* (AAU, QCA)
Combretum rotundifolium Rich.
   Prov.: N, P; liana; *Brandbyge & Azanza 31404* (AAU)
Terminalia amazonica (J. F. Gmel.) Exell
   Prov.: N, M-S; tree; *Korning & Thomsen 47419* (AAU); *Little et al. 717* (US)
Terminalia guianensis Eichler
   Prov.: M-S; tree; *Little et al. 317* (US)
Terminalia oblonga (Ruíz & Pavón) Steudel
   Prov.: N; tree; *SEF 8612* (AAU); *Neill & Palacios 7102* (QCA)

Commelinaceae

J. F. Macbride, Fl. Peru 1(3), Publ. Field Mus. Nat. Hist., Bot. Ser. 13: 592–608. 1936. This listing checked by R. Faden, Aug 1988.

Commelina erecta L.
Prov.: N; herb; *Alarcón 19547* (QCA)
Dichorisandra cf. *bonitana* Philipson
Prov.: N; herb; *Cerón 578* (QAME n.v.)
Dichorisandra hexandra (Aublet) Standley
Prov.: N; vine; *Korning & Thomsen 47200* (AAU)
Dichorisandra hexandra (Aublet) Standley aff.
Prov.: N; herb; *Lægaard 51512* (AAU, QCA); *Jaramillo & Coello 2774* (QCA)
Dichorisandra ulei J. F. Macbr.
Prov.: N; herb; *Foster 3821* (AAU, QCA); *Jaramillo & Coello 3003* (QCA)
Floscopa elegans Huber
Prov.: N; vine; *Cerón 616* (QAME n.v.)
Floscopa peruviana Hassk. ex C. B. Clarke
Prov.: N, P; vine; *Luteyn et al. 9076* (AAU); *Balslev & Alarcón 3026* (QCA)
Geogenanthus ciliatus Brückn.
Prov.: N; herb; *Alarcón 19552* (QCA); *Brandbyge et al. 33000* (AAU)
Geogenanthus rhizianthus (Ule) Brückn.
Prov.: N; herb; *Brandbyge et al. 30439* (AAU, US); *Irvine 359* (F)
Tradescantia zanonia (L.) Sw.
Prov.: N, P; herb; *Holm-Nielsen & Jeppesen 855* (AAU); *Balslev & Alarcón 2954* (QCA)
Tripogandra serrulata (Vahl) Handlos
Prov.: N; herb; *Gentry 9737* (AAU, GB, MO, QCA); *Irvine 780* (QCA)

Connaraceae

E. Forero, Fl. Neotropica 36. 1983.

Cnestidium rufescens Planchon
Prov.: N; liana; *Gentry et al. 21809* (MO, QCA)
Connarus fasciculatus (DC.) Planchon
Prov.: N; tree; *Lawesson et al. 44311* (QCA); *Jaramillo 6887* (QCA)
Connarus punctatus Planchon
Prov.: N; tree; *Brandbyge et al. 33629* (AAU, QCA)
Connarus ruber (Poeppig & Endl.) Planchon
Prov.: N; tree; *Foster 3635* (QCA); *Lescure 2030* (QCA)
Rourea amazonica (Huber) Radlk.
Prov.: N; shrub or liana; *Jaramillo & Coello 2943* (AAU); *Gentry et al. 21807* (AAU, QCA)
Rourea cuspidata Benth. ex Baker
Prov.: N; shrub or liana; *Lawesson et al. 44489* (AAU, QCA); *Irvine 389* (F)

Convolvulaceae

D. F. Austin, Fl. Ecuador 15, 1982.

Aniseia martinicensis (Jacq.) Choisy
Prov.: N; climber; *Holm-Nielsen et al. 20019* (AAU)

Convolvulaceae (cont.)

Dicranostyles sp.
    Prov.: N; tree; *Jaramillo & Coello 4435* (QCA); *Gentry 21750* (AAU)
    Probably *D. ampla* Ducke, *D. scandens* Benth., or *D. sericea* Gleason
Ipomoea alba L.
    Prov.: N, P; vine; *Holm-Nielsen & Jeppesen 936* (AAU); *Løjtnant & Molau
    13283* (AAU, GB)
Ipomoea batatas (L.) Lam.
    Prov.: N, P, M-S; vine; *Vickers 258* (F); *Davis & Yost 1053* (QCA); *Balslev 4902*
    (QCA); *Øllgaard et al. 34592* (AAU). Reaches 1000 m alt.
Ipomoea batatoides Choisy
    Prov.: N; vine; *Holm-Nielsen et al. 19689* (AAU); *Lugo 3434* (GB, QCA)
Ipomoea chondrosepala H. Hall.
    Prov.: N; vine; *Bohlin & Bohlin 289* (GB); *Lugo 2559* (GB); *Harling &
    Andersson 16641* (GB). Reaches 1000 m alt.
Ipomoea lindenii Martens & Galleotti
    Prov.: N; vine; *Bénoist 4798* (P n.v.)
Ipomoea ophioides Standley & Steyermark
    Prov.: N; vine; *Andrade 33001* (AAU); *Lugo 2116* (GB, QCA)
Ipomoea phyllomega (Vell.) House
    Prov.: N, P, M-S; vine; *Lugo 3176* (GB, QCA); *3116* (AAU).   Reaches 1000 m
    alt. in M-S: *Holm-Nielsen et al. 4541* (AAU, S)
Ipomoea quamoclit L.
    Prov.: N; vine; *Holm-Nielsen et al. 19773* (AAU); *Jaramillo & Rivera 131*
    (AAU, QCA)
Ipomoea ramosissima (Poir.) Choisy
    Prov.: N, P; vine; *Holm-Nielsen et al. 19110* (AAU); *Lugo 312* (GB, QCA)
    Reaches 750 m alt.
Ipomoea regnellii Meisner
    Prov.: N; vine; *Harling 11096* (GB); *Andrade 33129* (AAU)
Ipomoea reticulata O'Donell
    Prov.: N, P, M-S; vine; *Lugo 1545* (AAU); *Brandbyge et al. 36185* (AAU)
    Reaches slightly higher alts.: *Harling & Andersson 12891* (GB)
Ipomoea squamosa Choisy
    Prov.: N, P; vine; *Harling & Andersson 11763* (GB); *Sparre 13019* (S)
Jacquemontia ciliata Sandw.
    Prov.: N, P, M-S; vine; *Lugo 3958* (GB). Reaches 1000 m alt. in M-S: *Lugo 3758*
    (AAU, GB)
Jacquemontia hirtiflora (C. Martius & Galleotti) O'Donell
    Prov.: N, M-S; vine; *Lugo 263, 2973* (GB); *Sparre 13207* (S); *Harling 996* (S)
Maripa nicaraguensis Hemsley
    Prov.: N; vine; *Harling & Andersson 16596* (AAU, GB, QCA)
Maripa pauciflora Austin
    Prov.: N; vine; *Øllgaard et al. 39003* (AAU); *Brandbyge et al. 33320* (AAU)
Maripa peruviana Ooststr.
    Prov.: P; vine; *Jaramillo et al. 31523* (AAU)
Merremia umbellata (L.) H. Hall.
    Prov.: N, P; vine; *Løjtnant & Molau 13417* (AAU). Reaches 1000 m alt.

Costaceae
P. J. M. Maas, Fl. Ecuador 6, 1976. This listing checked by P. Maas, Jan 1989.

Costus amazonicus (Loes.) J. F. Macbr.
Prov.: N, P, M-S; herb; *Jaramillo et al. 30904* (AAU); *Davis & Yost 1029* (QCA) Reaches 1100 m alt. in Pastaza: *Asplund 19189* (S)

Costus arabicus L.
Prov.: N, P; herb; *Brandbyge & Azanza 31696* (AAU)

Costus asplundii (Maas) Maas
Prov.: N, P, M-S; herb; *Øllgaard et al. 34692* (AAU). Reaches 1000 m alt.

Costus chartaceus Maas
Prov.: P; herb; *Holm-Nielsen et al. 22005* (AAU)

Costus erythrocoryne K. Schum.
Prov.: P; herb; *Holm-Nielsen et al. 22117* (AAU)

Costus erythrophyllus Loes.
Prov.: N, P; herb; *Holm-Nielsen et al. 19842* (AAU); *Harling 3575* (S)

Costus guanaiensis Rusby
Prov.: N; herb; *Holm-Nielsen et al. 20180* (AAU)

Costus laevis Ruíz & Pavón
Prov.: N, P, M-S; herb; *Grubb et al. 1544* (K n.v.); *Øllgaard et al. 39107* (AAU) Reaches 1650 m in M-S: *Camp E-2395* (US)

Costus lasius Loes.
Prov.: N, P, M-S; herb; *Brandbyge & Azanza 31808* (AAU, QCA)

Costus lima K. Schum.
Prov.: N; herb; *Brandbyge et al. 30255* (AAU); *Dwyer & MacBryde 9776* (QCA)

Costus longibracteolatus Maas
Prov.: N, P, M-S; herb; *Andrade 33050* (AAU, QCA); *Balslev et al. 62240* (QCA) Reaches 900 m alt. in M-S: *Asplund 19765* (S)

Costus pulverulentus Presl
Prov.: N; herb; *Jaramillo 6898* (AAU, QCA); *Øllgaard et al. 57169* (AAU)

Costus scaber Ruíz & Pavón
Prov.: N, P, M-S; herb; *Brandbyge & Azanza 32245* (AAU, QCA); *Davis & Yost 940* (QCA). Reaches 1500 m alt. in M-S: *Harling & Andersson 12806* (GB)

Dimerocostus strobilaceus Kuntze
Prov.: N, P, M-S; herb; *Holm-Nielsen et al. 21044* (AAU); *Alarcón 19374* (QCA); *Balslev 2810* (QCA). Reaches 900 m alt. in M-S: *Asplund 19784* (S)

Crassulaceae

Bryophyllum sp.
Prov.: N; herb; *Balslev & Alarcón 2886, 2898* (QCA)

Kalanchoe pinnata (Lam.) Pers.
Prov.: N; herb; *Vickers 184* (F); *Irvine 711* (F)

Cucurbitaceae
J. F. Macbride, Fl. Peru 6(2), Publ. Field Mus. Nat. Hist., Bot. Ser. 13: 321–383. 1937. Identifications mostly by M. Nee, NY.

Calycophysum pedunculatum Triana
Prov.: N, M-S; vine; *Brandbyge & Azanza 32389* (AAU)

Cucurbitaceae (cont.)

Cayaponia amazonica (Poeppig & Endl.) Cogn.
Prov.: N; vine; *Lawesson et al. 43337* (AAU)
Cayaponia cf. coriacea Cogn.
Prov.: P; vine; *Brandbyge & Azanza 31415* (AAU)
Cayaponia cruegeri (Naudin) Cogn.
Prov.: N; vine; *Lawesson et al. 43554* (AAU)
Cayaponia duckei Harms aff.
Prov.: N; vine; *Brandbyge & Azanza 30424, 30071, 30497* (AAU)
Cayaponia glandulosa (Poeppig & Endl.) Cogn.
Prov.: N, P, M-S; vine; *Holm-Nielsen et al. 21412* (AAU); *Brandbyge & Azanza 32284* (AAU, QCA)
Cayaponia macrocalyx Harms
Prov.: P; vine; *Holm-Nielsen et al. 22544* (AAU); *Gentry 12487A* (MO, QCA)
Cayaponia oppositifolia Harms
Prov.: N; liana; *Brandbyge & Azanza 30435* (AAU)
Cayaponia ruizii Cogn.
Prov.: N, M-S; vine; *Davis & Yost 959* (QCA); *Alarcón 80* (QCA)
Citrullus cf. lanatus (Thunb.) Mats. & Nakai
Prov.: M-S; vine; *Cerón 216* (QAME n.v.)
Cyclanthera cordifolia Cogn.
Prov.: N; vine; *Jaramillo & Coello 3958* (AAU, QCA)
Elateriopsis oerstedii (Cogn.) Pittier
Prov.: M-S; vine; *Balslev & Boom 4382* (AAU, QCA)
Fevillea cordifolia L.
Prov.: N; vine; *Holm-Nielsen et al. 19710* (AAU); *Pinkley 103* (ECON)
Fevillea pergamentacea Cogn.
Prov.: N, P; vine; *Øllgaard et al. 34778* (AAU), *Balslev 2321* (AAU, QCA)
Gurania acuminata Cogn.
Prov.: N, P, M-S; vine; *Barfod & Azanza 32250* (AAU, QCA)
Gurania capitata Cogn.
Prov.: N; vine; *Jaramillo & Rivera 186* (AAU, QCA)
Gurania eriantha (Poeppig & Endl.) Cogn.
Prov.: N, P, M-S; vine; *Holm-Nielsen 19212* (AAU, QCA)
Gurania guentheri Harms
Prov.: N, P; vine; *Brandbyge et al. 33290* (AAU); *Foster 3828* (AAU, F)
Gurania pachypoda Harms
Prov.: P, M-S; vine; *Barfod & Azanza 32214* (AAU)
Gurania pedata Sprague
Prov.: N, P; vine; *Holm-Nielsen 19249* (AAU)
Gurania rhizantha (Poeppig & Endl.) C. Jeffrey
Prov.: N, P, M-S; vine; *Holm-Nielsen et al. 22570* (AAU, QCA)
Gurania spinulosa (Poeppig & Endl.) Cogn.
Prov.: N, P, M-S; vine; *Balslev & Madsen 10279* (AAU); *Irvine 782* (QCA)
Gurania sp.
Prov.: N; vine; *Holm-Nielsen et al. 19679* (AAU)
Lagenaria siceraria (Molina) Standley
Prov.: N; liana; *Vickers 131* (F); *Pinkley 540* (ECON)
Luffa aegyptiaca Mill.
Prov.: N, P; vine; *Lawesson et al. 39655* (AAU); *Irvine 774* (QCA)
Melothria trilobata Cogn.
Prov.: N; vine; *Holm-Nielsen et al. 21462B* (AAU)

Cucurbitaceae   (cont.)

Melothria warmingii Cogn.
Prov.: P; vine; *Løjtnant & Molau 13400* (AAU)
Momordica charantia L.
Prov.: P; liana; *Løjtnant & Molau13423* (AAU)
Psiguria triphylla (Miq.) C. Jeffrey
Prov.: N; vine; *Holm-Nielsen et al. 21128* (AAU)
Pteropepon sp.
Prov.: N; vine; *Gentry 9809* (AAU).   Distributed as *P. monospermus* (Vell.)
Cogn. Prob. = *P. deltoideus* Cogn.
Selysia prunifera (Poeppig & Endl.) Cogn.
Prov.: N; vine; *Holm-Nielsen et al. 21045* (AAU)

Cyclanthaceae
G. Harling, Fl. Ecuador 1, 1973. This listing checked by R. Erikson, GB, 1990.

Asplundia alata Harling
Prov.: N; terrestrial shrub or vine; *Balslev et al. 62271* (QCA); *Alarcón 58* (QCA); *Luteyn et al. 8636* (NY, QCA)
Asplundia aulacostigma Harling
Prov.: N, P, M-S; vine; *Pennington 1595* (K, OXF); *Harling et al. 9979* (GB)
Reaches 1000 m alt.
Asplundia ecuadoriensis (Harling) Harling
Prov.: N; vine; *Harling et al. 7352* (GB)
Asplundia heliotricha (Harling) Harling
Prov.: N, P; vine; *Harling 3558* (S)
Asplundia peruviana Harling
Prov.: N, M-S; vine; *Holm-Nielsen & Jeppesen 825* (AAU)
Asplundia schitzopetalum Harling
Prov.: P; vine; *Holm-Nielsen et al. 22316* (AAU)
Carludovica palmata Ruíz & Pavón
Prov.: N, P; terrestrial herb or shrub; *Brandbyge & Azanza 30094* (AAU); *Alarcón 99* (QCA); *Vickers 159* (F)
Cyclanthus bipartitus Poit.
Prov.: N, P, M-S; terrestrial herb; *Holm-Nielsen et al. 21469* (AAU); *Davis & Yost 965* (QCA); *Pinkley 410* (ECON); *Neill & Palacios 6769* (QCA)
Dicranopygium coma-pyrrhae (Harling) Harling
Prov.: N; terrestrial herb; *Harling et al. 6944* (GB)
Dicranopygium cuatrecasanum Harling   aff.
Prov.: N; terrestrial herb; *Balslev 2317* (QCA)
Dicranopygium cf. euryphyllum (Harling) Harling
Prov.: N; terrestrial herb; *Brandbyge et al. 33205* (AAU)
Dicranopygium lugonis Harling
Prov.: N; terrestrial herb or shrub; *Lawesson et al. 39536* (AAU); *Balslev 2425* (QCA)
Dicranopygium mirabile Harling
Prov.: N; terrestrial herb; *Balslev 4840, 4864* (QCA)
Dicranopygium rheithrophyllum (Harling) Harling
Prov.: N; terrestrial herb; *Molau & Öhmann 1556* (QCA)

Cyclanthaceae (cont.)

***Dicranopygium schultezii* Harling**
Prov.: N; terrestrial herb; *Cerón 881* (QAME n.v.)
***Dicranopygium* cf. *stenophyllum* Harling**
Prov.: N; terrestrial herb or shrub; *Holm-Nielsen 19229* (AAU)
***Dicranopygium* cf. *williamsii* (Standley) Harling**
Prov.: M-S; terrestrial herb; *Brandbyge & Azanza 32039* (AAU)
***Evodianthus funifer* (Poit.) Lindm.**
Prov.: N, P; vine; *Holm-Nielsen et al. 22360* (AAU); *Vickers 78* (F)
***Ludovia integrifolia* (Woodson) Harling**
Prov.: N, P; vine; *Holm-Nielsen et al. 21208* (AAU)
***Ludovia lancifolia* Brongn.**
Prov.: N; epiphytic herb or vine; *Holm-Nielsen et al. 20063* (AAU)
***Schultesiophytum chorianthum* Harling**
Prov.: P; shrub; *Øllgaard et al. 34861* (AAU)
***Thoracocarpus bissectus* (Vell.) Harling**
Prov.: N, P; vine; *Løjtnant & Molau 13508* (AAU, GB)

Cyperaceae
J. F. Macbride, Fl. Peru 1(1), Publ. Field Mus. Nat. Hist., Bot. Ser. 13: 261–320. 1936. Identifications by T. Koyama, NY, G. Davidse, MO, and S. Lægaard, AAU. This listing checked by P. Goetghebeur, May 1989.

***Bequerelia cymosa* Brongn.**
Prov.: P; herb; *Jaramillo et al. 31324* (AAU)
***Calyptrocarya bicolor* (Pfeiffer) Koyama**
Prov.: N; herb; *Holm-Nielsen et al. 20166* (AAU); *Palacios 2399* (QAME n.v.)
***Calyptrocarya glomerulata* (Brongn.) Urban**
Prov.: N, P, M-S; herb; *Holm-Nielsen et al. 4231* (AAU)
***Cyperus articulatus* L.**
Prov.: N; herb; *Vickers 17* (F)
***Cyperus* cf. *corymbosus* Rottb.**
Prov.: N; herb; *Brandbyge et al. 32840* (AAU)
***Cyperus distans* L.f.**
Prov.: N; herb; *Holm-Nielsen et al. 19825* (AAU)
***Cyperus iria* L.**
Prov.: N; herb; *Molau & Öhman 1582* (QCA)
***Cyperus laxus* Willem.**
Prov.: N, P, M-S; herb; *Brandbyge et al. 32127* (AAU); *Irvine 772* (QCA)
Syn. *C. diffusus* Vahl ssp. *chalaranthus* (Presl) Kukk.
***Cyperus luzulae* (L.) Retz.**
Prov.: N, P, M-S; herb; *Brandbyge et al. 30270* (AAU)
***Cyperus miliifolius* Poeppig & Kunth**
Prov.: N, P; herb; *Holm-Nielsen et al. 19880* (AAU)
***Cyperus prolixus* H.B.K.**
Prov.: N, P; herb; *McElroy 419* (QCA); *Vickers 186* (QCA)
***Cyperus rotundus* L.**
Prov.: N; herb; *Holm-Nielsen et al. 19824* (AAU)
***Cyperus simplex* Kunth**
Prov.: N, P; herb; *Løjtnant & Molau 13281* (AAU, GB); *Lægaard* (AAU, QCA)
***Cyperus sphacelatus* Rottb.**
Prov.: N, M-S; herb; *Lægaard 51189* (AAU, QCA)

Cyperaceae   (cont.)

Cyperus surinamensis Rottb.
Prov.: N; herb; *Holm-Nielsen & Jeppesen 206* (AAU); *Lægaard 51561* (AAU, QCA)
Diplasia karataefolia L. C. Rich.
Prov.: N, P; herb; *Brandbyge et al. 30059* (AAU); *Foster 3741* (F, QCA)
Eleocharis elegans (Kunth) Roemer & Schultes
Prov.: N; herb; *Lawesson et al. 39771* (AAU, QCA)
Eleocharis geniculata (L.) Roemer & Schultes
Prov.: N; herb; *Balslev 2289* (QCA)
Eleocharis interstincta (Vahl) Roemer & Schultes
Prov.: P; herb; *Løjtnant & Molau 13615* (AAU)
Eleocharis retroflexa (Poir.) Urban
Prov.: P; herb; *Holm-Nielsen & Jeppesen 505* (AAU); *Jaramillo 4069* (QCA) Reaches 1000 m alt.
Fimbristylis dichotoma (L.) Vahl
Prov.: N, P, M-S; herb; *Brandbyge et al. 32132* (AAU); *Alarcón 19527* (QCA)
Fimbristylis miliacea (L.) Vahl
Prov.: N, P; herb; *Jaramillo et al. 2636* (AAU, QCA)
Hypolytrum laxum Nees
Prov.: N; herb; *Lægaard 51072* (AAU, QCA)
Hypolytrum longifolium Schrad. ex Nees
ssp. sylvaticum (Poeppig & Kunth) Koyama
Prov.: N; herb; *Lægaard 51120* (AAU, QCA)
Hypolytrum schraderianum Nees
Prov.: N; herb; *Lægaard 51215* (AAU, QCA)
Kyllinga brevifolia Rottb.
Prov.: N; herb; *Cerón 872* (QAME n.v.)
Kyllinga pumila Michx.
Prov.: M-S; herb; *Brandbyge & Azanza 32256* (QCA).   Reaches 2100 m alt.
Oxycaryum cubense (Poeppig & Kunth) Lye
Prov.: P; herb; *Øllgaard et al. 35061* (AAU).   Syn. *Scirpus cubensis*
Rhynchospora amazonica Poeppig & Kunth ex Kunth
Prov.: N; herb; *Øllgaard et al. 35707* (AAU)
Rhynchospora corymbosa (L.) Britton
Prov.: N, P; herb; *Øllgaard et al. 35524* (AAU)
Rhynchospora gigantea Link
Prov.: P; h; *Øllgaard et al. 35072* (AAU)
Rhynchospora radicans (Cham. & Schlecht.) Pfeiffer
Prov.: P; herb; *Øllgaard et al. 35150* (AAU).   Reaches 2100 m alt.
Rhynchospora watsonii (Britt.) Davidse
Prov.: N; herb; *Cerón 1008* (QAME n.v.)
Scleria cf. cyperina Kunth
Prov.: P; herb; *Løjtnant & Molau 13410* (AAU), *13366* (QCA)
Scleria flagellum-nigrorum Berg.
Prov.: N; herb; *Brandbyge et al. 33874* (AAU)
Scleria macrophylla Presl
Prov.: P; herb; *Øllgaard et al. 35060* (AAU)
Scleria melaleuca Reichb. ex Cham. & Schlecht.
Prov.: N; herb; *Cerón 1305* (QAME n.v.)

Cyperaceae   (cont.)

Scleria microcarpa Nees ex Kunth
Prov.: N, P; herb; *Holm-Nielsen et al. 19992* (AAU); *Løjtnant & Molau 13277* (QCA)
Scleria mitis Berg.
Prov.: N; herb; *Alarcón 3000* (QCA)
Scleria pterota Presl
Prov.: N, P, M-S; herb; *Brandbyge et al. 30266* (AAU)
Scleria secans (L.) Urban
Prov.: N, P, M-S; herb; *Lawesson et al. 43355* (AAU)
Torulinium odoratum (L.) Hooper
Prov.: N, P, M-S; herb; *Lægaard 51484* (AAU, QCA); *Cerón 2039* (QAME n.v.)

Dichapetalaceae
G. T. Prance, Fl. Ecuador 12, 1980

Dichapetalum asplundeanum Prance
Prov.: N; tree; *Korning & Thomsen 58634* (AAU)
Dichapetalum rugosum (Vahl) Prance
Prov.: N; shrub or liana; *Asplund 10179* (S).   Reaches ca. 700 m alt.
Dichapetalum spruceanum Baillon
Prov.: N, P; shrub or vine; *Jaramillo et al. 30732* (AAU); *Neill et al. 6077* (QCA)
Reaches 1050 m alt. in Napo: *Asplund 18496* (S)
Stephanopodium angulatum (Little) Prance
Prov.: N; tree; *Lawesson et al. 44375* (AAU, QCA); *Lescure 2093* (QCA)
Tapura amazonica Poeppig & Endl.
Prov.: N; shrub; *Brandbyge et al. 33892* (AAU); *Neill et al. 6508* (AAU, QCA)
Tapura coriacea J. F. Macbr.
Prov.: N; tree; *Palacios 1253* (QAME n.v.)
Tapura guianensis Aublet
Prov.: N; *Irvine 671* (F, QCA); *Neill 7505* (QAME n.v.)
Tapura peruviana Krause
Prov.: N, P; tree; *Brandbyge & Azanza 32446* (AAU, QCA); *Irvine 667* (QCA)
Tapura sp. nov.
Prov.: N, P; tree; *Palacios 744* (QAME n.v.); *Zaruma et al. 573* (QAME n.v.)
This new species will be described by G. Prance as *T. magnifolia*.

Dilleniaceae
K. Kubitzki, Mitt. Bot. München 8: 1–98, 1970; ibid. 9: 1–105, 1971; ibid. 9: 707–720, 1973.

Doliocarpus dentatus (Aublet) Standley
Prov.: N, P; shrub; *Øllgaard et al. 34916* (AAU).   Reaches 900 m alt. in Napo: *Asplund 18894* (S).
Doliocarpus cf. *hispidus* Standley & Williams
Prov.: N; scandent; *Brandbyge et al. 33583* (AAU)
Doliocarpus major J. F. Gmel.
Prov.: N, P; tree or shrub; *Brandbyge et al. 30546* (AAU)
Doliocarpus novogranatensis Kubitzki
Prov.: N; shrub; *Holm-Nielsen & Jeppesen 884* (AAU).   Reaches 1200 m alt.

Dilleniaceae   (cont.)

Tetracera volubilis L.
Prov.: N; shrub; *Jaramillo & Coello 4451* (AAU)
Tetracera sp.
Prov.: N; liana; *Øllgaard et al. 57065* (AAU)

Dioscoreaceae
J. F. Macbride, Fl. Peru 1(3), Publ. Field Mus. Nat. Hist., Bot. Ser. 13: 690–707. 1936.

Dioscorea ramiflora Eichler
Prov.: N; vine; *Holm-Nielsen & Jeppesen 771* (AAU, S)
Syn. *D. samydea* (C. Martius) Griseb.
Dioscorea trifida L.f.
Prov.: N; vine; *Balslev 4880* (QCA); *Irvine 1064* (F, QCA)

Ebenaceae
J. F. Macbride, Fl. Peru 5(1), Publ. Field Mus. Nat. Hist., Bot. Ser. 13: 205–214. 1959.

Diospyros cf. digyna Jacq.
Prov.: N; tree; *Lawesson et al. 39400* (AAU, QCA)
Diospyros melinonii (Hieron.) A. C. Smith
Prov. N; tree; *Palacios 1086* (QAME n.v.)
Diospyros peruviana Hieron.
Prov. N; tree; *Zaruma et al. 60* (QAME n.v.)
Diospyros pseudoxylopia Mildbr.
Prov.: N; tree; *SEF 8577* (AAU, QCA); *Palacios 1341* (QAME n.v.)
Diospyros sp.
Prov.: N; tree; *Korning & Thomsen 47137* (AAU)

Elaeocarpaceae
J. F. Macbride, Fl. Peru 3A(2), Publ. Field Mus. Nat. Hist., Bot. Ser. 13: 413–442. 1956.

Sloanea guianensis (Aublet) Benth.
Prov.: N; tree; *Brandbyge & Azanza 30592* (AAU)
Sloanea laxiflora Spruce ex Benth.
Prov.: N; tree; *Korning & Thomsen 47417* (AAU)
Sloanea meianthera F. D. Smith
Prov.: P; tree; *Neill 6759* (QAME n.v.)
Sloanea pubescens (Poepp. & Endl.) Benth.
Prov.: N; tree; *Palacios 1213* (QAME n.v.)
Sloanea cf. robusta Uittien
Prov.: N; tree; *Marles 64* (QAME n.v.)
Sloanea rufa Planchon ex Benth.
Prov.: N; tree; *Palacios 1114* (QAME n.v.)
Sloanea spathulata C. E. Smith
Prov.: N; tree; *Luteyn et al. 9095* (AAU, NY); *SEF 8758* (AAU, QCA)

Elaeocarpaceae   (cont.)

***Sloanea terniflora* (Mociño & Sessé ex DC.) Standley**
    Prov.: N; shrub; *Jaramillo & Coello 4456* (AAU)
***Sloanea tuerckheimii* F. D. Smith**
    Prov.: N; tree; *Øllgaard et al. 39216* (AAU); *Gentry 9817* (AAU, MO, S)
***Sloanea* sp. 1**
    Prov.: N; tree; *Brandbyge et al. 36196* (AAU)
***Sloanea* sp. 2**
    Prov.: N; tree; *Lawesson et al. 44457* (AAU)

Ericaceae
J. L. Luteyn, Fl. Neotropica 35. 1983.

***Cavendishia tarapotana* (Meissner) Benth. & Hook.**
    Prov.: N; shrub; *Holm-Nielsen & Jeppesen 639* (AAU); *MacBryde 818* (QCA)

Eriocaulaceae
J. F. Macbride, Fl. Peru 1(3), Publ. Field Mus. Nat. Hist., Bot. Ser. 13:
489–494. 1936.

***Tonina fluviatilis* Aublet**
    Prov.: N, P; herb; *Holm-Nielsen et al. 19614* (AAU); *Cerón 2160* (QAME n.v.)

Erythroxylaceae
T. Plowman, Fl. Ecuador 36, 1989.

***Erythroxylum citrifolium* A. St. Hil.**
    Prov.: N; tree; *SEF 9231* (AAU, QCA); *Korning & Thomsen 58646* (AAU)
***Erythroxylum fimbriatum* Peyr.**
    Prov.: N; tree; *Zaruma et al. 398* (QAME n.v.)
***Erythroxylum gracilipes* Peyr.**
    Prov.: N, P; shrub; *Brandbyge & Azanza 31026* (AAU, QCA)
***Erythroxylum macrophyllum* Cav.**
    Prov.: N, P, M-S; tree; *Brandbyge & Azanza 31034* (AAU, QCA)
***Erythroxylum ulei* O. E. Schultz**
    Prov.: N; shrub; *Foster 3582* (AAU, QCA); *Vickers 144* (F)

Euphorbiaceae
J. F. Macbride, Fl. Peru 3A(1), Publ. Field Mus. Nat. Hist., Bot. Ser. 13:
3–200. 1951.

***Acalypha benensis* Britt.**
    Prov.: N; treelet; *Berg & Akkermans 1016* (AAU)
***Acalypha cuneata* Poeppig**
    Prov.: N; tree; *Palacios 1407* (QAME n.v.); *Neill 7040* (QAME n.v.)

Euphorbiaceae   (cont.)

Acalypha diversifolia Jacq.
   Prov.: N, P; shrub; *Jaramillo 93* (AAU, QCA); *Hopkins 415* (QCA)
Acalypha mapirensis Pax vel sp. aff.
   Prov.: N; shrub; *Gentry 9814* (GB, S), *9712* (GB)
Acalypha obovata Benth.
   Prov.: N; tree, shrub; *Luteyn et al. 9117* (AAU, QCA); *Irvine 268* (AAU)
Acalypha stachyura Pax
   Prov.: N; tree; *Luteyn et al. 9105* (QCA); *Zarucchi 2356* (QCA)
Alchornea brevistyla Pax & Hoffm.
   Prov.: N; tree; *Cerón 2142* (QAME n.v.)
Alchornea discolor Poeppig & Endl.
   Prov.: N; tree; *Cerón 3077* (QAME n.v.)
Alchornea glandulosa Poeppig & Endl.
   Prov.: N, M-S; tree; *SEF 8662* (AAU, QCA); *Irvine 807* (QCA); *Little et al. 738*
   (US). Reaches 750 m alt. in Napo: *Asplund 8987* (S)
Alchornea cf. grandiflora Muell. Arg.
   Prov.: N; tree; *Cerón 2075* (QAME n.v.)
Alchornea latifolia Swartz
   Prov.: N, M-S; tree; *Neill 7461* (QAME n.v.)
Alchornea triplinervia (Sprengel) Muell. Arg.
   Prov.: N; tree; *Irvine 856* (F, QCA)
Alchorneopsis floribunda (Benth.) Muell. Arg.
   Prov.: N; tree; *Zaruma et al. 631* (QAME n.v.); *Irvine 195* (F, QCA)
Aparisthmium cordatum (Juss.) Baillon
   Prov.: N, P, M-S; tree; *Korning & Thomsen 47085* (AAU); *McElroy 138* (QCA)
Caryodendron grandifolium (Muell. Arg.) Pax
   Prov.: N; tree; *SEF 8502* (AAU, QCA); *Korning & Thomsen 58614* (AAU, QCA)
Caryodendron orinocense Karsten
   Prov.: N; tree; *Korning & Thomsen 47495* (AAU); *Marles 124* (QAME n.v.)
Chamaesyce hirta (L.) Millspaugh
   Prov.: N; herb; *Vickers 33* (F); *Korning & Thomsen 47012* (AAU)
Conceveiba guianensis Aublet
   Prov.: N; tree; *Korning & Thomsen 47602* (AAU)
Conceveiba rhytidocarpa Muell. Arg.
   Prov.: N; tree; *Øllgaard et al. 57020* (AAU); *Palacios 1306* (QAME n.v.)
Croton lechleri Muell. Arg.
   Prov.: N; tree; *Zaruma et al. 9* (QAME n.v.)
Croton pungens Jacq.
   Prov.: N; tree; *Little & Campuzano 8* (US)
Croton sampatik Muell. Arg.
   Prov.: N; tree; *Little & Campuzano 48* (US)
Dalechampia friedrichsthalii Muell. Arg.
   Prov.: N; tree; *Cerón 1286* (QAME n.v.)
Drypetes amazonica Steyerm.
   Prov.: P, M-S; shrub; *Brandbyge & Azanza 32045* (AAU); *Irvine 321* (F, QCA)
Drypetes fanshawei Sandw.
   Prov.: N; tree; *Korning & Thomsen 58704* (AAU)
Drypetes variabilis Uittien
   Prov.: N; tree; *SEF 8878* (AAU, QCA)
Elaeophora polyadenia (Muell. Arg.) Ducke
   Prov.: N; vine; *Gentry 9717* (AAU)

Euphorbiaceae (cont.)

Euphorbia cotinifolia L.
>   Prov.: N; shrub, tree; *Alarcón 130* (QCA); *Balslev & Azanza 4367* (QCA)

Euphorbia cf. graminea Jacq.
>   Prov.: N; tree; *Cerón 2042* (QAME n.v.)

Euphorbia lasiocarpa Klotzsch
>   Prov.: N; tree; *Cerón 2434* (QAME n.v.)

Euphorbia thymifolia L.
>   Prov.: N, P; herb; *Løjtnant & Molau 13461* (AAU, QCA); *Alarcón 73* (QCA)
>   (= *E. prostrata* Ait. ?)

Glycydendron amazonicum Ducke
>   Prov.: N; tree; *SEF 8555* (AAU, QCA)

Hevea brasiliensis (Willd. ex Juss.) Muell. Arg.
>   Prov.: M-S; tree; *Pennington 10756* (QCA). Collected at 900 m alt.

Hevea guianensis Aublet
>   Prov.: N; tree; *Davis & Yost 1018* (AAU, QCA); *Oldeman & Arévalo 34* (QCA)

Hura crepitans L.
>   Prov.: M-S; tree; *Little et al. 688* (US)

Hyeronima alchorneoides Fr. Allemão
>   Prov.: N, P; tree; *Neill 8317* (QAME n.v.); *Øllgaard et al. 34835* (AAU)

Hyeronima andina Pax & Hoffm.
>   Prov.: N; tree; *Foster 3819* (F)

Hyeronima chocoensis Cuatrec.
>   Prov.: N; tree; *Little et al. 748* (US); *Chaguaro 116* (QCA)

Hyeronima laxiflora (Tul.) Muell. Arg.
>   Prov.: N; tree; *SEF 8737* (AAU, QCA); *Lawesson et al. 39938* (AAU)

Hyeronima oblonga (Tul.) Muell. Arg.
>   Prov.: N; tree; *Oldeman 88* (P)

Mabea elata Steyerm.
>   Prov.: M-S; tree; *Gentry et al. 30936* (AAU, F, MO, S); *Little et al. 637* (NY, US)
>   Reaches slightly higher altitudes.

Mabea nitida Benth.
>   Prov.: N; tree; *Foster 3596* (AAU, DAV, F, MO)

Mabea occidentalis Benth.
>   Prov.: N, M-S; tree; *Korning & Thomsen 57034* (AAU); *Luteyn et al. 8512* (NY)
>   Reaches 900 m alt. in M-S: *Pennington & Tenorio 10773* (QCA)

Mabea piriri Aublet
>   Prov.: N; tree; *Irvine 329* (F, QCA). Syn. *M. maynensis* Muell. Arg.

Mabea speciosa Muell. Arg.
>   Prov.: N; tree; *Foster 3676* (DAV, F, QCA); *Lawesson et al. 44469* (AAU, QCA)

Manihot brachiloba Muell. Arg.
>   Prov.: N; tree; *Cerón 640* (QAME n.v.)

Manihot esculenta Crantz
>   Prov.: N, P, M-S; shrub; *Balslev 4611* (QCA); *Jaramillo & Rivera 180* (AAU)

Margaritaria nobilis (L. f.) Muell. Arg.
>   Prov.: N; tree; *Andrade 33148* (AAU); *Foster 3879* (QCA); *Irvine 519* (QCA)

Omphalea diandra L.
>   Prov.: P; tree; *Neill 6823* (QAME n.v.)

Pausandra trianae (Muell. Arg.) Baillon
>   Prov.: N; tree; *Gentry 9741* (QCA, S); *SEF 10180* (AAU, QCA)

Phyllanthus acuminatus Vahl
>   Prov.: N; herb; *Vickers 254* (F); *Pinkley 254* (S)

Euphorbiaceae   (cont.)

Phyllanthus anisolobus Muell. Arg.
  Prov.: N; tree; *Cerón 1104* (QAME n.v.)
Phyllanthus brasiliensis (Aublet) Poir.
  Prov.: N; herb; *Jaramillo 75, 4204* (AAU, QCA); *Andrade 32941* (AAU)
Phyllanthus caroliniensis Walter
  Prov.: N; herb; *Holm-Nielsen et al. 19822* (AAU)
Phyllanthus pseudoconami Muell. Arg.
  Prov.: N; herb; *Vickers 45* (F)
Phyllanthus stipulatus (Raf.) Webster
  Prov.: N; tree; *Cerón 2026* (QAME n.v.)
Phyllanthus urinaria L.
  Prov.: N; tree; *Cerón 2040* (QAME n.v.)
Plukenetia polyadenia Muell. Arg.
  Prov.: N; climber; *Brandbyge & Azanza 30405* (AAU)
Plukenetia volubilis L.
  Prov.: N; liana; *Lawesson et al. 39481* (AAU, QCA); *Zarucchi 2378* (QCA);
  Madison et al. 5403 (QCA, SEL).   Reaches 750 m alt. in Napo: *Asplund 9437* (S)
Richeria racemosa (Poeppig & Endl.) Pax & Hoffm.
  Prov.: N, M-S; tree; *Øllgaard et al. 57184* (AAU).   Reaches 1000 m alt. in M-S:
  Little et al. 486 (US)
Ricinus communis L.
  Prov.: N; shrub; *Balslev & Alarcón 3006* (QCA); *Irvine 1059* (F, QCA)
  Reaches ca. 750 m alt. in N: *Asplund 9267* (S)
Sagotia racemosa Baillon
  Prov.: N; tree; *Cerón 3284* (QAME n.v.)
Sapium eglandulosum Ule
  Prov.: N; tree; *Palacios 1110* (QAME n.v.)
Sapium marmieri Huber
  Prov.: N, M-S; tree; *SEF 10047* (AAU, QCA); *Irvine 216* (QCA); *Pennington
  10585* (QCA).   Reaches 900 m alt. in M-S: *Little et al. 304* (US)
Sapium utile Preuss.
  Prov.: N; tree; *Irvine 853* (F, QCA)
Securinega congesta Muell. Arg.
  Prov.: N; shrub; *Jaramillo & Coello 2928* (AAU, QCA)
Tetrorchidium andinum Muell. Arg.
  Prov.: N; tree; *Lawesson et al. 39793* (AAU, QCA)
Tetrorchidium macrophyllum Muell. Arg.
  Prov.: N, M-S; tree; *Luteyn et al. 8509* (AAU).   Reaches ca. 750 m alt. in Napo:
  Asplund 9162 (S) and 1300 in M-S: *Gentry et al. 30910* (AAU)
Tetrorchidium cf. parvulum Muell. Arg.
  Prov.: N; tree; *Cerón 2658* (QAME n.v.)
Tetrorchidium rubrivenium Poeppig & Endl.
  Prov.: N; tree; *Neill 7246* (QAME n.v.); *Irvine 1104* (F, QCA)

Fabaceae   (see Leguminosae)

Flacourtiaceae (excl. Lacistemataceae)

H. O. Sleumer, Fl. Neotropica 22. 1980.

***Banara guianensis* Aublet**
Prov.: N, P, M-S; shrub or tree; *Holm-Nielsen & Jeppesen 446* (AAU, QCA).
Reaches 1100 m in Pastaza: *Neill et al. 5808* (AAU)

***Banara nitida* Spruce ex Benth.**
Prov.: N, P; tree; *SEF 9142* (AAU, QCA). Reaches 1000 m alt. in Pastaza:
Asplund 18593 (S)

***Carpotroche amazonica* C. Martius ex Eichler**
Prov.: N, M-S; tree; *Brandbyge & Azanza 32057* (AAU)

***Carpotroche longifolia* (Poeppig) Benth.**
Prov.: N, P, M-S; tree; *Holm-Nielsen et al. 22204* (AAU); *Davis & Yost 945*
(QCA); *Pinkley 28* (ECON); *Gentry 9752* (S); *Irvine 676* (AAU)

***Casearia acuminata* DC.**
Prov.: N; tree; *Palacios 820* (QAME n.v.)

***Casearia arborea* (L. C. Rich.) Urban**
Prov.: N, P, M-S; tree; *Korning & Thomsen 58682* (AAU); *Neill et al. 6111*
(AAU); *Little et al. 490* (US). Reaches 1000 m alt. in Pastaza: *Asplund 19717* (S)

***Casearia combaymensis* Tul.**
Prov.: P; tree; *Neill & Palacios 6766* (QCA)

***Casearia decandra* Jacq.**
Prov.: N, M-S; tree; *Little et al. 629* (US); *Palacios 1085* (QAME n.v.)

***Casearia fasciculata* (Ruíz & Pavón) Sleumer**
Prov.: N, P; shrub; *Luteyn et al. 9000* (AAU); *Davis & Yost 1033* (QCA); *Gentry
12432* (QCA). Reaches 1100 m in Pastaza: *Neill et al. 6136* (AAU)

***Casearia javitensis* H.B.K.**
Prov.: N, M-S; tree; *Brandbyge & Azanza 32021* (AAU); *Lawesson et al. 39410*
(QCA); *Neill et al. 6197* (AAU)

***Casearia nigricans* Sleumer**
Prov.: N; tree; *Zaruma et al. 145* (QAME n.v.); *Palacios 2151* (QAME n.v.)

***Casearia obovalis* Poeppig ex Griseb.**
Prov.: N; tree; *Zaruma et al. 153* (QAME n.v.)

***Casearia pitumba* Sleumer**
Prov.: N; tree; *Brandbyge 33662* (AAU, QCA). Syn. *C. macrophylla* Vahl.

***Casearia prunifolia* H.B.K.**
Prov.: N, P; *Davis & Yost 1031* (QCA); *Gentry 12434* (QCA). Reaches 900 m alt.
in Pastaza: *Fagerlind & Wibom 1176* (S)

***Casearia sylvestris* Sw.**
Prov.: N, P; tree; *SEF 10279* (AAU, QCA); *Irvine 682* (F, QCA); *Balslev &
Boom 4399* (AAU). Reaches ca. 1000 m alt.: *Neill et al. 5971* (AAU)

***Casearia ulmifolia* Vahl ex Ventenant**
Prov.: N; tree; *Palacios & Neill 898* (QAME n.v.); *Irvine 530* (F, QCA)

***Hasseltia floribunda* H.B.K.**
Prov.: N, M-S; tree; *Balslev 2315* (QCA); *Holm-Nielsen et al. 21101* (AAU)

***Laetia procera* (Poeppig & Endl.) Eichler**
Prov.: N; tree; *Korning & Thomsen 47686* (AAU); *Neill et al. 6197* (QCA)

***Lindackeria paludosa* (Benth.) Gilg**
Prov.: N, P; tree; *Jaramillo et al. 31393* (AAU, QCA)

***Lunania parviflora* Spruce ex Benth.**
Prov.:N; tree; *Oldeman & Arévalo 26* (QCA); *Lawesson et al. 44338* (QCA)

***Mayna grandifolia* (Karsten) Warburg**
Prov.: N; shrub; *Alarcón 126* (QCA)

Flacourtiaceae   (cont.)

Mayna odorata Aublet
> Prov.: N, P, M-S; shrub; *Holm-Nielsen & Jeppesen 954* (AAU); *Alarcón 114*
> (QCA); *Irvine 470* (F, QCA)

Neosprucea grandiflora (Spruce ex Benth.) Sleumer
> Prov.: N, M-S; tree; *Brandbyge & Azanza 32322* (AAU); *Brandbyge et al. 33440*
> (AAU); *Pennington 10626* (QCA)

Neosprucea sp.
> Prov.: N; tree; *Jaramillo 4052* (AAU, QCA); *Brandbyge et al. 30477* (AAU)
> (= *N. sucumbiensis* Cuatrec. ?)

Pleuranthodendron lindenii (Turcz.) Sleumer
> Prov.: M-S; tree; *Brandbyge & Azanza 32233* (AAU, QCA); *Neill et al. 6215*
> (AAU). Reaches 700 m alt. in M-S: *Pennington & Tenorio 10796* (QCA)

Ryania speciosa Vahl
> Prov.: N, P, M-S; tree; *Brandbyge et al. 36024* (AAU). Reaches 1000 m alt.

Tetrathylacium macrophyllum Poeppig & Endl.
> Prov.: N, P, M-S; tree or shrub; *Brandbyge & Azanza 32303* (AAU, QCA)

Xylosma tessmannii Sleumer
> Prov.: N; tree; *Neill 7237* (QAME n.v.)

Gentianaceae
P. J. M. Maas et al., Fl. Neotropica 41. 1986. This listing checked by P.
Maas, Jan 1989.

Irlbachia alata (Aublet) Maas
> Prov.: N, P, M-S; herb; *Holm-Nielsen et al. 20450* (AAU)

Irlbachia purpurascens (Aublet) Maas
> Prov.: P; herb; *Brandbyge et al. 34724* (AAU)

Voyria aphylla (Jacq.) Pers.
> Prov.: N; saprophytic herb; listed in Maas & Maas (1987) without voucher

Voyria aurantiaca Splitgerber
> Prov.: P; saprophytic herb; *Holm-Nielsen et al. 21841* (AAU)

Voyria flavescens Griseb.
> Prov.: N, P; saprophytic herb; *Brandbyge et al. 33738* (AAU)

Voyria spruceana Benth.
> Prov.: N; saprophytic herb; *Øllgaard et al. 39190* (AAU)

Voyria tenella W. J. Hooker
> Prov.: N, P, M-S; saprophytic herb; *Brandbyge & Azanza 32148* (AAU)

Gesneriaceae
Identifications by L. Skog, US, and L. P. Kvist, AAU.

Besleria aggregata (C. Martius) Hanst.
> Prov.: N, P, M-S; shrub, tree; *Jaramillo et al. 30772* (AAU); *Lugo 2141* (GB, SEL)
> Reaches 1500 m alt.

Besleria barbata (Poeppig) Hanst.
> Prov.: N, P, M-S; shrub; *Holm-Nielsen et al. 27290* (AAU, QCA); *Irvine 981* (F,
> QCA). Reaches 800 m alt.

Besleria comosa Morton
> Prov.: P; shrub; *Brandbyge & Azanza 31422* (AAU); *Lugo 2581* (SEL)
> Reaches higher alts.

Gesneriaceae   (cont.)

Besleria immitis Morton
    Prov.: N; shrub; *Øllgaard et al. 38844* (AAU)
Besleria miniata Morton
    Prov.: N; shrub; *Brandbyge et al. 30519* (AAU)
Besleria modica Morton
    Prov.: P, M-S; shrub; *Brandbyge & Azanza 32319* (AAU, QCA)
Besleria pauciflora Rusby
    Prov.: P; shrub; *Øllgaard et al. 34710* (AAU)
Besleria quadrangulata L. Skog
    Prov.: N, P; shrub; *Jaramillo & Coello 4639* (AAU).   Reaches 1100 m in Pastaza:
    Harling et al. 9741 (QCA, SEL)
Besleria stricta L. Skog
    Prov.: N, P, M-S; shrub; *Lawesson et al. 44371* (AAU)
Besleria variabilis Morton
    Prov.: N, P, M-S; shrub; *Holm-Nielsen 19210* (AAU); *Balslev 2307* (QCA)
    Reaches 750 m alt.
Besleria sp. 1
    Prov.: N; herb; *Holm-Nielsen et al. 26783* (AAU)
Besleria sp. 2
    Prov.: N; shrub; *Korning & Thomsen 47103* (AAU)
Besleria sp. 3
    Prov.: N; herb; *Holm-Nielsen et al. 26940* (AAU)
Besleria sp. 4
    Prov.: P; herb; *Holm-Nielsen et al. 22661* (AAU)
Besleria sp. 5
    Prov.: N; herb; *Balslev & Boom 4391* (AAU); *Holm-Nielsen19224* (AAU)
Chrysothemis pulchella (Donn. Smith ex Sims) Decne.
    Prov.: N; herb; *Andrade 33013* (AAU)
Codonanthe crassifolia (Focke) Morton
    Prov.: N; epiphytic herb; *Lawesson et al. 43489* (AAU, QCA)
Codonanthe uleana Fritsch
    Prov.: N; epiphytic herb; *Holm-Nielsen et al. 20256* (AAU); *Brandbyge &
    Azanza 30012* (AAU, QCA)
Codonanthopsis dissimulata (H. E. Moore) Wiehler
    Prov.: N; herb; *Vickers 161, 256* (F)
Codonanthopsis ulei Mansf.
    Prov.: N, P; epiphytic herb; *Holm-Nielsen et al. 21510* (AAU)
Columnea angustata (Wiehler) L. Skog
    Prov.: N, P; epiphytic herb; *Kvist et al. 60325* (AAU, QCA, US).   Expected in the
    area below 600 m alt.
Columnea brenneri (Wiehler) B. Morley
    Prov.: P, M-S; herb; *Lugo 1075* (GB).   Rarely below 600 m alt.
Columnea elongatifolia Kvist & L. Skog
    Prov.: N; epiphytic herb; *Holm-Nielsen & Jeppesen 664* (AAU)
    Syn. *Trichantha angustifolia* Wiehler
Columnea ericae Mansf.
    Prov.: N, P, M-S; herb; *Brandbyge et al. 32449* (AAU, QCA).   Reaches 2500 m
    alt.
Columnea inaequilatera Poeppig
    Prov.: N, P, M-S; herb; *Brandbyge & Azanza 30621* (AAU); *Jaramillo & Coello
    3642* (QCA).   Reaches 2000 m alt.

Gesneriaceae (cont.)

Columnea sanguinea (Pers.) Hanst.
Prov.: N; epiphytic herb; *Korning & Thomsen 47056* (AAU)
Columnea tenensis (Wiehler) B. Morley
Prov.: N; herb *Brandbyge & Azanza 33788* (AAU)
Columnea villosissima Mansf.
Prov.: N, P, M-S; herb; *Brandbyge & Azanza 30056* (AAU, QCA). Reaches 2000 m alt.
Cremosperma ecuadoranum Kvist & L. Skog
Prov.: N; herb; *Brandbyge et al. 30462* (AAU)
Diastema affine Fritsch
Prov.: M-S; herb; *Kvist et al. 60430* (AAU, QCA, US). Expected below 600 m alt.
Diastema scabrum (Poeppig) Benth. ex Walp.
Prov.: N, P; herb; *Lawesson et al. 39817* (AAU). Reaches 1000 m alt.
Drymonia affinis (Mansf.) Wiehler)
Prov.: N, P, M-S; shrub; *Holm-Nielsen et al. 21898* (AAU)
Drymonia coriacea (Oersted ex Hanst.) Wiehler
Prov.: N; herb, shrub, treelet or woody vine; *Øllgaard et al. 39020* (AAU)
Drymonia hoppii (Mansf.) Wiehler
Prov.: N, P, M-S; shrub; *Lawesson et al. 44329* (AAU); *Foster 3831* (AAU) Reaches 1000 m alt.
Drymonia macrophylla (Oersted) H. E. Moore
Prov.: N, P; shrub, climber; *Holm-Nielsen 19254* (AAU, QCA)
Drymonia pendula (Poeppig) Wiehler
Prov.: N, P; vine; *Lawesson et al. 39328* (AAU)
Drymonia serrulata (Jacq.) C. Martius
Prov.: N, P, M-S; shrub or vine; *Holm-Nielsen et al. 20213* (AAU). Reaches 2600 m alt.
Drymonia urceolata Wiehler
Prov.: N, P; shrub; *Jaramillo & Coello 3433* (AAU, QCA). More common between 1000 and 2000 m alt.
Drymonia warszewicziana Hanst.
Prov.: N, P; vine or shrub; *Brandbyge et al. 30450* (AAU); *Irvine 971* (F, QCA) Reaches 1200 m alt.
Drymonia sp.
Prov.: N, P; vine; *Holm-Nielsen et al. 20107* (AAU)
Episcia cupreata (Hook.) Hanst.
Prov.: N; herb; *Poulsen 80957* (AAU)
Gasteranthus corallinus (Fritsch) Wiehler
Prov.: N, P; shrub; *Lawesson et al. 39792* (AAU, QCA)
Gasteranthus oncogastrus (Hanst.) Wiehler
Prov.: N; herb, shrub; *Brandbyge et al. 30292* (AAU)
Gasteranthus sp.
Prov.: N; herb; *Lawesson et al. 39424* (AAU)
Gloxinia perennis (L.) Fritsch
Prov.: N, P; herb; *Holm-Nielsen et al. 19154* (AAU, QCA); *Vickers 249* (F)
Kohleria spicata (Kunth) Oersted
Prov.: N, M-S; herb, shrub; *Kvist et al. 60350* (AAU, QCA, US)
Monopyle macrocarpa Benth.
Prov.: N, P; shrub; *Holm-Nielsen & Jepppesen 934* (AAU)
Nautilocalyx ecuadoranus Wiehler
Prov.: N, P; herb; *Holm-Nielsen et al. 20154* (AAU)

Gesneriaceae (cont.)

Nautilocalyx glandulifera Wiehler
Prov.: N; herb; *Brandbyge & Azanza 30167* (AAU)

Nautilocalyx vinosus Wiehler
Prov.: N, P; herb; *Jaramillo et al. 30965A* (AAU); *Davis & Yost 922* (QCA, SEL)

Paradrymonia ciliosa (C. Martius) Wiehler
Prov.: N, P; vine; *Holm-Nielsen et al. 26820* (AAU)

Paradrymonia longifolia (Poeppig) Wiehler
Prov.: N, P, M-S; shrub, vine; *Brandbyge & Azanza 32087* (AAU)

Paradrymonia metamorphophylla (J. D. Smith) Wiehler
Prov.: N, M-S; shrub; *Harling & Andersson 16272* (GB, SEL). Reaches 2000 m
alt. in Napo: *Øllgaard et al. 35946* (AAU)

Parakohleria abunda Wiehler
Prov.: N, P, M-S; herb; *Lawesson et al. 39624* (AAU, QCA). Reaches 1500 m alt.

Parakohleria hispidissima Wiehler
Prov.: P, M-S; herb; *Brandbyge & Azanza 31943* (AAU). Ranges from 500 to
2500 m alt.

Parakohleria jamesoniana (Fritsch) Wiehler
Prov.: N, P, M-S; herb; *Holm-Nielsen & Jeppesen 964* (AAU). Reaches 2500 m

Parakohleria rhodotricha (Cuatrec.) Wiehler
Prov.: N, P; shrub; *Lugo 3562* (GB, SEL); *Besse et al. 68* (QCA, SEL)

Parakohleria sprucei (Britton) Wiehler
Prov.: N; herb; *Besse et al. 77* (QCA, SEL)

Pearcea hypocyrtiflora (Hook.) Regel
Prov.: P; herb; *Jaramillo & Coello 3566* (AAU, QCA)

Reldia multiflora Kvist & L. Skog
Prov.: N; herb; *Lawesson et al. 39509* (AAU)

Haemadoraceae
J. F. Macbride , Fl. Peru 1(3), Publ. Field Mus. Nat. Hist., Bot. Ser.
13: 630–631. 1936.

Xiphidium caeruleum Aublet
Prov.: N, P; herb; *Løjtnant & Molau 11512* (AAU); *Alarcón 19386* (QCA);
Irvine 986 (F, QCA). Reaches 1100 m alt.

Haloragaceae
J. F. Macbride, Fl. Peru 5(1), Publ. Field Mus. Nat. Hist., Bot. Ser.
13: 3–8. 1959.

Myriophyllum elatinoides Gaudin
Prov.: N; herb; *Lawesson et al. 44251* (AAU)

Heliconiaceae

L. Andersson, Fl. Ecuador 22, 1985. This listing checked by J. Kress, Mar 1989.

Heliconia aemygdiana Burle-Marx
Prov.: N, P, M-S; herb; *Holm-Nielsen et al. 21035* (AAU, QCA). Reaches 1000 m alt. in Pastaza: *Asplund 19105* (S)

Heliconia apparicioi Souza Barr.
Prov.: N; herb; *Lugo 2959* (AAU, GB)

Heliconia chartacea Lane ex Souza Barr.
Prov.: N, P, M-S; herb; *Brandbyge & Azanza 31897* (AAU, QCA)

Heliconia episcopalis Vell.
Prov.: N, P, M-S; herb; *Holm-Nielsen & Jeppesen 834* (AAU, S)

Heliconia hirsuta L.f.
Prov.: N, P, M-S; herb; *Brandbyge & Azanza 32402* (AAU, QCA); *Foster 3811* (F). Reaches 700 m alt.

Heliconia julianii Souza Barr.
Prov.: N; herb; *Lawesson et al. 43319* (AAU, QCA); *Foster 3723* (AAU, F)

Heliconia juruana Loes.
Prov.: N; herb; *Holm-Nielsen et al. 21220* (AAU); *Foster 3820* (AAU, F)

Heliconia marginata (Griggs) Pittier
Prov.: N; herb; *Fagerlind & Wibom s.n.* (S); *Gentry et al. 21869* (MO)

Heliconia metallica Planchon & Linden ex Hook.
Prov.: N; herb; *Harling et al. 7366, 7517* (AAU, GB, QCA)

Heliconia obscura Dodson & Gentry
Prov.: N, P; herb; *Jaramillo & Coello 3695* (AAU). Reaches 1100 m alt. in Napo: *Løjtnant & Molau 11508* (AAU)

Heliconia orthotricha L. Anderss.
Prov.: N, P, M-S; herb; *Holm-Nielsen et al. 22282* (AAU); *Harling & Andersson 17428* (GB); *Luteyn et al. 8511* (AAU, GB, QCA). Reaches 1000 m alt.

Heliconia rostrata Ruíz & Pavón
Prov.: N, P, M-S; herb; *Holm-Nielsen et al. 22632* (AAU); *Harling et al. 7041* (GB, QCA). Reaches 900 m alt. in M-S: *Harling & Andersson 12897* (GB)

Heliconia schumanniana Loes.
Prov.: N, P, M-S; herb; *Holm-Nielsen & Jeppesen 832* (AAU); *Irvine 965* (F, QCA). Reaches 1500 m alt. in M-S: *Harling & Andersson 12804* (GB)

Heliconia spathocircinata Aristeg.
Prov.: N, P, M-S; herb; *Holm-Nielsen et al. 19656* (AAU)

Heliconia standleyi J. F. Macbr.
Prov.: N; herb; *Jaramillo & Coello 4240* (AAU)

Heliconia stricta Huber
Prov.: N, P, M-S; herb; *Holm-Nielsen & Jeppesen 872* (AAU); *Foster 3657* (AAU). Reaches 1000 m alt. in Pastaza: *Asplund 18465* (S)

Heliconia vellerigera Poeppig
Prov.: N, P, M-S; herb; *Brandbyge & Azanza 31969* (AAU); *Irvine 1132* (F, QCA). Reaches 800 m alt. in Pastaza: *Harling & Andersson 17177* (GB)

Heliconia velutina L. Anderss.
Prov.: N, P, M-S; herb; *Lawesson et al. 43493* (AAU, QCA).

Hernandiaceae

J. F. Macbride , Fl. Peru 2(3), Publ. Field Mus. Nat. Hist., Bot. Ser. 13: 931–933. 1938.

Sparattanthelium cf. *amazonum* C. Martius

Prov.: N; *Zaruma et al. 260* (QAME n.v.). Reaches altitudes above 600 m. Possibly = *S. tarapotanum* Meissner ?

Hippocastanaceae

Billia colombiana   Planchon & Lindley

Prov.: N; tree; *Neill 7137* (AAU, QCA)

Hippocrateaceae

J. F. Macbride, Fl. Peru 3A(1), Publ. Field Mus. Nat. Hist., Bot. Ser. 13: 200–220. 1951. This listing checked by A. M. Mennega, Oct 1989.

Cheiloclinium cognatum (Miers) A. C. Smith

Prov.: N, P; shrub, tree or climber; *Holm-Nielsen et al. 21680* (AAU)

Cheiloclinium hippocrateoides (Peyr.) A. C. Smith

Prov.: N; liana; *Korning & Thomsen 58741* (AAU); *Neill 6711* (MO)

Cheiloclinium pedunculatum (A. C. Smith) A. C. Smith

Prov.: N; liana; *Palacios 893* (QAME n.v.)

Hippocratea volubilis L.

Prov.: N; shrub; *Holm-Nielsen et al. 21655* (AAU); *Foster 3648* (AAU)

Peritassa huanucana (Loesn.) A. C. Smith

Prov.: N; liana; *Øllgaard et al. 39118* (AAU)

Pristimera nervosa (Miers) A. C. Smith

Prov.: N; tree; *Korning & Thomsen 58741* (AAU)

Salacia elliptica (C. Martius) G. Don

Prov.: P; tree; *Jaramillo et al. 30997* (AAU)

Salacia cf. *macrantha* A. C. Smith

Prov.: N; tree; *Foster 3747* (AAU)

Salacia multiflora (Lam.) DC.

Prov.: N; liana; *Gentry 12431* (QCA)

Salacia opacifolia (J. F. Macbr.) A. C. Smith

Prov. M-S; tree; *Zaruma et al. 800* (QAME n.v.)

Salacia spectabilis A. C. Smith

Prov. N; tree; *Brandbyge et al. 33327* (AAU)

Tontelea attenuata Miers

Prov.: N, M-S; tree; *Brandbyge et al. 36117* (AAU); *Little et al. 514* (US)

Tontelea corymbosa (Huber) A. C. Smith vel sp. aff.

Prov.: N; tree; *Jaramillo & Coello 3541* (AAU)

Humiriaceae
J. F. Macbride, Fl. Peru 3(2) as Linaceae, Publ. Field Mus. Nat. Hist., Bot. Ser. 13: 621–632. 1949.

Humiriastrum sp.
Prov.: N; tree; *Brandbyge et al. 33923* (AAU)

Hydrocharitaceae
R. R. Haynes and L. B. Holm-Nielsen, Fl. Ecuador 26, 1986.

Elodea granatensis Humb. & Bonpl.
Prov.: N; herb; *Brandbyge et al. 36149* (AAU); *Jaramillo 6907* (AAU, QCA)

Icacinaceae
J. F. Macbride, Fl. Peru 3A(1), Publ. Field Mus. Nat. Hist., Bot. Ser. 13: 221–233. 1951. This listing checked by R. A. Howard, Feb 1989.

Calatola colombiana Sleumer
Prov.: N; tree; *SEF 10076* (AAU)
Calatola venezuelana Pittier
Prov.: N; tree; *Neill 6958* (QAME n.v.)
Citronella incarum (J. F. Macbr.) Howard
Prov.: N, P; tree; *Brandbyge & Azanza 30411* (AAU); *Neill et al. 6296* (AAU, QCA); *Pennington 10635* (QCA)
Dendrobangia boliviana Rusby
Prov.: N; tree; *Korning & Thomsen 47555* (AAU)
Discophora guianensis Miers
Prov.: N, P; tree; *Korning & Thomsen 47694* (AAU); *Irvine 847* (QCA)
Humirianthera ampla (Miers) Baehni
Prov.: N; shrub; *Brandbyge & Azanza 30407* (AAU)
Leretia cordata Vell.
Prov.: N; shrub; *Jaramillo & Coello 2631* (AAU, QCA); *Alarcón 104* (QCA)
Metteniusa tessmanniana (Sleumer) Sleumer
Prov.: N, P, M-S; tree; *Neill et al. 6863* (QCA), *6542* (AAU). Reaches 1050 m alt. in Pastaza: *Asplund 18711* (S)

Iridaceae

Eleutherine bulbosa (Mill.) Urban
Prov.: N; herb; *Balslev & Santos Dea 2819* (QCA); *Balslev & Alarcón 2999* (QCA); *Vickers 172* (F)

Lacistemaceae
H. O. Sleumer, Fl. Neotropica 22, 1980.

Lacistema aggregatum (Berg.) Rusby
Prov.: N; tree; *Lawesson et al. 39337* (AAU); *Palacios 509* (QAME n.v.) Reaches 750 m alt. in Napo: *Asplund 10180* (S)

Lacistemaceae   (cont.)

Lacistema nena J. F. Macbr.
Prov.: P; shrub; *McElroy 139* (QCA); *Little 614* (US)
Lacistema sp.
Prov.: N; tree; *SEF 8797, 8826* (AAU)
Lozania klugii (Mansf.) Mansf.
Prov.: N; tree; *Zaruma 425* (AAU)
Lozania mutisiana J. A. Schultes
Prov.: N; tree; *Davis 421* (S); *Asplund 18315* (S).   Collected at Tena,   750 m alt.

Lamiaceae
J. F. Macbride, Fl. Peru 5(2), Publ. Field Mus. Nat. Hist., Bot. Ser. 13: 721–829. 1960.   Identifications by R. M. Harley who is preparing treatments for Flora of Ecuador and Flora of Peru.

Hyptis capitata Jacq.
Prov.: N; herb; *Andrade 33010* (AAU, QCA); *Vickers 182* (F)
Hyptis mutabilis (A. Rich.) Briq.
Prov.: N; herb; *Brandbyge et al. 30268* (AAU); *Molau & Öhman 1572* (QCA)
Hyptis obtusiflora Presl ex Benth.
Prov.: N, P, M-S; herb; *Øllgaard et al. 35432* (AAU).   Reaches 1000 m alt.
Hyptis pachycephala Epling
Prov.: N; shrub; *Jaramillo & Coello 3021* (AAU)
Hyptis pectinata (L.) Poit.
Prov.: N; shrub; *Harling et al. 17277* (GB); *Balslev & Alarcón 3054* (QCA); *Alarcón 19545* (QCA).   Reaches ca. 750 m alt. in Napo: *Asplund 9245* (S)
Hyptis sidaefolia (L'Hér.) Briq.
Prov.: P; herb; *Øllgaard et al. 34994* (AAU).   Also higher alts.: *Spruce 6022* (S)
Hyptis sp.
Prov.: N; herb; *Korning & Thomsen 47028* (AAU)
Mentha suaveolens Ehrh.
Prov.: N; herb; *Alarcón 2* (QCA)
Ocimum campechianum Mill.
Prov.: N; shrub; *Brandbyge & Azanza 32873* (AAU); *Vickers 12* (F); *Irvine 705* (F, QCA).   Syn. *O. micranthum* Willd.

Lauraceae
J. F. Macbride, Fl. Peru 2(3), Publ. Field Mus. Nat. Hist., Bot. Ser. 13: 819–931. 1938; J. G. Rohwer, Mitt. Inst. Allg. Bot. Hamburg 20: 1–278. 1986; K. Kubitzki & S. Renner, Fl. Neotropica 31. 1982.   This listing checked by J. Rohwer, HBG, August 1990.

Aniba hostmanniana (Nees) Mez
Prov.: N; tree; *SEF 8888* (AAU); *Neill et al. 3612* (QCA)
Aniba megaphylla Mez
Prov.: P; tree; *Jaramillo et al. 31306* (AAU)
Aniba panurensis (Meissner) Mez
Prov.: N; tree; *Korning & Thomsen 47765* (AAU); *SEF 8594* (AAU, QCA)
Aniba cf. *puchury-minor* (C. Martius) Mez
Prov.: N; tree; *Palacios 1969* (QAME n.v.)

Lauraceae (cont.)

Aniba riparia (Nees) Mez
    Prov.: N, P; tree *SEF 8958* (AAU, QCA); *Lugo 4032* (GB)
Beilschmiedia sulcata (Ruíz & Pavón) Kosterm.
    Prov.: M-S; tree; *Neill 7477* (QAME n.v.)
Caryodaphnopsis fosteri van der Werff
    Prov.: N; tree; *SEF 8965* (AAU)
Caryodaphnopsis tomentosa van der Werff
    Prov.: N; tree; *Palacios 4337* (AAU, MO, F, HBG, QAME, NY, US)
Cinnamomum napoense van der Werff
    Prov.: N; tree; *Palacios 2886* (AAU, MO, QAME, NY, US)
Endlicheria acuminata Kosterm.
    Prov.: N; shrub, tree; *Luteyn et al. 8541* (AAU)
Endlicheria anomala (Nees) Mez
    Prov.: N; tree; *Lawesson et al. 44403* (AAU), *43389* (AAU, QCA)
Endlicheria dysodantha (Ruíz & Pavón) Mez
    Prov.: N, P; tree; *Brandbyge & Azanza 31785* (AAU, QCA)
Endlicheria formosa A. C. Smith
    Prov.: N; P; tree; *Øllgaard et al. 35039* (AAU); *Pennington 10570* (QCA)
Endlicheria klugii O. C. Schmidt
    Prov.: N; tree; *Neill 7152* (QCA)
Endlicheria krukovii (A. C. Smith) Kosterm.
    Prov.: N; tree; *Neill 7164* (AAU, QCA); *Luteyn et al. 8586* (AAU, QCA)
Endlicheria paniculata (Sprengel) J. F. Macbr.
    Prov.: N; tree; *Palacios 1030* (QAME n.v.)
Endlicheria pyriformis (Nees) Mez
    Prov.: N, P; tree; *Lawesson et al. 44450* (AAU); *Palacios 1005* (QAME n.v.)
Endlicheria sericea Nees
    Prov.: N; tree; *SEF 8740, Korning & Thomsen 47630* (AAU)
Endlicheria sprucei (Meissner) Mez
    Prov.: P; tree; *Jaramillo et al. 31147* (AAU)
Endlicheria tessmannii O. C. Schmidt
    Prov.: M-S; treelet; *Brandbyge & Azanza 32418* (AAU)
Endlicheria sp.
    Prov.: N; tree; *Korning & Thomsen 47526, 47610, 47810* (AAU)
Licaria armeniaca (Nees) Kosterm.
    Prov.: N; tree; *Holm-Nielsen 20040* (AAU)
Licaria canella (Meissner) Kosterm.
    Prov.: N; tree; *Korning & Thomsen 47546* (AAU); *Neill 7226* (QAME n.v.)
Licaria sp.
    Prov.: N; tree; *SEF 10397* (AAU)
Nectandra caucana (Meissner) Mez
    Prov.: M-S; tree; *Neill 7428* (QAME n.v.)
Nectandra longifolia (Ruíz & Pavón) Nees
    Prov.: M-S; tree; *Zaruma et al. 354* (QAME n.v.)
Nectandra matthewsii Meissner
    Prov.: P; shrub; *Øllgaard et al. 35184* (AAU)
Nectandra membranacea (Sw.) Griseb.
    Prov.: N; tree; *Palacios et al. 496* (AAU)
Nectandra pearcei Mez
    Prov.: M-S; tree; *Neill 7155* (QAME n.v.); *Cerón & Palacios 3148*(QAME n.v.)
Nectandra pulverulenta Nees
    Prov.: N; tree; *Lugo 5065* (GB)

Lauraceae (cont.)

Nectandra purpurea (Ruíz & Pavón) Mez
Prov.: P; tree; *Lugo 4243, 4194, 4396, 4395* (GB); *Neill 7393* (QAME n.v.)

Nectandra reticulata Mez
Prov.: N, P, M-S; tree; *Neill et al. 6238* (AAU, QCA); *Lugo 4448* (GB)

Nectandra sp. 1
Prov.: N; tree; *Neill 6982* (QAME n.v.). This new species will be described by J. Rohwer as *N. crassiloba*

Nectandra sp. 2
Prov.: N; tree; *Lugo 5414, 5599* (GB). This new species will be described by J. Rohwer as *N. gracilis*

Nectandra sp. 3
Prov.: N, tree; *Palacios et al. 1885* (QAME n.v.). This new species will be described by J. Rohwer as *N. coeloclada*

Nectandra sp. 4
Prov.: P; tree; *Øllgaard et al. 35153* (AAU). This new species will be described by J. Rohwer as *N. parviflora*

Nectandra sp. 5
Prov.: N; tree; *Foster 3866* (AAU). This new species will be described by J. Rohwer as *N. canaliculata*

Ocotea aciphylla (Nees) Mez
Prov.: M-S; tree; *Palacios et al. 1483* (QAME n.v.)

Ocotea amazonica (Meissner) Mez
Prov.: N; tree; *Brandbyge et al. 33773* (AAU)

Ocotea bofo H.B.K.
Prov.: N; tree; *Palacios et al. 966* (QAME n.v.)

Ocotea cernua (Nees) Mez
Prov.: P; shrub; *Øllgaard et al. 35162* (AAU)

Ocotea costulata (Nees) Mez
Prov.: M-S; tree; *Neill 400* (QAME n.v.). Reaches 700 m alt. in M-S; *Pennington & Tenorio 10762* (QCA)

Ocotea floribunda (Sw.) Benth.
Prov.: N; tree; *SEF 8534* (AAU); *Korning & Thomsen 58653* (AAU); *Neill et al. 6941* (AAU). Syn. *O. wachenheimii* Bénoist.

Ocotea grandifolia (Nees) Mez aff.
Prov.: N, tree; *Pennington 10555* (MO)

Ocotea javitensis (H.B.K.) Pittier
Prov.: N; tree; *Brandbyge & Azanza 30422* (AAU); *Neill 7059* (QAME n.v.)

Ocotea laxiflora (Meissner) Mez
Prov.: M-S; tree; *Little et al. 742* (US)

Ocotea longifolia H.B.K.
Prov.: N, P; tree; *SEF 8672* (AAU); *Brandbyge & Azanza 31438* (AAU)

Ocotea ucayalensis O. C. Schmidt
Prov.: N; tree; *Neill 7221* (QAME n.v.)

Ocotea venenosa Kosterm. & Pinkley
Prov.: N; tree; *Pinkley 538, 555* (ECON); *Cerón 182* (MO)

Ocotea sp. 1
Prov.: N; tree; *SEF 8815* (AAU, QCA); *Korning & Thomsen 47629* (AAU)

Ocotea sp. 2
Prov.: N; tree; *SEF 8576, 8638, 8879* (AAU)

Ocotea sp. 3
Prov.: N; tree; *SEF 9127* (AAU); *Korning & Thomsen 47684, 47700* (AAU)

Ocotea sp. 4
Prov.: N; tree; *Korning & Thomsen 58667* (AAU)

Lauraceae   (cont.)

Persea americana Mill.
    Prov.: N; tree; *Brandbyge & Azanza 32832* (AAU); *Balslev & Irvine 4610*
    (QCA); *Pinkley 153* (S); *Neill 6423* (QAME n.v.)
Phoebe triplinervis (Ruíz & Pavón) Mez
    Prov.: M-S; tree; *Gentry 30935* (AAU, MO).   Collected at 1050 m alt.
Phoebe sp.
    Prov.: N; tree; *SEF 9137* (AAU)
Pleurothyrium cuneifolium Nees aff.
    Prov.: N; tree; *Lugo 303, 320* (GB); *Neill & Palacios 7019* (AAU, QCA)
Pleurothyrium krukovii A. C. Smith
    Prov.: N; tree; *Neill 6555* (AAU, QCA)
Pleurothyrium poeppigii Nees
    Prov.: N; tree; *Neill et al. 6555* (QAME n.v.)
Pleurothyrium trianae (Mez) Rohwer
    Prov.: N; tree; *Palacios 1415* (QAME n.v.)
Rhodostemonodaphne grandis (Mez) Rohwer
    Prov.: M-S; tree; *Pennington & Tenorio 10760* (QCA); *Zaruma et al. 810*
    (QAME n.v.).   Collected at 700 m alt.   Syn. *Nectandra grandis* (Mez) Kosterm.
Rhodostemonodaphne kunthiana (Mez) Rohwer
    Prov.: N, tree; *Cerón 3435* (QAME n.v.)
Rhodostemonodaphne synandra van der Werff
    Prov.: N; tree; *Neill & Palacios 7129* (HBG, MO, QAME n.v.)

Lecythidaceae
G. T. Prance and S. Mori, Fl. Neotropica 21(I). 1979 and S. Mori and G. T.
Prance, Fl. Neotropica 21(II). 1990.

Couratari guianensis Aublet
    Prov.: N; tree; *Korning & Thomsen 47444* (AAU); *Foster 3748* (QCA, S)
Couroupita guianensis Aublet
    Prov.: N, P, M-S; tree; *Lawesson et al. 39306* (AAU, QCA); *Lugo 2207* (GB, NY)
Eschweilera andina (Rusby) J. F. Macbr.
    Prov.: N, P, M-S; tree; *Brandbyge et al. 36241* (AAU); *Little et al. 706* (NY)
Eschweilera bracteosa (Poeppig ex Berg) Miers
    Prov.: N; tree; *Brandbyge et al. 36092* (AAU, NY)
Eschweilera caudiculata R. Knuth
    Prov.: P, M-S, tree; *Little et al. 358* (US).   At 800 m alt., *Harling & Andersson*
    17111 (GB, NY)
Eschweilera coriacea (A. DC.) Mori
    Prov.: N, P; tree; *Øllgaard et al. 39174, 57035* (AAU)
Eschweilera decolorans Sandw.
    Prov.: N; tree; *Brandbyge et al. 33925* (AAU, NY)
Eschweilera gigantea (R. Knuth) J. F. Macbr.
    Prov.: P; tree; *Neill & Palacios 6559* (AAU); *Irvine 546* (F, QCA)
Eschweilera itayensis R. Knuth
    Prov.: N; tree; *Cerón 3012* (QAME n.v.)
Eschweilera juruensis R. Knuth
    Prov.: N; tree; *Palacios 1707* (QAME n.v.)
Eschweilera laevicarpa Mori
    Prov.: N, tree; *Neill 7270* (QAME n.v.)

Lecythidaceae (cont.)

Eschweilera parvifolia C. Martius ex A. DC.
> Prov.: N; tree; *Foster 3592* (AAU); *Brandbyge et al. 33725* (AAU)

Grias neuberthii J. F. Macbr.
> Prov.: N, P, M-S; tree; *Holm-Nielsen et al. 21916* (AAU); *Neill et al. 6319* (QCA);
> *Alarcón 57* (QCA); *Davis & Yost 973* (QCA). Syn. *G. foetidissima* Dugand

Grias peruviana Miers
> Prov.: P; tree; *Palacios & Neill 593* (AAU)

Gustavia hexapetala (Aublet) Smith
> Prov.: P, M-S; tree; *Holm-Nielsen et al. 22587D* (AAU); *Little et al. 722* (US)

Gustavia longifolia Poeppig ex Berg
> Prov.: N; tree; *Brandbyge et al. 33218* (AAU); *Davis & Yost 1017* (QCA)

Gustavia macarenensis Philipson
> Prov.: N; tree; *Lugo 1036* (GB); *Irvine 420* (F, QCA); *Zaruma 283* (AAU)
> Reaches 750 m alt. in Napo: *Asplund 10282* (S)

Gustavia terminaliflora Mori
> Prov.: N; tree; *Palacios 2190* (QAME n.v.)

Lecythis zabucaja Aublet
> Prov.: M-S, tree; *Little et al. 746* (US, NY); *Ortega 79* (NY)

Leguminosae (Caesalpiniaceae, Fabaceae, Mimosaceae)

J. F. Macbride, Fl. Peru 3(1), Publ. Field Mus. Nat. Hist., Bot. Ser. 13:
3–507. 1943. H. Hopkins, Fl. Neotropica 43. 1986; R. S. Cowan, Fl.
Neotropica 1. 1968; H. S. Irwin & R. Barneby, Mem. New York Bot. Gard.
35: 1–918. 1982.

Abarema jupunba (Willd.) Britton & Killip
> Prov.: N; tree; *Neill et al. 6326* (QAME n.v.); *Little 719* (US)

Abarema laeta (Poeppig & Endl.) Barneby & Grimes
> Prov.: N; tree; *Neill et al. 7181* (QAME n.v.)

Acacia amazonica Benth.
> Prov.: N; vine; *Mexía 7115* (NY, US)

Acacia glomerosa Benth.
> Prov.: N, P, M-S; tree; *Neill 7108* (QAME n.v.). Reaches 1300 m alt.

Acacia hayesii Benth.
> Prov.: N; vine, shrub, treelet; *Asplund 9156* (S); *Brandbyge et al. 30314* (AAU)
> Including *A. macbridei* Britt. & Rose ex J. F. Macbr.

Acacia multipinnata Ducke
> Prov.: N, P; vine or shrub; *Irvine 379* (F, MO, QCA); *Brandbyge 30256* (AAU)

Acacia tubulifera Benth.
> Prov.: N, P; vine or treelet; *Dwyer 9650* (MO, QCA); *Gentry 9715A* (MO)
> Reaches 1300 m alt.

Aeschynomene americana L.
> Prov.: N, P; shrub; *Løjtnant & Molau 13457* (AAU); *Vickers 42* (F)

Albizia guachapele (H.B.K.) Dugand
> Prov.: N; tree; *Neill et al. 6368* (AAU, QCA)

Andira inermis (Wright) Kunth ex DC.
> Prov.: N; tree; *SEF 8533* (AAU, QCA)

Andira macrothyrsa Ducke
> Prov.: N; tree; *Neill et al. 8056* (QAME n.v.)

Leguminosae   (cont.)

Arachis hypogaea L.
> Prov.: N, M-S; shrub; *Brandbyge & Azanza 32429* (AAU); *Villegas & Meneses 7* (QCA); *Irvine 1048* (F, QCA)

Bauhinia arborea Wunderlin
> Prov.: N; tree; *SEF 8762, 8935* (AAU, QCA); *Pennington 10592* (QCA)

Bauhinia brachycalyx Ducke
> Prov.: N; tree; *Brandbyge et al. 30287* (AAU); *SEF 10133* (AAU, QCA)

Bauhinia glabra Jacq.
> Prov.: N, P; tree; *Holm-Nielsen et al. 22547* (AAU)

Bauhinia guianensis Aublet
> Prov.: N, P; tree or climber; *Holm-Nielsen et al. 22189* (AAU); *Gentry 12507* (QCA). Reaches 1300 m alt. in Pastaza: *Neill et al. 5862* (QCA).

Bauhinia tarapotensis Benth.
> Prov.: N, P; tree; *Holm-Nielsen et al. 19121* (AAU, QCA); *Alarcón 19533* (QCA); *Besse et al. 25* (QCA, SEL); *Neill et al. 6022* (QCA)

Brownea grandiceps Jacq.
> Prov.: N; tree; *Balslev & E. Madsen 10596* (AAU); *Jaramillo & Coello 2813* (QCA); *Plowman & Davis 4082* (S)

Brownea macrophylla Linden ex Mast.
> Prov.: N; tree; *Neill et al. 6218* (AAU, MO); *Alarcón 19390* (QCA)

Browneopsis ucayalina Huber
> Prov.: N; tree; *Lawesson et al. 39304* (AAU, QCA); *Neill et al. 6889* (QCA)

Caesalpinia pulcherrima (L.) Sw.
> Prov.: N; tree; *Villegas & Meneses 40* (QCA)

Cajanus cajan (L.) Millsp.
> Prov.: N; shrub; *Madison et al. 5469* (QCA, SEL).   Syn. *C. bicolor* DC.

Calliandra angustifolia Spruce ex Benth.
> Prov.: N; shrub; *Irvine 710* (QCA); *Balslev & Azanza 4359* (QCA)

Calliandra carbonaria Benth.
> Prov.: N, P, M-S; tree; *Neill & Gómez 6424* (QCA); *Neill et al. 6140* (AAU) Reaches 900 m alt. in Pastaza: *Fagerlind & Wibom 1249* (S)

Calliandra cf. haematocephala Hassk.
> Prov.: N; tree; *Korning & Thomsen 47395* (AAU)

Calliandra subnervosa Benth.
> Prov.: N; shrub; *Holm-Nielsen & Jeppesen 708* (AAU)

Calliandra trinervia Benth.
> Prov.: P, M-S; tree; *Lugo 4297, 4382, 5110, 5033, 5052* (GB).   Reaches 900 m alt.

Calopogonium mucunoides Desv.
> Prov.: N, P, M-S; herb; *Holm-Nielsen & Jeppesen 1013* (AAU)

Canavalia sp.
> Prov.: N; vine; *Brandbyge et al. 33431* (AAU)

Cedrelinga catenaeformis Ducke
> Prov.: N, M-S; tree; *SEF 8591* (AAU, QCA); *Neill et al. 6893* (QCA)

Centrolobium paraense Tul.
> Prov.: N; tree; *Neill et al. 6192* (QCA); *Palacios et al. 818* (AAU)

Centrosema plumieri (Turp. ex Pers.) Benth. vel sp. aff.
> Prov.: N; liana; *Korning & Thomsen 47009* (AAU)

Centrosema triquetrum Benth.
> Prov.: N; vine; *Holm-Nielsen & Jeppesen 662* (AAU), *Gentry 12453* (QCA)

Clitoria cf. amazonum C. Martius ex Benth.
> Prov.: N, P; woody vine; *Holm-Nielsen 19208* (AAU); *Gentry 9735* (AAU, QCA)

Leguminosae   (cont.)

Crudia glaberrima (Steud.) J. F. Macbr.
Prov.: N; treelet; *Øllgaard et al. 57150* (AAU)
Dalbergia monetaria L. f.
Prov.: N; vine; *Brandbyge et al. 33706* (AAU)
Desmodium adscendens (Sw.) DC.
Prov.: N, P; *Balslev et al. 84569* (AAU), *Løjtnant & Molau 13256* (AAU, QCA)
Desmodium heterocarpon (L.) DC.
Prov.: N; herb; *Neill 7174* (QAME n.v.)
Desmodium heterophyllum (Willd.) DC.
Prov.: N; scandent herb; *Holm-Nielsen et al. 20244* (AAU); *Madison et al. 5470* (QCA, SEL)
Dialium guianense (Aublet) Sandw.
Prov.: N; tree; *Brandbyge & Azanza 30593* (AAU, QCA)
Dioclea malacocarpa Ducke
Prov.: N; vine; *Asdall 82-69* (QCA)
Dioclea ucayalina Harms
Prov.: N; vine; *Pinkley 36* (ECON)
Dioclea sp. 1
Prov.: N; liana; *Balslev & E. Madsen 10603* (AAU)
Dioclea sp. 2
Prov.: N; liana; *Pennington 10622* (QCA); *Lescure 2026* (QCA)
Dioclea sp. 3
Prov.: N; liana; *Alarcón 94* (QCA); *Balslev & Alarcón 3047* (QCA)
Diplotropis ? sp.
Prov.: N; tree; *Korning & Thomsen 58739* (AAU)
Dussia tessmannii Harms
Prov.: N; *Neill 7344* (QAME n.v.)
Entada polyphylla Benth.
Prov.: N, P; liana; *Neill et al. 6487* (AAU).   Reaches 800 m alt. in Pastaza: *Grimes & Todzia 2572* (QCA)
Entada polystachya (L.) DC.
Prov.: N; liana; *Neill et al. 6056* (QCA)
Enterolobium barnebianum Mesq. & Silva
Prov.: N, P, M-S; tree; *Øllgaard et al. 57062* (AAU); *Little et al. 689* (US); *Davis & Yost 1026* (QCA)
Erythrina amazonica Krukoff
Prov.: N, P; tree; *Holm-Nielsen & Jeppesen 709* (AAU); *MacBryde & Simmons 1466* (QCA)
Erythrina peruviana Krukoff
Prov.: N; tree; *Neill et al. 7439* (QAME n.v.)
Erythrina poeppigiana (Walp.) O. F. Cook
Prov.: P, M-S; tree; *Holm-Nielsen et al. 22529* (AAU); *Lugo 4176, 4509* (GB)
Reaches 1100 m alt. in M-S: *Holm-Nielsen et al. 20566* (AAU)
Erythrina rubrinervia H.B.K.
Prov.: N; tree; *Alarcón 19131* (QCA)
Erythrina schimpfii Diels aff.
Prov.: N, P; tree; *Navarrete 35* (QCA); *Irvine 1069* (QCA); *McElroy 429* (QCA)
Reaches 1100 m alt. in Pastaza: *Neill et al. 5826* (QCA)
Erythrina ulei Harms
Prov.: N; tree; *Lugo 2218* (GB); *Palacios & Neill 929* (AAU); *Neill et al. 6356* (QCA).   Reaches 700 m alt.
Erythrina sp.
Prov.: P, M-S; tree; *Løjtnant & Molau 14563, 14561* (AAU)

Leguminosae   (cont.)

Hymenaea courbaril L.
Prov.: N; tree; *Balslev & Alarcón 3010* (QCA)
Hymenaea oblongifolia Huber
Prov.: N; tree; *Neill 7052* (QAME n.v.); SEF 8694 (AAU, QCA)
Hymenolobium heterocarpon Ducke aff.
Prov.: N; tree; *Palacios 4706* (QAME n.v.)
Indigofera sp.
Prov.: N; shrub; *Jaramillo & Coello 4146* (AAU); *Holm-Nielsen 19722* (AAU)
Inga acrocephala Steudel
Prov.: N; tree; *Cerón 219* (QAME n.v.)
Inga alba (Sw.) Willd.
Prov.: N; tree; *Cerón 3861* (QAME n.v.)
Inga aliena J. F. Macbr.
Prov.: N; tree; *Gentry 59999* (MO n.v.)
Inga cf. brachyrhachis Harms
Prov.: N; treelet; *Christensen 82965* (AAU)
Inga capitata Desv. vel sp. aff.
Prov.: N; tree; *Gentry 12421* (AAU, QCA, S)
Inga cf. ciliata Presl
Prov.: N; tree; *Cerón 206, 772* (QAME n.v.)
Inga cinnamomea Spruce ex Benth.
Prov.: N, P; tree; *Holm-Nielsen et al. 22548* (AAU); *SEF 9105* (AAU)
Inga cordatoalata Ducke
Prov.: N; tree; *Pennington 12218* (K n.v.)
Inga cordistipula C. Martius
Prov.: N; tree; *Palacios 672* (QAME n.v.)
Inga coriacea (Pers.) Desv.
Prov.: N; tree; *Neill et al. 7963* (QAME n.v.)
Inga densiflora Benth.
Prov.: N; tree; *Lugo 1740* (GB)
Inga edulis C. Martius
Prov.: N, P, M-S; tree; *Brandbyge et al. 36126* (AAU); *Alarcón 131* (QCA); *Irvine 152* (F, QCA). Reaches 900 m alt. Syn. *L. minutula* (Schery) Elias
Inga fagifolia (L.) Willd. ex Benth.
Prov.: N; tree; *Neill et al. 7228* (QAME n.v.)
Inga fastuosa (Jacq.) Willd.
Prov.: N; tree; *Cerón 166* (QAME n.v.)
Inga marginata Willd.
Prov.: N, P; tree; *Holm-Nielsen et al. 20209* (AAU); *Vickers 80* (QCA); *Irvine 155* (F, QCA). Reaches 1900 m in Pastaza: *Asplund 10346* (S)
Inga cf. mathewsiana Benth.
Prov: N, P; tree; *Holm-Nielsen et al. 22535* (AAU)
Inga myriantha Benth.
Prov.: N; tree; *Palacios 1444* (QAME n.v.)
Inga nobilis Willd.
Prov.: N, P; tree; *Luteyn et al. 8560* (AAU)
Inga pavoniana G. Don
Prov.: N; tree; *Palacios 1157* (QAME n.v.)
Inga pezizifera Benth. aff.
Prov.: N; tree; *SEF 10233* (AAU, QCA)

Leguminosae   (cont.)

Inga pilosiuscula **(Rich.) Desv.** aff.
>   Prov.: N; tree; *SEF 9298* (AAU, QCA)

Inga poeppigiana **Benth.**
>   Prov.: N; tree; *Neill 7289* (QAME n.v.)

Inga punctata **Willd.**
>   Prov.: N; tree; *Luteyn et al. 9097* (AAU); *Mexía 7160* (S); *Irvine 134* (QCA)

Inga quaternata **Poeppig & Endl.**
>   Prov.: N; tree; *Lawesson et al. 43451* (AAU); *Grimes & Todzia 2580* (MO)
>   Reaches 750 m alt. in Napo: *Asplund 9279* (S)

Inga rufiseta **Benth.**
>   Prov.: N; tree; *MacBryde 1285* (QAME n.v.)

Inga ruiziana **G. Don**
>   Prov.: N; tree; *Pinkley 403* (S)

Inga setifera **DC.**
>   Prov.: N; tree; *Lugo 276* (GB)

Inga cf. *setosa* **G. Don**
>   Prov.: N; treelet; *Christensen 72359* (AAU)

Inga spectabilis **(Vahl) Willd.**
>   Prov.: N, P; tree; *Øllgaard et al. 35015* (AAU); *Irvine 722* (QCA)

Inga stipularis **DC.**
>   Prov.: N; tree; *SEF 8745* (QCA)

Inga cf. *tenuistipula* **Ducke**
>   Prov.: N; treelet; *Holm-Nielsen et al. 21314* (AAU)

Inga tessmannii **Harms**
>   Prov.: N; tree; *Cerón 2046* (QAME n.v.)

Inga thibaudiana **DC.**
>   Prov.: N; tree; *Holm-Nielsen et al. 20046* (AAU); *Vickers 40* (F)

Inga cf. *umbratica* **Poeppig & Endl.**
>   Prov.: N; tree; *SEF 10035* (AAU, QCA)

Inga vera **Willd.**
>   Prov.: N; tree; *Gentry 60015* (QAME n.v.)

Inga vismiifolia **Poeppig**
>   Prov.: N; tree; *Neill 6366* (QAME n.v.)

Lecointea peruviana **J. F. Macbr.** var. *lasiogyne* **Barneby**
>   Prov.: N; tree; *Neill et al. 6051* (AAU, QCA); *SEF 8750, 8732* (AAU, QCA)

Lonchocarpus araripensis **Benth.**
>   Prov.: M-S; tree; *Neill et al. 7431* (QAME)

Lonchocarpus nicou **(Aublet) DC.**
>   Prov.: N; herb, shrub; *Davis Yost 968, 979* (QCA); *Vickers 53* (F)

Lonchocarpus **sp.**
>   Prov.: N; climber; *Holm-Nielsen & Jeppesen 850* (AAU)

Machaerium cuspidatum **Kuhlm. & Hoehne**
>   Prov.: N; climber; *Foster 3783* (AAU)

Machaerium floribundum **Benth.**
>   Prov.: N; treelet; *Holm-Nielsen et al. 21229* (AAU)

Macrolobium acaciaefolium **(Benth.) Benth.**
>   Prov.: N; tree; *Foster 3598* (AAU); *Holm-Nielsen et al. 21199* (AAU)

Macrolobium cf. *angustifolium* **(Benth.) R. Cowan**
>   Prov.: N; tree; *Palacios 2370* (QAME n.v.)

Macrolobium archeri **R. Cowan**
>   Prov.: N; tree; *Øllgaard et al. 57069* (AAU); *SEF 9024* (AAU, QCA)

Leguminosae (cont.)

Macrolobium colombianum (Britt. & Killip) Killip
 Prov.: N; tree; *Korning & Thomsen 47535* (AAU); *Neill & Palacios 7018* (AAU)
Macrolobium stenocladum Harms vel sp. aff.
 Prov.: N; tree; *Palacios 2372* (QAME n.v.)
Macrolobium unijugum (Poeppig & Endl.) R. Cowan
 Prov.: N; tree; *Korning & Thomsen 47702* (AAU); *Irvine 945* (F, QCA)
 Syn. *M. limbatum* Spruce ex Benth.
Mimosa myriadena (Benth.) Benth.
 Prov.: N, P; shrub; *Holm-Nielsen et al. 21969* (AAU)
Mimosa polydactyla Humb. & Bonpl. ex Willd.
 Prov.: N, P; shrub; *Løjtnant & Molau 13271* (AAU); *Lawesson et al. 39698*
 (AAU). Reaches 1100 m alt.
Mimosa punctulata Spruce ex Benth.
 Prov.: N; liana; *Holm-Nielsen et al. 21731* (AAU); *Neill et al. 6462* (QCA)
Mimosa tetragona Poir.
 Prov.: P; shrub; *Løjtnant & Molau 13469* (AAU)
 Syn. *Schrankia hamata* Humb. & Bonpl. ex Willd.
Mucuna elliptica (Ruíz & Pavón) DC.
 Prov.: N; liana; *Lugo 306* (GB)
Mucuna urens (L.) DC.
 Prov.: N; tree; *Holm-Nielsen et al. 19111* (AAU); *Lugo 2122* (GB)
Mucuna sp.
 Prov.: N, P; liana; *Jaramillo & Coello 3195* (AAU, QCA)
Myroxylon balsamum (L.) Harms
 Prov.: N, tree; *Palacios & Neill 1292A* (AAU)
Ormosia amazonica Ducke
 Prov.: N; tree; *Neill et al. 6251* (QCA); *Vickers 270* (F)
Ormosia sp. nov.
 Prov.: N; tree; *Cerón 407* (QAME n.v.). This new species will be described by
 C. H. Stirton as *O. oblongifolia.*
Parkia balslevii H. C. Hopkins
 Prov.: N; tree; *Holm-Nielsen et al. 21181* (AAU); *Hopkins 428* (AAU, QCA)
Parkia multijuga Benth.
 Prov.: N; tree; *Neill et al. 6409* (AAU, QCA); *Hopkins 426* (QCA)
Parkia nitida Miq.
 Prov.: N; tree; *Hopkins 406* (AAU, QCA); *Neill et al. 6254* (QCA)
Parkia panurensis Benth. ex H. C. Hopkins
 Prov.: N; tree; *Hopkins & Balslev 404* (AAU, QCA)
Parkia velutina Bénoist
 Prov.: P; tree; *Neill 6632* (QAME n.v.); *Balslev et al. 84659* (AAU)
Phaseolus caracalla L.
 Prov.: N; tree; *Irvine 217* (F, QCA). Syn. *Vigna caracalla* (L.) Verdc.
Piptadenia anolidurus Barneby
 Prov.: M-S; scandent shrub; *Cazalet & Pennington 7728* (K, NY, US)
Piptadenia cf. flava (Sprengel) Benth.
 Prov.: N; tree; *Cerón 236* (QAME n.v.)
Piptadenia pteroclada Benth.
 Prov.: N; tree; *Neill 7201* (QAME n.v.)
Pithecellobium amplum Spruce ex Benth.
 Prov.: N; tree; *Øllgaard et al. 38843* (AAU)
Pithecellobium auriculatum Benth.
 Prov.: N; tree; *Neill et al. 6326* (AAU, QCA)

Leguminosae   (cont.)

Pithecellobium basijugum Ducke
    Prov.: N; tree; *Øllgaard et al. 39234* (AAU); *Luteyn et al. 8663* (AAU, GB)
Pithecellobium coccineum Benth.
    Prov.: N, tree; *Neill 7285* (QAME n.v.)
Pithecellobium inaequale (Humb. & Bonpl.) Benth.
    Prov.: N; tree; *Lawesson et al. 43395* (AAU)
Pithecellobium laetum (Poeppig & Endl.) Benth.
    Prov.: N; tree; *Zaruma et al. 409* (QAME n.v.)
Pithecellobium longifolium (Humb. & Bonpl.) Standley
    Prov.: N, P; tree; *Holm-Nielsen et al. 21167* (AAU);*Whitmore 802* (S); *Neill & Palacios 6560* (AAU, QCA); *Irvine 762* (F, QCA)
Pithecellobium macrophyllum Spruce ex Benth.
    Prov.:N, P; tree; *Balslev1597* (AAU, QCA); *SEF 9271* (AAU, QCA); *Irvine 680* (F, QCA).   Reaches 1050 m alt. in Pastaza: *Harling 3128* (S).
Platymiscium pinnatum (Jacq.) Dugand
    Prov.: N; tree; *SEF 10009, 10286* (AAU, QCA)
Platymiscium stipulare Benth.
    Prov.: N; tree; *Neill et al. 7041* (QCA); *Palacios et al. 361* (AAU)
Pterocarpus amazonum (C. Martius ex Benth.) Amshoff
    Prov.: N; tree; *Jaramillo 90* (AAU, QCA); *Neill et al. 6464* (AAU), *7163* (QCA)
Pterocarpus magnicarpus Schery
    Prov.: N; tree; *Korning & Thomsen 47759, 47767* (AAU)
Pterocarpus rohrii Vahl
    Prov.: N; tree; *Neill et al. 6464* (QAME n.v.)
Pterocarpus ulei Harms
    Prov.: N; tree; *Holm-Nielsen et al. 21170* (AAU); *Foster 3692* (QCA)
Schizolobium parahyba (Vell.) S. F. Blake
    Prov.: N; tree; *Neill & Gómez 6445* (AAU, QCA)
Sclerolobium sp.
    Prov.: N; tree; *Bravo & Gómez 127* (QCA); *Nowak 154* (QCA)
Senna acuparata Irwin & Barneby
    Prov.: M-S; climber; *Brandbyge & Azanza 32047* (AAU)
Senna alata (L.) Roxb.
    Prov.: N, P; shrub; *Irvine 804* (QCA);*Neill et al. 6869* (AAU).   Reaches 900 m alt. in Pastaza: *Grimes & Todzia 2576* (QCA)
Senna bacillaris (L. f.) Irwin & Barneby
    Prov.: N, P, M-S; tree; *Holm-Nielsen et al. 19155* (AAU, QCA); *Neill 7166* (QCA).   Reaches 900 m alt. in Pastaza: *Grimes & Todzia 2577* (QCA).
Senna cernua (Balbis) Irwin & Barneby
    Prov.: N; tree; *Pinkley 154* (ECON)
Senna cowanii (J. F. Macbr.) Irwin & Barneby
    Prov.: N; tree; *Holm-Nielsen et al. 21189* (AAU, QCA)
Senna fruticosa (Mill.) Irwin & Barneby
    Prov.: N; tree; *Holm-Nielsen & Jeppesen 1036* (AAU); *Irvine 731* (QCA); *Pinkley 177* (S); *Gentry 12460* (S).   Reaches 1200 m alt.
Senna grandis L. f.
    Prov.: N; tree; *Oldeman & Arévalo 44* (QCA)
Senna hirsuta (L.) Irwin & Barneby
    Prov.: N; *Zaruma et al. 488* (QAME n.v.)
Senna macrocarpa (Kunth) Irwin & Barneby
    Prov.: N; tree; *Pinkley 154* (NY)

Leguminosae   (cont.)

Senna macrophylla (Kunth) Irwin & Barneby
Prov.: N, P, M-S; tree; *Brandbyge & Azanza 32361* (AAU, QCA); *Neill et al.*
5830 (QCA); *Oldeman & Arévalo 92* (QCA).   Reaches 2050 m alt.
Senna multijuga (L. C. Rich.) Irwin & Barneby
Prov.: N, P, M-S; tree; *Holm-Nielsen 19272* (AAU); *Neill et al. 6196* (QCA)
Reaches 760 m alt.
Senna obliqua (Ruíz & Pavón ex G. Don) Irwin & Barneby
Prov.: N, P, M-S; shrub or climber; *Brandbyge et al. 33615* (AAU, QCA)
Senna pendula (H.B.K. ex Willd.) Irwin & Barneby
Prov.: N, shrub; *Jaramillo & Coello 4144* (AAU, QCA); *Gentry 12487* (QCA)
Senna quinquangulata (L. C. Rich.) Irwin & Barneby
Prov.: N, P, M-S; shrub, tree; *Brandbyge & Azanza 31894* (AAU, QCA)
Senna reticulata (Willd.) Irwin & Barneby
Prov.: N; tree; *Andrade 33004* (AAU, QCA)
Senna ruiziana (G. Don) Irwin & Barneby
Prov.: N, P; tree; *Brandbyge et al. 33316* (AAU, QCA).   Reaches 1000 m alt.
Senna spinescens (Vog.) Irwin & Barneby
Prov.: N; tree; *Brandbyge et al. 33721* (AAU)
Senna trolliiflora Irwin & Barneby
Prov.: N; tree; *Brandbyge & Azanza 32694* (AAU)
Stryphnodendron porcatum Neill & Occhioni f.
Prov.: N, M-S; *Neill 7953, 7837, 6365* (QAME n.v.)
Swartzia arborescens (Aublet) Pittier
Prov.: N, M-S; tree; *Korning & Thomsen 57135* (AAU); *Little et al. 779* (US)
Swartzia auriculata Poeppig
Prov.: N; tree; *Foster 3660* (QCA); *Balslev & Irvine 4583* (QCA)
Swartzia benthamiana Miq.
Prov.: N; tree; *Korning & Thomsen 47518* (AAU)
Swartzia cardiosperma Spruce ex Benth.
Prov.: N; tree; *SEF 9192, 10190* (AAU, QCA)
Swartzia laevicarpa Amshoff
Prov.: N; tree; Neill 7332 (QAME n.v.)
Swartzia leptopetala Benth.
Prov.: N; tree; *Neill 7088* (QAME n.v.)
Swartzia macrosema Harms
Prov.:N, P; tree; *Lugo 270* (AAU); *Korning & Thomsen 47597* (AAU).   Reaches
1050 m alt. in Pastaza: *Asplund 18819* (S)
Swartzia polyphylla DC.
Prov.: N; tree; *Mowbray 703123* (MO n.v.)
Swartzia simplex (Sw.) Sprengel
Prov.: N, P; tree; *Holm-Nielsen et al. 21087B* (AAU); *Irvine 642* (F, QCA)
Tachigalia sp.
Prov.: N; tree; *Irvine 735* (F, QCA)
Tephrosia sinapou (Buc' hoz) A. Chev.
Prov.: N; shrub; *Vickers 198* (QCA); *Pinkley 75* (ECON); *Irvine 1073* (F, QCA)
Vatairea erythrocarpa (Ducke) Ducke
Prov.: P; tree; *Neill 6727* (QAME n.v.)
Zygia latifolia (L.) Fawcett & Rendle
Prov.: N, P, M-S; tree; *Foster 3824* (QCA); *Neill & Palacios 6737* (AAU, QCA)
Syn. *Pithecellobium latifolium* (L.)Benth.

Liliaceae
J. F. Macbride, Fl. Peru 1(3), Publ. Field Mus. Nat. Hist., Bot. Ser. 13: 617–630. 1936.

Allium cepa L.
Prov.: N; herb; *Balslev & Alarcón 3019, 2985* (QCA)

Limnocharitaceae
R. R. Haynes & L. B. Holm-Nielsen, Fl. Ecuador 26, 1986.

Limnocharis flava (L.) J. Buch.
Prov.: N, P; herb; *Harling et al. 19791* (AAU, GB)

Loganiaceae
J. F. Macbride, Fl. Peru 5(1), Publ. Field Mus. Nat. Hist., Bot. Ser. 13: 239–269. 1959.

Cynoctonum mitreola (L.) Britton
Prov.: N, P; herb; *Jaramillo & Coello 3800* (AAU)
Potalia amara Aublet
Prov.: N, P ; shrub; *Holm-Nielsen et al. 19877* (AAU); *Balslev & Santos Dea 2905* (QCA); *Pinkley 393* (ECON)
Sanango racemosum (Ruíz & Pavón) Barringer
Prov.: N; tree; *Cerón 2172* (QAME n.v.); *Neill 7017* (QAME n.v.)
Spigelia anthelmia L.
Prov.: N; herb; *Holm-Nielsen et al. 19723* (AAU); *Villegas & Meneses 67* (QCA)
Spigelia humboldtiana Cham. & Schldl.
Prov.: N, P; herb; *Brandbyge & Azanza 32903* (AAU)
Spigelia sp.
Prov.: N, P; herb; *Brandbyge & Azanza 31638* (AAU)
Strychnos darienensis Seemann
Prov.: N; shrub, tree; *Øllgaard et al. 39287* (AAU); *Pinkley 516* (S)
Strychnos erichsonii R. Schomb.
Prov.: N; tree; *Jaramillo & Coello 4424* (AAU)
Strychnos jobertiana Baillon
Prov.: N; tree; *Korning & Thomsen 47677* (AAU); *Pinkley 385* (S)
Strychnos peckii B. L. Robinson
Prov.: N; tree; *Pinkley 79* (S)
Strychnos toxifera R. Schomb. ex Benth.
Prov.: N; shrub; *Pinkley 566* (S)

Loranthaceae
J. Kuijt, Fl. Ecuador 24, 1986.

Oryctanthus alveolatus (H.B.K.) Kuijt
Prov.: N, P; epiphytic herb; *Holm-Nielsen et al. 21191* (AAU).   Reaches 1200 m
Oryctanthus florulentus (Rich.) van Tieghem
Prov.: N, M-S; epiphytic herb; *Holm-Nielsen 19841* (AAU); *Alarcón & Balslev 2972* (QCA)

Loranthaceae   (cont.)

Oryctanthus spicatus (Jacq.) Eichler
Prov.: N; epiphytic herb *Lawesson et al. 43548* (AAU).   Usually at higher alts.

Phthirusa pyrifolia (H.B.K.) Eichler
Prov.: N, P, M-S; epiphytic herb; *Lawesson et al. 44282* (AAU); *Balslev & Alarcón 3072* (QCA); *Fagerlind & Wibom 2249* (S).   Reaches 1000 m alt. in Pastaza: *Asplund 18923* (S).   Syn. *Phthirusa platyclada* Ule

Phthirusa robusta Rusby
Prov.: N, P, M-S; epiphytic herb; *Jaramillo & Coello 2929* (AAU); *Fagerlind & Wibom 2250* (S).   Reaches 1050 m alt. in Pastaza: *Asplund 19346* (S).

Psittacanthus barlowii Kuijt
Prov.: N; epiphytic herb; *Davis & Yost 999* (QCA)

Psittacanthus corynocephalus Eichler
Prov.: N; epiphytic herb; *Holm-Nielsen et al. 21409* (AAU)

Psittacanthus cucullaris (Lam.) Blume
Prov.: N, P; epiphytic herb; *Holm-Nielsen et al. 20237* (AAU, QCA); *Alarcón 67* (QCA); *Lugo 901* (GB)

Psittacanthus plagiophyllus Eichler
Prov.: N; epiphytic herb; *Brandbyge et al. 33578* (AAU, QCA)

Psittacanthus wiensii Kuijt
Prov.: P, M-S; epiphytic herb; *Øllgaard et al. 34505* (AAU, QCA); *McElroy 201* (QCA).   Reaches 650 m alt.

Struthanthus orbicularis (H.B.K.) Blume
Prov.: N, P; epiphytic herb; *Øllgaard et al. 35087* (AAU); *Dwyer & MacBryde 9789* (QCA).   Reaches higher altitudes.   Syn. *S. chordocladus* (Oliver) Eichler

Lythraceae
A. Lourteig, Fl. Ecuador 37, 1989.

Adenaria floribunda H.B.K.
Prov.: N, P, M-S; shrub, tree; *Løjtnant & Molau 13586* (AAU, QCA)

Cuphea bombonasae Sprague
Prov.: P; shrub; *Øllgaard et al. 35157* (AAU); *Lugo 4175* (GB).   Reaches 1900 m

Cuphea carthagenensis (Jaq.) J. F. Macbr.
Prov.: P; herb; *Løjtnant & Molau 13566* (GB).   Reaches 1050 m alt. in Pastaza: *Øllgaard et al. 35550* (AAU)

Cuphea strigulosa H.B.K.
Prov.: P; herb; *Løjtnant & Molau 13566* (AAU).   Reaches higher altitudes

Lafoensia punicifolia Bertero ex DC.
Prov.: N; tree; *Zaruma et al. 483* (QAME n.v.)

Magnoliaceae

Talauma ovata A. St. Hil.
Prov.: N; tree; *Øllgaard et al. 57126* (AAU); *Neill 6987, 7087* (QAME n.v.).   Maybe = *T. amazonica* Ducke ?

Malpighiaceae

J. F. Macbride, Fl. Peru 3(3), Publ. Field Mus. Nat. Hist., Bot. Ser. 13: 781–871. 1950; B. Gates, Fl. Neotropica 30. 1982.

Banisteriopsis caapi (Spruce ex Griseb.) Morton
  Prov.: N; vine; *Holm-Nielsen 19172* (AAU); *Balslev & Santos Dea 2830* (QCA)
Banisteriopsis longialata (Niedenzu) B. Gates
  Prov.: N; vine; *Pinkley 449* (S)
Banisteriopsis muricata (Cav.) Cuatrec.
  Prov.: N; vine; *Davis & Yost 967, 975* (QCA)
Banisteriopsis pubipetala (A. Juss.) Cuatrec.
  Prov.: N; *Zaruma et al. 378* (QAME n.v.)
Bunchosia argentea (Jacq.) DC.
  Prov.: N; tree; *Brandbyge & Azanza 30386* (AAU)
Bunchosia cf. armeniaca (Cav.) DC.
  Prov.: N; tree; *Foster 3871* (QCA)
Bunchosia hookeriana Juss.
  Prov.: P; tree; *Neill & Palacios 6646* (QCA)
Byrsonima japurensis Juss.
  Prov.: M-S; tree; *Little et al. 707* (US)
Byrsonima putumayensis Cuatrec.
  Prov.: N; tree; *Irvine 1004* (F, QCA)
Callaeum antifebrile (Griseb.) D. M. Johnson
  Prov.: P; liana; *McElroy 371* (QCA)
Dicella julianii (J. F. Macbr.) W. Anderson
  Prov.: P; liana *Brandbyge & Azanza 31435* (AAU)
Diplopteris cabrerana (Cuatrec.) B. Gates
  Prov.: N; vine; *Irvine 699* (QCA); *Vickers 212* (F)
Jubelina uleana (Niedenzu) Cuatrec.
  Prov.: N; *Palacios 2352* (QAME n.v.)
Mascagnia divaricata (H.B.K.) Niedenzu
  Prov.: N; *Cerón 2028* (QAME n.v.)
Mascagnia macrodisca (Triana & Planchon) Niedenzu
  Prov.: N; *Cerón 1250* (QAME n.v.)
Mascagnia ovatifolia (H.B.K.) Griseb. aff.
  Prov.: N; liana; *Madison et al. 5484* (QCA, SEL)
Stigmaphyllon bogotense Triana & Planchon
  Prov.: N; liana; *Azanza & Barfod 41117* (AAU); *Besse et al. 059* (AAU, QCA)
Stigmaphyllon maynense Huber
  Prov.: N; *Cerón 1688* (QAME n.v.)
Tetrapterys mucronata Cav.
  Prov.: N; *Neill 7256* (QAME n.v.)

Malvaceae

J. F. Macbride, Fl. Peru 3A(2), Publ. Field Mus. Nat. Hist., Bot. Ser. 13: 442–593. 1956. This listing checked by P. Fryxell, TEX, May 1991.

Abelmoschus moschatus Medic.
    Prov.: N; shrub; *Andrade 33140* (AAU). Syn. *Hibiscus abelmoschus* L.

Abutilon dianthum K. Presl
    Prov.: N; shrub; *Lugo 2381* (AAU, GB) *A. dianthum* Presl is the next oldest name for *Abutilon sylvaticum* (Cav.) Schum., the basionym of which [*Sida sylvatica* Cav.] is a problematical name.

Gossypium barbadense L.
    Prov.: N, M-S; shrub; *Brandbyge & Azanza 32348* (AAU); *Alarcón 10* (QCA)

Hibiscus peruvianus R. E. Fries
    Prov.: N, P; shrub; *Øllgaard et al. 35134* (AAU)

Hibiscus rosa-sinensis L.
    Prov.: N; shrub; *Vickers 166* (F); *Pinkley 91* (ECON)

Malachra alceifolia Jacq.
    Prov.: N; shrub; *Brandbyge et al. 33550* (AAU)

Malachra fasciata Jacq.
    Prov.: N; shrub; *Alarcón 4* (QCA)

Malachra ruderalis Garcke
    Prov.: P, M-S; shrub; *Lugo 3787* (AAU)

Malachra rudis Benth.
    Prov.: N, P; shrub; *Brandbyge et al. 30215* (AAU). Reaches 1050 m alt.

Malvaviscus concinnus H.B.K.
    Prov.: N, P, M-S; shrub; *Holm-Nielsen & Jeppesen 563* (AAU)

Pavonia castaneifolia A. St. Hil. & Naudin
    Prov.: N, P; shrub; *Holm-Nielsen et al. 21598* (AAU)

Pavonia fruticosa (Miller) Fawcett & Rendle
    Prov.: N, P, M-S; shrub; *Holm-Nielsen et al. 20518* (AAU) Reaches 1100 m alt.

Pavonia leucantha Garcke
    Prov.: P; shrub; *Løjtnant & Molau 13593* (AAU, GB)

Pavonia oxyphyllaria J. D. Smith
    Prov.: N, P; shrub; *Brandbyge et al. 30464* (AAU)

Pavonia schiedeana Steudel
    Prov.: N; shrub; *Brandbyge et al. 32505* (AAU). Reaches higher altitudes.

Sida acuta Burm. f.
    Prov.: N; shrub; *Alarcón 8* (QCA)

Sida glomerata Cav.
    Prov.: N; shrub; *Brandbyge & Azanza 32854* (AAU); Vickers 29 (F)

Sida setosa C. Martius ex Colla
    Prov.: N, P; shrub; *Øllgaard et al. 35105* (AAU)

Wissadula excelsior (Cav.) Presl
    Prov.: P; shrub; *Øllgaard et al. 35396* (AAU)

Marantaceae
H. Kennedy et al., Fl. Ecuador 32, 1988 .

Calathea allouia (Aublet) Lindley
    Prov.: N, P; herb; *Brandbyge & Azanza 32811* (AAU); *Vickers 177* (FLAS)
Calathea altissima (Poeppig & Endl.) Koern.
    Prov.: N, P, M-S; herb; *Brandbyge et al. 33345* (AAU, GB, QCA)
Calathea anderssonii Kennedy
    Prov.: N; herb; *Kennedy et al. 4383* (AAU, GB, QCA)
Calathea attenuata Kennedy
    Prov.: N, P, M-S; herb; *Holm-Nielsen et al. 22278* (AAU).   Reaches 900 m alt.
Calathea bantae Kennedy
    Prov.: N, P, M-S; herb; *Øllgaard et al. 35506* (AAU).   Reaches 1400 m alt.
Calathea capitata (Ruíz & Pavón) Lindley
    Prov.: N, P; herb; *Holm-Nielsen et al. 20136* (AAU); *Foster 3556* (QCA)
Calathea chrysoleuca (Poeppig & Endl.) Koern.
    Prov.: N; herb; *Kennedy et al. 4282* (GB); *Foster 3830* (QCA, S, US)
Calathea clivorum Kennedy
    Prov.: N; herb; *Kennedy et al. 4368* (AAU, GB, QCA)
Calathea contrafenestra Kennedy
    Prov.: N; herb; *Korning & Thomsen 47387* (AAU); *Madison et al. 5400* (QCA)
Calathea crotalifera Watson
    Prov.: N, P, M-S; herb; *Holm-Nielsen et al. 20282* (AAU).   Reaches 850 m alt.
Calathea curaraya Kennedy
    Prov.: N, P; herb; *Holm-Nielsen et al. 22035* (AAU)
Calathea ecuadoriana Kennedy
    Prov.: N, P; herb; *Lugo 4177* (GB)
Calathea exscapa (Poeppig & Endl.) Koern.
    Prov.: P; herb; *Lugo 4416* (GB)
Calathea fucata Kennedy
    Prov.: N, P; herb; *Lawesson et al. 43508* (AAU); *Løjtnant & Molau 13347* (AAU)
Calathea laetevirens Huber
    Prov.: N; herb; *Kennedy et al. 4350* (AAU, GB)
Calathea lagoagriana Kennedy
    Prov.: N, P, M-S; herb; *Brandbyge & Azanza 31872* (AAU, GB, QCA)
Calathea lanicaulis Kennedy
    Prov.: N, P; herb; *Kennedy et al. 4373* (AAU, QCA, SEL)
Calathea lateralis (Ruíz & Pavón) Lindley
    Prov.: N, P, M-S; herb; *Jaramillo & Coello 3206* (AAU, QCA)
Calathea leonia (Sander) Schum.
    Prov.: N, P; herb; *Øllgaard et al. 39182* (AAU)
Calathea libbyana Kennedy
    Prov.: N; herb; *Kennedy et al. 4334* (AAU, GB, QCA, SEL)
Calathea loeseneri J. F. Macbr.
    Prov.: P, M-S; herb; *Brandbyge & Azanza 31232* (AAU, GB)
Calathea majestica (Linden) Kennedy
    Prov.: N; herb; *Andrade 33098* (AAU, QCA); *Balslev & Santos Dea 2825* (QCA)
Calathea marantina (Willd. ex Koern.) Koch
    Prov.: N, P, M-S; herb; *Andrade 33028* (QCA); *Holm-Nielsen et al. 16296*
    (AAU); *Irvine 789* (F, QCA).   Reaches 1450 m alt.
Calathea micans (Mathieu) Koern.
    Prov.: N, P; herb; *Holm-Nielsen et al. 22459* (AAU); *Foster 3818* (QCA, S)
Calathea microcephala (Poeppig & Endl.) Koern.
    Prov.: N, P; herb; *Øllgaard et al. 35259* (AAU)

Calathea mishuyacu J. F. Macbr.
   Prov.: N, P, M-S; herb; *Holm-Nielsen et al. 21507* (AAU); *Harling & Andersson 17717* (GB, QCA)
Calathea ornata (Linden) Koern. aff.
   Prov.: N; herb; *Vickers 202* (F)
Calathea pallidicosta Kenndey
   Prov.: P, M-S; herb; *Holm-Nielsen et al. 21138* (AAU).   Reaches 1100 m alt.
Calathea paucifolia Kennedy
   Prov.:P; herb, *Lugo 1605* (GB)
Calathea plurispicata Kennedy
   Prov.: N; herb; *Øllgaard et al. 39137* (AAU)
Calathea poeppigiana Loes. ex Kennedy
   Prov.: P; herb; *Brandbyge & Azanza 31671 (AAU)*
Calathea propinqua (Poeppig & Endl.) Koern.
   Prov.: N, P; herb; *Brandbyge & Azanza 30833* (AAU).   Reaches 1100 m alt. in
   Pastaza: *Harling et al. 9772* (GB, QCA)
Calathea roseo-picta (Linden) Regel
   Prov.: N; herb; *Pinkley 304* (ECON)
Calathea standleyi J. F. Macbr.
   Prov.: N, P, M-S; herb; *Brandbyge et al. 33481* (AAU); *Davis & Yost 941* (F,
   QCA); *Harling & Andersson 17039* (GB).   Reaches 850 m alt.
Calathea striata Kennedy
   Prov.: N; herb; *Brandbyge & Azanza 30146* (AAU)
Calathea variegata Linden ex Koern.
   Prov.: N, P, M-S; herb; *Holm-Nielsen & Jeppesen 870* (AAU).   Reaches 800 m
   alt. in M-S: *Sparre 19222* (S)
Calathea zingiberina Koern.
   Prov.: P; herb; *McElroy 297* (BH)
Ctenanthe ericae Andersson
   Prov.: N; herb; *Heinrichs 502* (B)
Hylaeanthe hexantha (Poeppig & Endl.) Jonker & Jonker
   Prov.: N; herb; *Harling et al. 14769* (GB); *Madison et al. 5396* (QCA, SEL)
Hylaeanthe unilateralis (Poeppig & Endl.) Jonker & Jonker
   Prov.: N; herb; *Brandbyge et al. 32463* (AAU, GB)
Ischnosiphon cerotus Loes.
   Prov.: N, P; herb; *Jaramillo & Coello 3019* (AAU, QCA); *Lugo 3382* (GB, QCA)
Ischnosiphon hirsutus O. G. Peters.
   Prov.: N, P; herb; *Holm-Nielsen et al. 22388* (AAU)
Ischnosiphon killipii J. F. Macbr.
   Prov.: N, P; herb; *Holm-Nielsen et al. 22393* (AAU)
Ischnosiphon leucophaeus (Poeppig & Endl.) Koern.
   ssp. *leucophaeus*
   Prov.: N, P; herb; *Brandbyge & Azanza 31054* (AAU, QCA)
Ischnosiphon macarenae L. Andersson
   Prov.: N, P; herb; *Brandbyge & Azanza 31688* (AAU, GB); *Foster 3681* (F, QCA)
Ischnosiphon obliquus (Rudge) Koern.
   Prov.: N, P; herb; *Øllgaard et al. 35256* (AAU); *Davis & Yost 1045* (QCA)
Ischnosiphon puberulus Loes.
   Prov.: N, P; herb; *Harling & Andersson 16616* (AAU, GB, QCA)
Ischnosiphon rotundifolius (Poeppig & Endl.) Koern.
   Prov.: N, P; climber; *Neill 6201* (GB); *Harling & Andersson 17471* (GB)

Marantaceae   (cont.)

Maranta amazonica L. Andersson
> Prov.: N, P, M-S; herb; *Balslev et al. 62290* (AAU, QCA)

Monotagma juruanum Loes.
> Prov.: N; herb; *Holm-Nielsen et al. 20184* (AAU)

Monotagma laxum (Poeppig & Endl.) Schum.
> Prov.: N, P, M-S; herb; *Foster 3653* (F, QCA); *Balslev & Alarcón 3015* (QCA)

Monotagma secundum (Peters.) Schum.
> Prov.: N, P; herb; *Foster 3631* (F, QCA); *Renner 69079* (AAU)

Stromanthe stromanthoides (J. F. Macbr.) L. Andersson
> Prov.: N, P, M-S; herb; *Holm-Nielsen et al. 19355* (AAU); *Lugo 216* (AAU, GB, QCA); *Pinkley 46* (ECON).   Reaches 900 m alt. in M-S: *Camp E-1087* (US)

Marcgraviaceae
J. F. Macbride, Fl. Peru 3A(2), Publ. Field Mus. Nat. Hist., Bot. Ser. 13: 703–717. 1956.

Marcgravia macrophylla Gilg
> Prov.: N; epiphytic herb; *Alarcón 110* (QCA); *Lawesson et al. 39570* (AAU, QCA).   Reaches 2000 m alt.: *Øllgaard & Balslev 10205 (AAU)*

Marcgravia subcaudata Gilg
> Prov.: N; epiphytic herb;   *Lawesson et al. 39374* (AAU, QCA)

Marcgravia sp. 1
> Prov.: N; epiphytic herb; *Lawesson 43465* (AAU, QCA); *Balslev 2387* (QCA)

Marcgravia sp. 2
> Prov.: N; epiphytic herb; *Davis & Yost 954, 972* (QCA); *Balslev 2309* (QCA)

Norantea sp.
> Prov.: N; epiphytic herb; *Jaramillo & Coello 4439* (QCA)

Melastomataceae
J. J. Wurdack, Fl. Ecuador 13, 1980.

Aciotis aequatorialis **Cogn.**
  Prov.: P; herb; *Løjtnant & Molau 13404* (AAU); *Lugo 1467* (GB, QCA)
  Reaches 1000 m alt. in Pastaza: *Asplund 18663* (S)
Aciotis caulialata **(Ruíz & Pavón) Triana**
  Prov.: P; herb; *Lugo 4924* (AAU, GB). Reaches 1050 m alt. in Pastaza:
  Øllgaard et al. 35519 (AAU)
Aciotis indecora **(Bonpl.) Triana**
  Prov.: N; herb; *Lawesson et al. 44243* (AAU, QCA)
Aciotis polystachya **(Bonpl.) Triana**
  Prov.: N, P; herb; *Holm-Nielsen et al. 19737* (AAU); *Renner 69334* (AAU, QCA)
Aciotis purpurascens **(Aublet) Triana**
  Prov.: N, P, M-S; herb; *Renner 69323* (AAU, QCA); *Cazalet & Pennington 7755*
  (QCA). Reaches 1000 m alt. in Pastaza: *Asplund 18317* (S)
Adelobotrys adscendens **(Sw.) Triana**
  Prov.: N, P, M-S; liana; *Renner 69322* (AAU, QCA)
Adelobotrys boissieriana **Cogn.**
  Prov.: NP, M-S; liana; *Brandbyge et al. 33741* (AAU); *Lugo 692* (GB, QCA)
Adelobotrys klugii **Wurdack**
  Prov.: N, M-S; liana; *Øllgaard et al. 38870* (AAU, QCA)
Adelobotrys scandens **(Aublet) DC.**
  Prov.: N; liana; *Renner 69088* (AAU, QCA, US)
Adelobotrys tessmannii **Markgraf**
  Prov.: N, M-S; liana; *Brandbyge & Azanza 32031* (AAU); *Lugo 3221* (AAU)
Adelobotrys **sp.**
  Prov.: P; liana; *Jaramillo et al. 31194* (AAU, QCA, US); *Renner 69057A* (US)
Arthrostema ciliatum **Ruíz & Pavón**
  Prov.: N, P, M-S; shrub; *Holm-Nielsen & Jeppesen 949* (AAU); *Lawesson et al.*
  39656 (AAU, QCA). Reaches 1000 m alt. in M-S: *Asplund 19730* (S)
Bellucia pentamera **Naudin**
  Prov.: N, P, M-S; tree; *Holm-Nielsen et al. 22110* (AAU); *Alarcón 120* (QCA);
  Neill et al. 6338 (AAU, QCA). Reaches 1800 m alt.
Blakea bracteata **Gleason**
  Prov.: N, P; epiphytic herb, climber; *Holm-Nielsen & Jeppesen 517* (AAU);
  Renner 69085 (AAU, QCA, US). Reaches 900 m alt.
Blakea glandulosa **Gleason**
  Prov.: N, P; tree or epiphytic shrub; *Holm-Nielsen 19327* (AAU). Reaches 1000 m
  alt. in Pastaza: *Lugo 77* (AAU, GB)
Blakea hirsuta **Triana**
  Prov.: P; tree; *Lugo 3989* (AAU, GB); *Lugo 4260* (GB, QCA)
Blakea hispida **Markgraf**
  Prov.: P; epiphytic herb; *Lugo 5711* (GB). Reaches 1100 m alt. in Pastaza: *Lugo*
  4878 (AAU, GB)
Blakea portentosa **Wurdack**
  Prov.: N; *Palacios et al. 840* (AAU, MO, QAME n.v.)
Blakea rosea **(Ruíz & Pavón) D. Don**
  Prov.: N, P; epiphytic herb; *Renner 69317* (AAU, QCA); *Vickers 255* (F)
Blakea sawadae **J. F. Macbr.**
  Prov.: N; liana; *Korning & Thomsen 47099* (AAU, QCA); *Øllgaard et al. 57084*
  (AAU, QCA)
Blakea subvaginata **Wurdack**
  Prov.: N, P; tree; *Holm-Nielsen et al. 26536* (AAU). Reaches 1000 m alt.

Melastomataceae   (cont.)

***Clidemia allardii* Wurdack**
> Prov.: N, P, M-S; shrub; *Renner 69055* (AAU, QCA, US).   Reaches 700 m alt.

***Clidemia bullosa* DC.**
> Prov.: N; shrub; *Brandbyge et al. 33560* (AAU, QCA)

***Clidemia capitellata* (Bonpl.) D. Don**
> Prov.: N; shrub; *Holm-Nielsen et al. 21734* (AAU); *Oldeman & Arévalo 84* (QCA)

***Clidemia dentata* D. Don**
> Prov.: N, P, M-S; shrub; *Holm-Nielsen et al. 19861* (AAU).   Reaches 1100 m alt.

***Clidemia dimorphica* J. F. Macbr.**
> Prov.: N, P, M-S; shrub; *Renner 69071* (AAU, QCA, US).   Reaches 1100 m alt.

***Clidemia epiphytica* (Triana) Cogn.**
> Prov.: N, P; vine; *Renner 69056* (AAU, QCA, US)

***Clidemia graciliflora* Huber**
> Prov.: P; shrub; *Øllgaard et al. 34709* (AAU)

***Clidemia heterophylla* (Desr.) Gleason**
> Prov.: N, P; shrub; *Lawesson et al. 39436* (AAU)

***Clidemia hirta* (L.) D. Don**
> Prov.: N, P; shrub; *Holm-Nielsen 19251* (AAU).   Reaches 600 m alt.

***Clidemia inobsepta* Wurdack**
> Prov.: N; shrub; *Harling et al. 7088* (GB)

***Clidemia japurensis* DC. var. *heterobasis* (DC.) Wurdack**
> Prov.: N, P; shrub; *Øllgaard et al. 35031* (AAU)

***Clidemia juruensis* (Pilger) Gleason**
> Prov.: P; shrub; *Øllgaard et al. 34707* (AAU)

***Clidemia octona* (Bonpl.) L. Williams**
> Prov.: N, P; shrub; *Holm-Nielsen & Jeppesen 1016* (AAU).   Reaches 700 m alt.

***Clidemia pilosa* D. Don**
> Prov.: P, M-S; shrub; *Lugo 4474* (AAU).   Reaches 1100 m alt.

***Clidemia procumbens* Gleason**
> Prov.: N; shrub; *Lugo 3245, 7764* (GB)

***Clidemia semijuga* (Gleason) Wurdack**
> Prov.: N, P; shrub; *Lugo 2147* (AAU, GB); *Jaramillo et al. 31715* (AAU)

***Clidemia septuplinervia* Cogn.**
> Prov.: N, P; shrub; *Holm-Nielsen et al.* 21060 (AAU); *Irvine 450* (F, QCA)

***Clidemia serpens* (Triana) Cogn.**
> Prov.: N, P, M-S; vine; *Holm-Nielsen & Jeppesen 951* (AAU); *Brandbyge & Azanza 31974* (AAU, QCA)

***Clidemia sessiliflora* (Naudin) Cogn.**
> Prov.: P, M-S; *Øllgaard & Balslev 9045* (AAU, QCA).   Reaches higher altitudes

***Clidemia sprucei* Gleason**
> Prov.: N, P, M-S; shrub; *Holm-Nielsen 19301* (AAU); *Renner 69330* (AAU, QCA)

***Clidemia variifolia* Wurdack**
> Prov.: N; shrub; *Holm-Nielsen et al. 21043* (AAU); *Lawesson et al. 39326* (AAU)

***Conostegia superba* D. Don ex Naudin**
> Prov.: N, P, M-S; tree; *Lugo 221* (QCA), *2012* (AAU).   Reaches 1100 m alt. in Pastaza: *Asplund 19128* (S). Syn. *C. poeppigii* Cogn.

***Graffenrieda colombiana* Gleason**
> Prov.: N, P; tree; *Holm-Nielsen & Jeppesen 657* (AAU).   Reaches 600 m alt.

***Graffenrieda galeottii* (Naudin) L. Williams**
> Prov.: N; tree; *Palacios 418* (QAME n.v.)

Melastomataceae   (cont.)

Graffenrieda gracilis (Triana) L. Williams
Prov.: N, P, M-S; tree; *Øllgaard et al. 35090* (AAU).   Reaches 1100 m alt. in
Pastaza: *Asplund 18361* (S)
Henriettea stellaris Berg ex Triana
Prov.: N; tree; *Jaramillo & Coello 2930* (AAU, QCA)
Henriettella fissanthera Gleason
Prov.: N; shrub; *Renner 69093* (AAU, QCA, US)
Henriettella lawrancei Gleason
Prov.: N, P; tree; *Brandbyge et al. 30290* (AAU); *Renner 69069* (AAU, QCA, US)
Henriettella loretensis Gleason
Prov.: N; tree; *Brandbyge et al. 33935* (AAU)
Henriettella odorata Markgraf
Prov.: N; tree; *Lugo 452* (GB, US)
Henriettella sylvestris Gleason
Prov.: N; tree; *Gentry et al. 22074* (AAU, QCA)
Henriettella verrucosa Berg ex Triana
Prov.: N, P; shrub, tree; *Lawesson et al. 39375* (AAU, QCA).   Reaches 1000 m
alt. in Pastaza: *Lugo 20* (AAU, GB)
Leandra aristigera (Naudin) Cogn.
Prov.: N, P; shrub; *Brandbyge et al. 33763* (AAU); *Foster 3664* (AAU, QCA)
Leandra candelabrum (J. F. Macbr.) Wurdack
Prov.: N, P; shrub, tree; *Holm-Nielsen et al. 21252* (AAU)
Leandra caquetana Sprague
Prov.: N, P, M-S; shrub; *Renner 69333* (AAU, QCA)
Leandra caquetensis Gleason
Prov.: P, M-S; shrub; *Holm-Nielsen et al. 20401* (AAU).   Reaches 700 m alt.
Leandra chaetodon (DC.) Cogn.
Prov.: N, P, M-S; shrub; *Renner 69063* (AAU, QCA, US)
Leandra longicoma Cogn.
Prov.: N, P, M-S; shrub; *Renner 69311* (AAU, QCA).   Reaches 900 m alt.
Leandra macdanielii Wurdack
Prov.: P; shrub; *Brandbyge & Azanza 31229* (AAU)
Leandra retropila Cogn.
Prov.: N, M-S; shrub; *Holm-Nielsen & Jeppesen 725* (AAU).   Reaches 900 m alt.
Leandra secunda (D. Don) Cogn.
Prov.: N, P, M-S; shrub; *Renner 69077* (AAU, QCA, US).   Reaches 1000 m alt.
Leandra secundiflora (DC.) Cogn.
Prov.: N, P; shrub; *Lawesson 43438* (AAU, QCA)
Leandra solenifera Cogn.
Prov.: N, P, M-S; shrub; *Holm-Nielsen & Jeppesen 1020* (AAU).   Up to 700 m alt.
Loreya spruceana Benth. ex Triana
Prov.: N; tree; *Holm-Nielsen et al. 21748* (AAU); *Davis & Yost 937* (QCA)
Syn. *L. collatata* Wurdack.
Loreya subandina Wurdack
Prov.: N, P; tree; *Øllgaard et al. 34595* (AAU, QCA)
Loreya umbellata (Gleason) Wurdack
Expected from Napo.
Maieta guianensis Aublet
Prov.: N, P; shrub; *Lawesson et al. 43514* (AAU)
Maieta poeppigii C. Martius ex Cogn.
Prov.: N, P; shrub; *Balslev et al. 60549* (AAU, QCA)

Melastomataceae (cont.)

Miconia abbreviata Markgraf
Prov.: N; shrub; *Renner 69070* (AAU, QCA, US)
Miconia affinis DC.
Prov.: N; tree; *Øllgaard et al. 38889* (AAU); *SEF 8711* (AAU, QCA)
Miconia amazonica Triana
Prov.: N; tree; *Renner 69318* (AAU, QCA, US)
Miconia ampla Triana
Prov.: N, P; tree; *Lawesson et al. 44406* (AAU, QCA)
Miconia appendiculata Triana
Prov.: N; tree; *Holm-Nielsen et al. 21449* (AAU); *Jaramillo & Coello 2945* (AAU, QCA)
Miconia astroplocama Donn. Smith
Prov.: N, M-S; tree; *Brandbyge & Azanza 31987* (AAU, QCA)
Miconia aulocalyx C. Martius ex Triana
Prov.: N; shrub; *Harling et al. 7419* (GB); *Jaramillo & Coello 4232* (AAU, QCA)
Miconia aurea (D. Don) Naudin
Prov.: N, M-S; shrub or tree; *Camp E-1133* (S, US); *Neill et al. 6481* (AAU)
Miconia aureoides Cogn.
Prov.: N, P, M-S; shrub; *Renner 69314* (AAU, QCA); *Foster 3568* (AAU)
Miconia barbeyana Cogn.
Prov.: N, M-S; shrub; *Holm-Nielsen et al. 20534* (AAU)
Miconia barbinervis (Benth.) Triana
Prov.: N, P; shrub; *Holm-Nielsen et al. 21612* (AAU). Reaches 3900 m alt.
Miconia benthamiana Triana
Prov.: N, P; shrub; *Øllgaard et al. 34744* (AAU, QCA). Reaches 900 m alt.
Miconia brachybotrya Triana
Prov.: N; tree; *Renner 69327* (AAU, QCA, US)
Miconia bubalina (D. Don) Naudin
Prov.: N, P, M-S; tree; *Holm-Nielsen et al. 22678* (AAU); *Foster 3760* (AAU, F)
Miconia calvescens DC.
Prov.: N, P; tree; *Holm-Nielsen 19343* (AAU). Reaches 1000 m alt.
Miconia cannabina Markgraf
Prov.: N; tree; *Brandbyge et al. 30523* (AAU)
Miconia carassana Cogn.
Prov.: P; tree; *Brandbyge & Azanza 31094* (AAU, QCA)
Miconia cazaletii Wurdack
Prov.: N, M-S; shrub; *Brandbyge et al. 33379* (AAU)
Miconia centrodesma Naudin
Prov.: N, P, M-S; shrub, tree; *Renner 69080* (AAU, QCA, US)
Miconia cercophora Wurdack
Prov.: P, M-S; tree; *Brandbyge & Azanza 32078* (AAU); *Gentry 9737* (US) Reaches 800 m alt.: *Holm-Nielsen & Jeppesen 499* (AAU)
Miconia chrysophylla (L. C. Rich.) Urban
Prov.: P; tree; *Øllgaard et al. 35363* (AAU)
Miconia conformis Wurdack
Prov.: P; shrub; *Jaramillo & Coello 3527* (AAU)
Miconia decurrens Cogn.
Prov.: N, M-S; tree; *Korning & Thomsen 47785* (AAU)
Miconia dodecandra (Desr.) Cogn.
Prov.: N, P; *Zaruma et al. 792* (QAME n.v.). Reaches 1000 m alt. in P: *Lugo 1799* (AAU); *Neill et al. 6008* (AAU)

Melastomataceae   (cont.)

Miconia dolichorrhyncha Naudin
Prov.: N; tree; *Holm-Nielsen et al. 21202* (AAU)
Miconia elata (Sw.) DC.
Prov.: N; tree; *SEF 8521* (AAU, QCA); *Neill 7133* (AAU, QAME n.v.)
Miconia erioclada Triana
Prov.: N, P, M-S; shrub; *Renner 69320*(AAU, QCA, US).   Reaches 750 m alt. in
M-S: *Harling & Andersson 12925* (AAU, GB)
Miconia filamentosa Gleason
Prov.: N; shrub; *Lawesson et al. 43343* (AAU, QCA)
Miconia fosteri Wurdack
Prov.: N; shrub; *Renner 69062B* (AAU, QCA, US)
Miconia goniostigma Triana
Prov.: P; shrub; *Lugo 4492* (AAU), *3620* (GB, US).   Reaches 1000 m alt.
Miconia grandifolia Ule
Prov.: N; tree; *Little 727* (US)
Miconia heterochaeta Wurdack
Prov.: P; tree; *Lugo 5508, 5636* (GB)
Miconia hookeriana Triana
Prov.: N, M-S; shrub; *Lugo 3373* (AAU, GB); *Jaramillo & Rivera 134* (AAU,
QCA).   Reaches 850 m alt. in M-S: *Holm-Nielsen et al. 20519* (AAU)
Miconia insularis Gleason
Prov.: N, P; tree; *Lugo 3883* (AAU, GB, QCA).   Reaches 1050 m alt.
Miconia lamprophylla Triana
Prov.: N; tree; *Renner 69321* (AAU, QCA, US)
Miconia longifolia (Aublet) DC.
Prov.: N, P; tree; *Brandbyge et al. 33635* (AAU, QCA)
Miconia lugonis Wurdack
Prov.: P; tree; *Lugo 2602* (QCA), *1729* (AAU); *Harling & Andersson 17632* (GB)
Miconia mazanana J. F. Macbr.
Prov.: N; tree; *Luteyn et al. 9107* (AAU, QCA); *Harling et al. 7494* (GB)
Miconia minutiflora (Bonpl.) DC.
Prov.: P; tree; *Øllgaard et al. 35494* (AAU)
Miconia napoana Wurdack
Prov.: N; tree; *Lugo 2529* (AAU, GB); *SEF 8926* (AAU, QCA)
Miconia nervosa (Smith) Triana
Prov.: N, P, M-S; shrub; *Holm-Nielsen et al. 19684* (AAU); *Irvine 237* (F, QCA);
Foster 3715 (AAU, F).   Reaches 1100 m alt.
Miconia nutans Donn. Smith
Prov.: N, P; shrub or tree; *Lugo 4620* (US), *1793* (AAU).   Reaches 1000 m alt.
Miconia oligantha Wurdack
Prov.: P; tree;   *Lugo 22* (AAU)
Miconia paleacea Cogn.
Prov.: N, P; shrub; *Holm-Nielsen & Jeppesen 970* (AAU); *Andrade 33044* (AAU,
QCA); *Foster 3826* (AAU, F)
Miconia phaeochaeta Wurdack
Prov.: N, M-S; tree; *Brandbyge & Azanza 30096* (AAU)
Miconia pilgeriana Ule
Prov.: N, P; shrub, tree; *Brandbyge et al. 33591* (AAU, QCA)
Miconia poeppigii Triana
Prov.: P; tree; *Lugo 5473, 5606* (GB)
Miconia porphyrotricha (Markgraf) Wurdack
Prov.: N, P; shrub; *Renner 69324* (AAU, QCA, US)

Melastomataceae   (cont.)

***Miconia prasina* (Sw.) DC.**
  Prov.: N; tree; *Korning & Thomsen 58660* (AAU); *Neill et al. 6244* (QAME)
***Miconia procumbens* (Gleason) Wurdack**
  Prov.: N, M-S; shrub; *Brandbyge et al. 33302* (AAU, QCA)
***Miconia pterocaulon* Triana**
  Prov.: N, P; shrub; *Jaramillo et al. 31302* (AAU); *Renner 69081* (AAU, QCA, US)
***Miconia punctata* (Desr.) D. Don**
  Prov.: N; tree; *Grubb et al. 1642* (NY, US); *SEF 9009* (AAU, QCA)
***Miconia quadripora* Wurdack**
  Prov.: P, M-S; shrub; *Lugo 5127* (AAU, GB).   Reaches 1100 m alt.
***Miconia radulaefolia* (Benth.) Naudin**
  Prov.: N; shrub; *Brandbyge et al. 36123* (AAU)
***Miconia rivalis* Wurdack**
  Prov.: N, P, M-S; shrub, tree; *Lugo 4946* (AAU, GB); *Renner 69325* (AAU, QCA, US).   Reaches 1000 m alt.
***Miconia schunkei* Wurdack**
  Prov.: N, P, M-S; shrub; *Renner 69061* (AAU, QCA, US).   Reaches 1000 m alt.
***Miconia sciurea* Uribe**
  Prov.: N, P; tree; *Holm-Nielsen et al. 21645* (AAU); *McElroy 382* (QCA)
***Miconia serrulata* (DC.) Naudin**
  Prov.: N, P, M-S; tree; *Renner 69316* (AAU, QCA)
***Miconia seticaulis* Wurdack**
  Prov.: P; shrub; *Harling & Andersson 17633* (AAU, GB)
***Miconia splendens* (Sw.) Griseb.**
  Prov.: N; tree; *Lawesson et al. 44301* (AAU, QCA); *Foster 3641* (AAU)
***Miconia subspicata* Wurdack**
  Prov.: N, P, M-S; shrub, tree; *Holm-Nielsen & Jeppesen 862* (AAU); *Madison et al. 5313* (QCA, SEL)
***Miconia tenensis* Markgraf**
  Prov.: N; shrub; *Lawesson et al. 39372* (AAU, QCA).   Reaches 900 m alt.
***Miconia ternatifolia* Triana**
  Prov.: N, M-S; tree; *Holm-Nielsen et al. 19122* (AAU, QCA).   Reaches 1080 m alt.
***Miconia tomentosa* (L. C. Rich.) D. Don ex DC.**
  Prov.: N, P; tree; *Renner 69310* (AAU, QCA, US); *Irvine 258* (F, QCA)
***Miconia triangularis* Gleason**
  Prov.: N, P, M-S; tree; *Asplund 9186* (S); *Lugo 4813* (AAU).   Reaches 1200 m in M-S: *Camp E-1223* (NY)
***Miconia trinervia* (Sw.) D. Don ex Loud.**
  Prov.: N, P; tree; *Brandbyge & Azanza 30053* (AAU, QCA); *Irvine 697* (F, QCA)
***Miconia triplinervis* Ruíz & Pavón**
  Prov.: N, P, M-S; tree; *Renner 69328* (AAU, QCA, US)
***Miconia venulosa* Wurdack**
  Prov.: N; tree; *Irvine 409* (F, QCA)
***Miconia zubenetana* J. F. Macbr.**
  Prov.: N, P; tree; *Lugo 22* (GB, US)
***Monolena primulaeflora* Hook. f.**
  Prov.: N, P, M-S; epiphytic herb; *Renner 69086* (AAU, QCA).   Reaches 1200 m
***Mouriri* cf. *floribunda* Markgraf**
  Prov.: N; tree; *SEF 8883* (AAU, QCA); *Jaramillo 9097* (QCA)
***Mouriri grandiflora* DC.**
  Prov.: N, P, M-S; tree; *Foster 3686* (QCA, S), *Holm-Nielsen et al. 21868* (AAU)

Melastomataceae (cont.)

***Mouriri myrtifolia* Spruce ex Triana**
Prov.: M-S; tree; *MacBryde 154* (QCA, US). Collected at 840 m alt.
***Mouriri myrtilloides* (Sw.) Poir.**
Prov.: P; tree; *Neill 6666* (QAME n.v.)
***Mouriri nigra* (DC.) Morley**
Prov.: M-S; tree; *Ortega 77* (US)
***Mouriri oligantha* Pilger**
Prov.: M-S; tree; *Ortega 187* (US)
***Myrmidone macrosperma* (C. Martius) C. Martius**
Prov.: N; shrub; *Korning & Thomsen 47109* (AAU, QCA, US)
***Ossaea boliviensis* (Cogn.) Gleason**
Prov.: N, P, M-S; shrub; *Brandbyge et al. 33697* (AAU, QCA); *Harling & Andersson 17455* (GB). Reaches 800 m alt.
***Ossaea bullifera* (Pilger) Gleason**
Prov.: N, P; shrub; *Øllgaard et al. 34510* (AAU, QCA); *Croat 58562* (AAU, MO)
***Ossaea capillaris* (Don) Cogn.**
Prov.: N, M-S; shrub; *Holm-Nielsen et al. 20544* (AAU). Reaches 850 m alt.
***Ossaea cucullata* Gleason**
Prov.: N, P; shrub; *Brandbyge & Azanza 31043* (AAU, QCA)
***Ossaea laxivenula* Wurdack**
Prov.: P; tree; *Holm-Nielsen et al. 22241* (AAU)
***Ossaea quadrisulca* (Naudin) Wurdack**
Prov.: P; shrub; *Øllgaard et al. 35249* (AAU)
***Ossaea quinquenervia* (Miller) Cogn.**
Prov.: N, P; shrub; *Øllgaard et al. 35173* (AAU)
***Ossaea robusta* (Triana) Cogn.**
Prov.: N, P; shrub; *Lawesson et al. 43407* (AAU, QCA); *Lugo 17* (AAU, GB)
***Salpinga secunda* DC.**
Prov.: N, P; shrub; *Renner 69082* (AAU, QCA, US)
***Tessmanianthus cenepensis* Wurdack**
Prov.: N; tree; *Palacios et al. 507* (QAME n.v., US)
***Tessmanianthus heterostemon* Markgraf**
Prov.: N, P; tree; *Løjtnant & Molau 13514* (AAU, GB); *SEF 9085* (AAU, QCA)
***Tibouchina longifolia* (Vahl) Baillon**
Prov.: N, P, M-S; herb; *Renner 69309* (AAU, QCA). Reaches 1000 m alt. in Pastaza: *Harling 3205* (S)
***Tococa capitata* Traill ex Cogn.**
Prov.: N; tree; *Lawesson et al. 43342* (AAU)
***Tococa caquetana* Sprague**
Prov.: N, P, M-S; shrub; *Renner 69062A* (AAU, QCA). Syn. *T. micrantha* Ule
***Tococa chuivensis* Wurdack**
Prov.: N, P, M-S; shrub; *Holm-Nielsen & Jeppesen 1019* (AAU); *Harling & Andersson 17489* (AAU, GB); *Foster 3577* (AAU). Reaches ca. 1000 m alt.
***Tococa coronata* Benth.**
Prov.: N; shrub; *Holm-Nielsen et al. 21303* (AAU, QCA); *Foster 3699* (QCA)
***Tococa discolor* Pilger**
Prov.: N, P; shrub; *Holm-Nielsen et al. 20081* (AAU); *Brandbyge & Azanza 31025* (AAU, QCA)
***Tococa guianensis* Aublet**
Prov.: N; shrub; *Jaramillo 6939* (AAU, GB); *Alarcón 27* (QCA)
***Tococa occidentalis* Naudin**
Prov.: P; shrub; *Øllgaard et al. 35248* (AAU). Reaches 1200 m alt.

Melastomataceae (cont.)

Tococa stenoptera Gleason
  Prov.: N; shrub; *Brandbyge et al. 36067* (AAU)
Tococa symphyandra (Triana) Cogn.
  Prov.: N, P; *Neill 7624* (QAME n.v.); *Øllgaard & Balslev 9055* (AAU, QCA)
Topobea asplundii Wurdack
  Prov.: N, P; epiphytic herb; *Neill et al. 6489* (AAU)
Topobea cutucuensis Wurdack
  Prov.: M-S; epiphytic herb; *Cerón 439* (QAME n.v.)
Triolena amazonica (Pilger) Wurdack
  Prov.: N, P; herb; *Lawesson et al. 39513* (AAU)
Triolena pileoides (Triana) Wurdack
  Prov.: N; subshrub; *Holm-Nielsen & Jeppesen 775* (AAU)
Triolena pluvialis (Wurdack) Wurdack
  Prov.: N, P; shrub; *Holm-Nielsen et al 19659* (AAU); *Alarcón 19508* (QCA);
  Vickers 219 (F). Reaches 750 m alt. Close to *T. hirsuta* (Benth.) Triana

Meliaceae
T. D. Pennington, Fl. Neotropica 28. 1981. This listing checked by T. D.
Pennington, Apr 1989.

Cabralea canjerana (Vell.) C. Martius
  Prov.: N; tree; *Korning & Thomsen 58710* (AAU); *Chaguaro 117* (QCA)
Cedrela fissilis Vell.
  Prov.: N; tree; *Neill et al. 6237* (AAU); *Oldeman & Arévalo 6896* (QCA)
Cedrela odorata L.
  Prov.: N, M-S; tree; *Neill et al. 6230* (AAU, QCA). Reaches 700 m alt. in M-S:
  Pennington & Tenorio 10765 (QCA)
Guarea carinata Ducke
  Prov.: N; tree; *Flores 148* (QCA); *Chaguaro 120* (QCA)
Guarea cinnamomea Harms
  Prov.: P; tree; *Brandbyge & Azanza 31023* (AAU, QCA)
Guarea cristata Pennington
  Prov.: P; tree; *Jaramillo et al. 31374* (AAU)
Guarea glabra Vahl
  Prov.: N, tree; *Oldeman 43* (P)
Guarea gomma Pulle
  Prov.: P; tree; *Jaramillo et al. 30770* (AAU)
Guarea grandifolia A. DC.
  Prov.: N, P; tree; *Holm-Nielsen 30147* (AAU); *Irvine 567* (QCA)
Guarea guentheri Harms
  Prov.: N, tree; *Palacios 957* (QAME n.v.); *Irvine 908* (F, QCA)
Guarea guidonia (L.) Sleumer
  Prov.: N; tree; *Holm-Nielsen et al. 20233* (AAU, QCA); *Irvine 142* (QCA)
Guarea humaitensis Pennington
  Prov.: N; tree; *Neill 901* (QAME n.v.)
Guarea kunthiana A. Juss.
  Prov.: N, P; shrub; *Holm-Nielsen et al. 22600* (AAU); *Irvine 740* (F, QCA)
Guarea macrophylla Vahl spp. pendulispica (C. DC.) Pennington
  Prov.: N, P; tree; *Holm-Nielsen et al. 22594* (AAU); *Vickers 83* (F); *Balslev &
  Irvine 4627* (QCA). Reaches 800 m alt. in M-S: *Sparre 19229* (GB, S)

Meliaceae   (cont.)

***Guarea pterorhachis* Harms**
 Prov.: P; tree; *Holm-Nielsen et al. 22538* (AAU)
***Guarea pubescens* (L. C. Rich.) A. Juss.**
 Prov.: N; tree; *Lawesson et al. 39594* (AAU, QCA)
***Guarea purusana* C. DC.**
 Prov.: N; tree; *SEF 8848* (AAU, QCA)
***Guarea silvatica* C. DC.**
 Prov.: N, P; M-S; tree; *Lawesson et al. 44447* (AAU, QCA)
***Guarea* sp. 1**
 Prov.: N; tree; *SEF 8728* (AAU); *Korning & Thomsen 47432* (AAU)
***Guarea* sp. 2**
 Prov.: N; tree; *Barfod & Azanza 31487* (AAU)
***Guarea* sp. 3**
 Prov.: N; tree; *Øllgaard et al. 35336* (AAU)
***Guarea* sp. 4**
 Prov.: N; tree; *SEF 8669, 9094* (AAU)
***Melia azedarach* L.**
 Prov.: N; tree; *Alarcón 19366* (QCA)
***Ruagea insignis* (C. DC.) Pennington**
 Prov.: N; tree; *Neill et al. 8452* (QAME n.v.); *Little 757* (US)
***Swietenia macrophylla* G. King**
 Prov.: N; tree; *Neill et al. 6894* (QCA)
***Trichilia elegans* A. Juss.**
 Prov.: N; tree; *Pennington 10603* (QCA)
***Trichilia euneura* C. DC.**
 Prov.: N; treelet; *Christensen 82953* (AAU)
***Trichilia inaequelatera* Pennington**
 Prov.: N; tree; *Lawesson et al. 44292* (AAU, QCA)
***Trichilia laxipaniculata* Cuatrec.**
 Prov.: N; tree; *Pennington 10626* (MO); *SEF 10325* (AAU, QCA)
***Trichilia maynasiana* C. DC.**
 Prov.: N, P; tree; *Lawesson et al. 43461* (AAU, QCA); *Neill et al. 6906* (QCA);
 Gentry 9770 (AAU, QCA, S).   Reaches 750 m alt. in Napo: *Asplund 9283* (S)
***Trichilia micrantha* Benth.**
 Prov.: N; tree; *SEF 9253* (AAU, QCA)
***Trichilia pallida* Sw.**
 Prov.: N, P, M-S; tree; *Brandbyge & Azanza 31787* (AAU, QCA)
***Trichilia pleeana* (A. Juss.) C. DC.**
 Prov.: N, M-S; tree; *Zaruma et al. 101* (AAU); *Irvine 135* (QCA).   Reaches 1000
 m alt. in M-S: *Pennington & Tenorio 10770* (QCA)
***Trichilia poeppigii* C. DC.**
 Prov.: N, P; tree; *Brandbyge et al. 30304* (AAU)
***Trichilia quadrijuga* Kunth**
 Prov.: N, P; tree; *Øllgaard et al. 34816* (AAU); *Pennington 10616* (QCA)
***Trichilia rubra* C. DC.**
 Prov.: N, M-S; tree; *Korning & Thomsen 47421* (AAU).   Reaches 800 m alt. in
 M-S: *Pennington & Tenorio 10776* (QCA)
***Trichilia septentrionalis* C. DC.**
 Prov.: N, M-S; tree; *Brandbyge & Azanza 31962* (AAU, QCA)
***Trichilia solitudinis* Harms**
 Prov.: N; tree; *Øllgaard et al. 57146* (AAU)

Meliaceae   (cont.)

Trichilia sp.
Prov.: N; tree; *SEF 9027* (AAU).   Possibly *T. stipitata* Pennington

Menispermaceae
J. F. Macbride, Fl. Peru 2(3), Publ. Field Mus. Nat. Hist., Bot. Ser. 13: 680–699. 1938.   Identifications by R. Barneby, NY.

Abuta grandifolia (C. Martius) Sandw.
Prov.: N, P; tree; *Brandbyge & Azanza 30801* (AAU); *Vickers 221* (QCA)
Abuta rufescens Aublet
Prov.: N; liana; *Øllgaard et al. 39077* (AAU); *Pinkley 286* (S)
Abuta solimoensis Krukoff & Barneby
Prov.: N; liana; *Neill et al. 8230* (AAU)
Anomospermum chloranthum Diels
ssp. *confusum* Krukoff & Barneby
Prov.: N; liana; *Brandbyge et al. 32491* (AAU, QCA); *Davis & Yost 943* (QCA)
Chondrodendron tecunarum Barneby & Krukoff
Prov.: N; vine; *Pinkley 285* (S)
Chondrodendron tomentosum Ruíz & Pavón
Prov.: N; vine; *Brandbyge & Azanza 32907* (AAU); *Gentry 9772* (QCA)
Cionomene javariensis Krukoff
Prov.: N; liana; *Neill 6543* (AAU)
Cissampelos grandifolia Triana & Planchon
Prov.: N; vine; *Holm-Nielsen et al. 19124* (AAU)
Cissampelos laxiflora Moldenke
Prov.: N, P; vine; *Brandbyge et al. 33232* (AAU, QCA)
Cissampelos pareira L.
Prov.: N; vine; *Holm-Nielsen et al. 19159* (AAU)
Cissampelos tropaeolifolia DC.
Prov.: N; vine; *Dwyer & Simmons 9764* (AAU)
Curarea toxicofera (Wedd.) Barneby & Krukoff
Prov.: N; vine; *Korning & Thomsen 47208* (AAU).   Syn. *Chondrodendron toxicoferum* (Wedd.) Krukoff & Moldenke
Disciphania dioscoreoides Barneby
Prov.: N; liana; *Neill 6373* (MO, NY); *Cerón 1079* (NY)
Disciphania ernestii Eichler
Prov.: N; vine; *Zarucchi 2376* (QCA)
Disciphania killipii Diels
Prov.: N, P; vine; *Balslev et al. 84517* (AAU, QCA)
Disciphania remota Diels
Prov.: M-S; vine; *Brandbyge & Azanza 32320* (AAU)
Disciphania sarcostephana Barneby
Prov.: N; vine; *Neill et al. 6271* (AAU, QCA)
Disciphania tricaudata Barneby
Prov.: N; vine; *Neill & Palacios 2269* (F, K, MO, NY, US)
Odontocarya tripetala Diels
Prov.: N; liana; *Palacios et al. 463* (AAU); *Holm-Nielsen et al. 21212* (AAU)
Odontocarya ulei Diels
Prov.: N, P; vine; *Brandbyge et al. 33592* (AAU, QCA)

Menispermaceae   (cont.)

Orthomene schomburgkii (Miers) Barneby & Krukoff
Prov.: N; vine; *Foster 3864* (QCA, S); *Brandbyge & Azanza 30409* (AAU)
Sciadotenia ramiflora Eichler
Prov.: N; vine; *Dwyer & MacBryde 9671* (QCA)

Monimiaceae
J. F. Macbride, Fl. Peru 2(3), Publ. Field Mus. Nat. Hist., Bot. Ser. 13: 784–819. 1938. S. Renner is treating the family for *Fl. Ecuador*.

Mollinedia caudata J. F. Macbr.
Prov.: N, P, M-S; shrub; *Holm-Nielsen et al. 22446* (AAU)
Mollinedia latifolia (Poeppig) Tul.
Prov.: N, P, M-S; treelet; *Holm-Nielsen et al. 4162* (AAU, S); *Palacios & Neill 1200* (AAU, MO); *Feil 91307* (AAU, QCA). Reaches slightly higher altitudes.
Siparuna bifida (Poeppig & Endl.) A. DC.
Prov.: N, P; shrub, treelet; *Brandbyge & Azanza 30018* (AAU)
Siparuna chiridota (Tul.) A. DC.
Prov.: N, P; shrub, treelet; *Balslev 2832* (AAU, QCA). Reaches 1000 m alt.
Siparuna cristata (Poeppig & Endl.) A. DC.
Prov.: N, P, M-S; shrub; *Holm-Nielsen et al. 19681* (AAU). Reaches 1200 m alt.
Siparuna decipiens (Tul.) A. DC.
Prov.: N, P, M-S; shrub, treelet; *Balslev & Santos Dea 2860* (AAU, QCA)
Siparuna macrophylla (Kunth in Humb. & Bonpl.) A. DC.
Prov.: N, P, M-S; shrub, treelet; *Jaramillo 7678* (AAU, NY, QCA). Reaches 2000 m alt.
Siparuna macrotepala Perkins
Prov.: N, P, M-S; treelet; *Brandbyge et al. 30245* (AAU)
Siparuna magnifica Perkins
Prov.: N, P, M-S; shrub, treelet; *Harling 7823* (AAU, GB). Reaches 1100 m alt.
Siparuna pauciflora (Beurl.) A. DC.
Prov.: N, P, M-S; shrub, treelet; *Jaramillo & Coello 3425* (AAU, MO, QCA)
Siparuna sp. 1
Prov.: N; shrub, treelet; *Cerón 5491* (AAU, QAME n.v.); *Feil 91312* (AAU, QCA)
Siparuna sp. 2
Prov.: P; shrub; *Holm-Nielsen et al. 22095, 22103, 22111* (AAU).   (=*S. hispida* A. DC.?)
Siparuna sp. 3
Prov.: N; shrub, tree; *Jaramillo & Coello 2954* (AAU, QCA)
Siparuna sp. 4
Prov.: N, P, M-S; treelet; *Brandbyge & Azanza 31913* (AAU)

Moraceae
C. C. Berg, Fl. Neotropica 7. 1972. This listing checked by C. C. Berg, Nov 1990.

Artocarpus altilis (S. Parkinson) Fosberg
Prov.: N; tree; *Andrade 33133* (AAU); *Irvine 717* (F, QCA).   Cultivated.
Batocarpus amazonicus (Ducke) Fosberg
Prov.: N; tree; *Irvine 645* (F, QCA); *Zaruma 379* (MO, QAME n.v.)

Moraceae (cont.)

Batocarpus costaricensis Standley & L. O. Williams
Prov.: N; tree; *SEF 8864* (AAU, QCA); *Palacios et al. 4680* (QAME n.v.)
Batocarpus orinocensis Karsten
Prov.: N; tree; *Korning & Thomsen 58689* (AAU); *Irvine 581* (F, QCA)
Brosimum alicastrum Sw. ssp. bolivarense (Pittier) C. C. Berg
Prov.: Zamora-Chinchipe; tree; *Montesdeoca 18-1* (QAME n.v.)
Brosimum guianense (Aublet) Huber
Prov.: N; tree; *Korning & Thomsen 47457* (AAU)
Brosimum lactescens (S. Moore) C. C. Berg
Prov.: N; tree; *Korning & Thomsen 58720* (AAU)
Brosimum potabile Ducke
Prov.: N; tree; *SEF 8704* (AAU)
Brosimum rubescens Taubert
Prov.: N; tree; *Palacios et al. 12441* (BG, QCA)
Brosimum utile (H.B.K.) Pittier ssp. ovatifolium (Ducke) C. C. Berg
Prov.: N; tree; *Lawesson et al. 39562* (AAU, QCA)
Brosimum utile (H.B.K.) Pittier ssp. longifolium (Ducke) C. C. Berg
Prov.: N; tree; *Neill et al. 7924* (QAME n.v.)
Castilla ulei Warb.
Prov.: N; tree; *SEF 9301* (AAU, QCA); *Valencia 355* (QCA)
Clarisia biflora Ruíz & Pavón
Prov.: N, M-S; tree; *SEF 10146* (AAU, QCA); *Neill et al. 6503* (AAU). Reaches
700 m alt. in M-S: *Zaruma 361* (AAU)
Clarisia racemosa Ruíz & Pavón
Prov.: N, P; tree; *Berg & Akkermans 1068* (AAU)); *Pennington 10589* (QCA)
Dorstenia umbricola A. C. Smith vel sp. aff.
Prov.: N; herb; *Korning & Thomsen 47180* (AAU)
Ficus albert-smithii Standley
Prov.: N; tree; *Balslev et al. 97090* (AAU, QCA)
Ficus americana Aublet
Prov.: N, P; tree; *Øllgaard et al. 35080* (AAU)
Ficus aripuanensis C. C. Berg
Prov.: N; tree; *Cerón 5516* (QAME n.v.)
Ficus caballina Standley
Prov. N; tree; *Balslev et al. 97122* (AAU, QCA)
Ficus caldasiana Dugand
Prov.: N; tree; *SEF 10097* (AAU, QCA)
Ficus casapiensis (Miq.) Miq.
Prov.: N; tree; *Balslev & Alarcón 2975* (AAU)
Ficus cervantesiana Standley & L. O.Williams
Prov.: N; tree; *Palacios 2964* (QAME n.v.)
Ficus cuatrecasana Dugand
Prov.: N; tree; *SEF 10182, 10202* (AAU, QCA); *Irvine 868* (F, QCA)
Ficus donnell-smithii Standley
Prov.: N; tree; *Palacios 2963* (QAME n.v.)
Ficus eximia Schott
Prov. N, M-S; tree; *Zaruma et al. 84, 281* (QCA)
Ficus gomelleira Kunth & Bouché
Prov.: N; tree; *Berg & Akkermans 1064* (AAU); *SEF 10124* (AAU, QCA)

Moraceae (cont.)

Ficus guianensis Desv.
Prov.: N; tree; *Berg & Akkermans 1007* (AAU); *Jaramillo 2950* (QCA); *Alarcón 85* (QCA). Including *Ficus clusiifolia* Schott ex Sprengel
Ficus insipida Willd.
Prov.: N, P, M-S; tree; *Holm-Nielsen et al. 20206* (AAU, QCA); *Irvine 652* (F, QCA); *Alarcón 75/23* (QCA); *Little et al. 755* (US). Syn. *F. glabrata* H.B.K.
Ficus jacobii Vázq.
Prov.: M-S; tree; *Little et al. 390* (US)
Ficus killipii Standley
Prov.: N; tree; *Pennington 10619* (K)
Ficus krukovii Standley
Prov. N, tree; *Gentry 12516* (AAU); *Palacios 2382* (QAME n.v.)
Ficus macbridei Standley
Prov.: N; tree; *Neill et al. 7243* (QAME n.v.)
Ficus mathewsii (Miq.) Miq.
Prov.: N; tree; *Little 392* (US). This is *Ficus guianensis* s. lat., including *Ficus erratica* Standley
Ficus maxima P. Miller
Prov.: N; tree; *Oldeman & Arévalo 17* (QCA); *Davis & Yost 1040* (AAU, QCA)
Ficus nymphiifolia P. Miller
Prov.: N; tree; *SEF 9272* (AAU, QCA); *Palacios 1346* (QCA)
Ficus obtusifolia H.B.K.
Prov.: N; tree; *Balslev et al. 97119* (AAU, QCA); *Palacios 2785* (QAME n.v.)
Ficus cf. padifolia Kunth
Prov.: M-S; tree; *Palacios 1482* (QAME n.v.)
Ficus paraensis (Miq.) Miq.
Prov.: N; tree; *Neill et al. 6504* (AAU); M-S; *Little et al. 653* (US)
Ficus pertusa L.f.
Prov.: N, P; tree; *Palacios & Neill 947* (AAU). Reaches 1300 m alt.
Ficus schippii Standley
Prov.: N; tree; *Lawesson et al. 43467* (AAU, QCA). Reaches 1600 m alt.
Ficus schultesii Dugand
Prov.: N; tree; *SEF 10416* (AAU, QCA)
Ficus sphenophylla Standley
Prov.: N; tree; *Balslev et al. 97003* (AAU, QCA)
Ficus trigona L. f.
Prov.: N; tree; *Brandbyge et al. 30491* (AAU); *Foster 3867* (QCA)
Ficus trigonata L.
Prov.: N; tree; *Neill et al. 7456* (QAME n.v.)
Ficus yoponensis Desv.
Prov.: N; tree; *Vickers 90* (F); *Palacios 1897* (QAME n.v.)
Helicostylis elegans (J. F. Macbr.) C. C. Berg
Prov.: N; tree; *Balslev et al. 97056* (AAU, QCA)
Helicostylis scabra (J. F. Macbr.) C. C. Berg
Prov.: M-S; tree; *Ortega 164* (AAU, QCA)
Helicostylis tomentosa (Poeppig & Endl.) J. F. Macbr.
Prov.: P; tree; *Brandbyge & Azanza 31044* (AAU, QCA)
Helicostylis turbinata C. C. Berg
Prov.: N; tree; *SEF AC2* (AAU, QCA)
Maclura tinctoria (L.) Steudel
Prov.: N, P, M-S; tree; *Irvine 610* (F, QCA); *Pennington & Tenorio 10786* (QCA); *Villegas & Meneses 13* (QCA). Syn. *Chlorophora tinctoria* (L.) Gaud.

Moraceae   (cont.)

Maquira calophylla **(Poeppig & Endl.) C. C. Berg**
Prov.: N; tree; *SEF 8775* (AAU, QCA); *Irvine 662* (F, QCA)
Maquira coriacea **(Karsten) C. C. Berg**
Prov.: N; tree; *Bloch et al. 68725* (AAU)
Maquira guianensis **Aublet s. lat.**
Prov.: N, P; tree; *Bloch et al. 68242* (AAU); *Palacios et al. 3383* (QAME n.v.)
Naucleopsis amara **Ducke**
Prov.: N; tree; *Holm-Nielsen 20266* (AAU)
Naucleopsis concinna **(Standley) C. C. Berg**
Prov.: M-S; tree; *Little et al. 522* (US)
Naucleopsis glabra **Spruce ex Pittier**
Prov.: N, P; tree; *Valencia et al. 359* (QCA); *Neill & Palacios 6829* (QCA)
Naucleopsis imitans **(Ducke) C. C. Berg**
Prov.: N; tree; *Lawesson et al. 39119* (AAU)
Naucleopsis krukovii **(Standley) C. C. Berg**
Prov.: N; tree; *Berg & Akkermans 1110* (AAU)
Naucleopsis mello-barretoi **(Standley) C. C. Berg**
Prov.: N; tree; *Bloch et al. 67928* (AAU, QCA)
Naucleopsis ulei **(Warb.) Ducke**
Prov.: N; tree; *SEF 8568* (AAU, QCA); *Foster 3714* (QCA, S)
Perebea angustifolia **(Poeppig & Endl.) C. C. Berg**
Prov.: N; tree; *Korning & Thomsen 47752* (AAU)
Perebea guianensis **Aublet**
Prov.: N, P, M-S; tree; *Brandbyge & Azanza 30052* (AAU); *Berg & Akkermans 1088* (AAU, S); *Lawesson et al. 39142* (AAU); *Davis & Yost 1009* (QCA)
Perebea humilis **C. C. Berg**
Prov.: N, P; tree; *Dwyer et al. 9757* (BG, QCA); *Jaramillo et al. 4255* (QCA)
Perebea mollis **(Poeppig & Endl.) Huber**
Prov.: N; tree; *Brandbyge et al. 30302* (AAU)
Perebea tessmannii **Mildbr.**
Prov.: M-S; tree; *Cerón 253* (QAME n.v.).   Reaches 1000 m alt. in M-S: *Little et al. 340* (US)
Perebea xanthochyma **Karsten**
Prov.: N; tree; *Brandbyge et al. 30496* (AAU); *Irvine 232* (F, QCA)
Poulsenia armata **(Miq.) Standley**
Prov.: N; tree; *SEF 9068* (AAU); *Pinkley 237* (S); *Irvine 958* (F, QCA)
Pseudolmedia laevigata **Trécul**
Prov.: N, M-S; tree; *Korning & Thomsen 47510* (AAU); *Foster 3696* (QCA, S)
Pseudolmedia laevis **(Ruiz & Pavón) J. F. Macbr.**
Prov.: N, M-S; tree; *Brandbyge et al. 30299* (AAU); *Vickers 231* (F)
Pseudolmedia macrophylla **Trécul**
Prov. N; tree; *Cerón 3459* (QAME n.v.)
Pseudolmedia rigida **(Klotzsch & Karsten) Cuatrec.**
Prov. N; tree; *Palacios 3568* (QAME n.v.)
Sorocea guilleminiana **Gaudich.**
Prov. N; tree; *Valencia et al. 361* (QCA); *Christensen 72530* (AAU)
Sorocea hirtella **Mildbr.**
Prov.: N, P; tree; *Brandbyge & Azanza 31238* (AAU); *Stein et al. 2575* (QCA)
Sorocea muriculata **Miq. ssp. *muriculata***
Prov.: N, P; tree; *Brandbyge & Azanza 30815* (AAU); *Irvine 818* (F, QCA)
Sorocea steinbachii **C. C. Berg**
Prov.: N, P; tree; *Brandbyge & Azanza 31631* (AAU)

Moraceae (cont.)

***Trophis caucana* (Pittier) C. C. Berg**
> Prov.: N, P, M-S; tree; *Holm-Nielsen & Jeppesen 784* (AAU). Reaches 800 m in
> M-S: *Gentry 9808* (QCA). Syn. *Olmedia aspera* Ruíz & Pavón

***Trophis racemosa* (L.) Urban**
> Prov.: N, P; tree; *Brandbyge & Azanza 31654* (AAU); *Foster 3877* (AAU, QCA)

***Trymatococcus amazonicus* Poeppig & Endl.**
> Prov.: N; tree; *H. Christensen 83330* (AAU, BG, QCA); *Bloch et al. 68396* (AAU)

Musaceae (excl. Heliconiaceae)
L. Andersson, Fl. Ecuador 22, 1985.

***Musa acuminata* Colla**
> Prov.: N; herb; *Balslev 2799* (QCA)

***Musa* × *paradisiaca* L.**
> Prov.: N; herb; *Balslev & Santos Dea 2884* (QCA); *Balslev & Irvine 4617* (AAU)

***Phenakospermum guyannense* (L. C. Rich.) Endl. ex Miq.**
> Prov.: N; tall herb; *Øllgaard et al. 57042* (AAU)

Myristicaceae
A. C. Smith *in* J. F. Macbride, Fl. Peru 2(3), Publ. Field Mus. Nat. Hist.,
Bot. Ser. 13: 766–784. 1938. This listing checked by W. Rodrigues, INPA.

***Compsoneura capitellata* (A. DC.) Warb.**
> Prov.: N; tree; *Øllgaard et al. 57050* (AAU); *SEF 9124* (AAU, QCA)

***Compsoneura sprucei* (A. DC.) Warb.**
> Prov.: N, P; tree; *Korning & Thomsen 47445* (AAU); *Foster 3644* (F)

***Iryanthera crassifolia* A. C. Smith**
> Prov.: P; tree; *Neill 6710* (AAU)

***Iryanthera elliptica* Ducke**
> Prov.: N; tree; *Davis & Yost 1020* (QCA)

***Iryanthera grandis* Ducke**
> Prov.: N; tree; *Brandbyge et al. 30282* (AAU)

***Iryanthera juruensis* Warb.**
> Prov.: N; tree; *Brandbyge et al. 33956* (AAU); *Davis & Yost 1014* (QCA)

***Iryanthera laevis* Markgraf**
> Prov.: N; tree; *Brandbyge et al. 36026* (AAU)

***Iryanthera lancifolia* Ducke**
> Prov.: N; tree; *Brandbyge et al. 36027* (AAU)

***Iryanthera macrophylla* (Benth.) Warb.**
> Prov.: N; *Neill 6757* (AAU)

***Iryanthera paraensis* Huber**
> Prov. N; tree; *Davis & Yost 1005* (QCA); *Flores 157* (QCA)

***Iryanthera ulei* Warb.**
> Prov.: N; tree; *Brandbyge et al. 33919* (AAU); *Foster 3697* (QCA)

***Osteophloeum platyspermum* (A. DC.) Warb.**
> Prov.: N, M-S; tree; *Palacios 1679* (AAU). Reaches 900 m alt. in M-S:
> *Pennington & Tenorio 10757* (QCA)

***Otoba glycycarpa* (Ducke) W. Rodr. ined.**
> Prov.: N; tree; *Neill et al. 7157* (QAME n.v.)

Myristicaceae   (cont.)

***Otoba novogranatensis* Moldenke**
Prov.: N; tree; *Brandbyge et al. 30241* (AAU)
***Otoba parvifolia* (Markgraf) A. Gentry**
Prov.: N, P; tree; *Holm-Nielsen & Jeppesen 913* (AAU); *Foster 3860* (AAU, QCA)
***Virola calophylla* Warb.**
Prov.: N, P; tree; *Brandbyge & Azanza 30590* (AAU); *Davis & Yost 1019* (QCA)
***Virola decorticans* Ducke**
Prov.: N; tree; *Neill et al. 8300* (QAME n.v.)
***Virola duckei* A. C. Smith**
Prov.: N; tree; *SEF 8630* (AAU); *Korning & Thomsen 47739* (AAU)
***Virola elongata* (Spruce ex Benth.) Warb.**
Prov.: N, P; tree; *Holm-Nielsen et al. 21184* (AAU, QCA)
***Virola flexuosa* A. C. Smith**
Prov.: N; tree; *Brandbyge et al. 33898* (AAU); *Oldeman & Arévalo 49* (QCA)
***Virola multinervia* Ducke**
Prov.: N; tree; *Korning & Thomsen 58749* (AAU)
***Virola* cf. *obovata* Ducke**
Prov.: N; tree; *SEF 8592* (AAU, QCA); *Korning & Thomsen 47426* (AAU)
***Virola pavonis* (A. DC.) A. C. Smith**
Prov.: N; tree; *Neill 8130* (QAME n.v.)
***Virola peruviana* (A. DC.) Warb.**
Prov.: N; tree; *Korning & Thomsen 47164* (AAU); *Pennington 10578* (QCA)
***Virola sebifera* Aublet**
Prov.: N, M-S; tree; *Brandbyge & Azanza 32223* (AAU); *Irvine 820* (F, QCA)
***Virola surinamensis* (Rol.) Warb.**
Prov.: N, P; tree; *Brandbyge et al. 36171* (AAU); *Neill 6673* (AAU, QCA)

Myrsinaceae
J. F. Macbride, Fl. Peru 5(1), Publ. Field Mus. Nat. Hist., Bot. Ser. 13: 163–203. 1959. Identifications by J. J. Pipoly.

***Ardisia guianensis* (Aublet) Mez**
Prov.: N, P; shrub, tree; *Holm-Nielsen et al. 22334* (AAU); *Irvine 812* (QCA)
***Ardisia panurensis* Mez vel sp. aff.**
Prov.: P; shrub; *Øllgaard et al. 34716* (AAU)
***Ardisia pellucida* Oerst.**
Prov.: N, P; shrub; *Øllgaard et al. 35161* (AAU)
***Ardisia* sp.**
Prov.: N; shrub; *Lawesson et al. 39451* (AAU)
***Cybianthus albiflorus* (A. C. Smith) Agostini**
Prov.: P; shrub; *Jaramillo et al. 30984* (AAU, QCA)
***Cybianthus* cf. *macrophyllus* Miq.**
Prov.: N; shrub; *Foster 3618* (QCA); *Balslev & Santos Dea* (QCA)
***Cybianthus occigranatensis* (Cuatrec.) Agostini**
Prov.: N; tree; *Neill 7494* (QAME n.v.)
***Cybianthus pseudoicacoreus* (Miq.) Agostini**
Prov.: N; shrub; *Brandbyge et al. 33949* (AAU)
***Cybianthus* cf. *simplex* (Hook. f.) Agostini**
Prov.: N; tree; *Holm-Nielsen 19295* (AAU, QCA); *Øllgaard et al. 39196* (AAU)

Myrsinaceae   (cont.)

Geissanthus longistamineus (A. C. Smith) Pipoly
    Prov.: N, P; shrub; *Jaramillo et al. 30920* (AAU)
Myrsine guianensis (Aublet) O. Kuntze
    Prov.: N; shrub; *Korning & Thomsen 47772* (AAU), *Neill 7448* (QAME n.v.)
Parathesis amazonica Mez
    Prov.: N; shrub; *Holm-Nielsen 19205* (AAU, QCA)
Stylogyne cauliflora (C. Martius ex Miq.) Mez
    Prov.: N, P; tree; *Brandbyge et al. 33544* (AAU)
Stylogyne laxiflora (Benth.) Mez
    Prov.: N; shrub; *Lawesson et al. 44333* (AAU, QCA)
Stylogyne longifolia (C. Martius ex Miq.) Mez
    Prov.: N; shrub; *Brandbyge et al. 33785* (AAU)
Stylogyne micrantha (H.B.K.) Mez
    Prov.: N, P; shrub; *Brandbyge et al. 33617* (AAU)

Myrtaceae
McVaugh *in* J. F. Macbride, Fl. Peru 4(2), Publ. Field Mus. Nat. Hist.,
Bot. Ser. 13: 567–818. 1958.   Identifications by L. Landrum, ASU, and J.
Miller, MO; mostly made in 1989.

Calyptranthes bipennis Berg
    Prov.: M-S; shrub; *Brandbyge & Azanza 32232* (AAU)
Calyptranthes longifolia Berg
    Prov.: N; tree; *Davis & Yost 944* (MO)
Calyptranthes macrophylla Berg
    Prov.: N, P; tree; *Brandbyge et al. 32669* (AAU); *Palacios & Neill 699* (AAU)
Calyptranthes maxima McVaugh
    Prov.: N; tree; *Zaruma et al. 238* (QAME n.v.)
Calyptranthes plicata McVaugh
    Prov.: N; tree; *Davis & Yost 944* (QCA)
Calyptranthes ruiziana Berg aff.
    Prov.: N; tree *Holm-Nielsen et al. 22294* (AAU)
Calyptranthes cf. simulata McVaugh
    Prov.: N; shrub, tree; *Andrade 33045* (AAU)
Calyptranthes speciosa Sagot
    Prov.: N; tree; *Brandbyge et al. 30446* (AAU)
Calyptranthes cf. tessmannii Burret ex Mc Vaugh
    Prov.: N; tree; *Brandbyge et al. 33532* (AAU)
Calyptranthes sp. 1
    Prov.: N; shrub; *Foster 3713* (AAU)
Calyptranthes sp. 2
    Prov.: N; tree; *Brandbyge et al. 30543* (AAU)
Calyptranthes sp. 3
    Prov.: N; shrub; *Lawesson et al. 39727* (AAU)
Calyptranthes sp. 4
    Prov.: P; shrub; *Jaramillo et al. 30778* (AAU).   Probably sp. nov.
Calyptranthes sp. 5
    Prov.: P; tree; *Holm-Nielsen et al. 22064* (AAU).   Possibly *Plinia* sp.
Calyptranthes sp. 6
    Prov.: N; shrub; *Foster 3717* (AAU).   Possibly *Marliera* sp.

Myrtaceae (cont.)

Campomanesia lineatifolia Ruíz & Pavón
    Prov.: N; shrub; *Vickers 234* (F)
Eugenia biflora (L.) DC.
    Prov.: N, M-S; tree; *Little 750* (US); *Asplund 9133* (S).   Syn. *E. loretensis* Diels
Eugenia cuspidifolia DC.
    Prov.: N; tree; *SEF 9152* (AAU, QCA)
Eugenia dittocrepis Berg
    Prov.: P; tree; *Neill & Palacios 6687* (QCA)
Eugenia feijoi Berg
    Prov.: P; shrub; *Jaramillo et al. 30726* (AAU); *Palacios 2387* (QAME n.v.)
Eugenia florida DC. aff.
    Prov.: N; tree; *Korning & Thomsen 47524* (QCA); *Lawesson et al. 44258* (AAU)
Eugenia riparia DC.
    Prov.: N; tree; *Palacios 931* (QAME n.v.).   Syn. *E. muricata* DC.
Eugenia stipitata McVaugh
    Prov.: N; tree; *Dodson et al. 14964* (AAU)
Eugenia sp. 1
    Prov.: N; tree; *Lawesson et al. 43464* (AAU)
Eugenia sp. 2
    Prov.: P; shrub; *Øllgaard et al. 34944* (AAU)
Eugenia sp. 3
    Prov.: P; shrub; *Øllgaard et al. 35314* (AAU)
Eugenia sp. 4
    Prov.: N; shrub; *Brandbyge et al. 36176* (AAU).   (=*E. egensis* DC. ?)
Eugenia sp. 5
    Prov.: N; tree; *Holm-Nielsen et al. 21206* (AAU)
Eugenia sp. 6
    Prov.: N; tree; *Korning & Thomsen 58693* (AAU)
Eugenia sp. 7
    Prov.: N; tree; *Korning & Thomsen 58651* (AAU)
Eugenia sp. 8
    Prov.: N; tree; *Brandbyge & Azanza 30587* (AAU)
Eugenia sp. 9
    Prov.: P; tree; *Brandbyge & Azanza 31089*
Eugenia sp. 10
    Prov.: N; tree; *Brandbyge et al. 33575*
Eugenia sp. 11
    Prov.: N; tree; *Brandbyge & Azanza 30348*
Myrcia acuminata (H.B.K.) DC.
    Prov.: N; tree; *Holm-Nielsen 39841* (AAU)
Myrcia obumbrans (Berg) McVaugh
    Prov.: P; tree; *Neill & Palacios 6634* (QCA)
Myrcia splendens (Sw.) DC.
    Prov.: P; tree; *Øllgaard et al. 35371* (AAU)
Myrcia sp. 1
    Prov.: N; tree; *Foster 3762* (AAU)
Myrcia sp. 2
    Prov.: N; tree; *Korning & Thomsen 58731* (AAU)
Myrcia sp. 3
    Prov.: P; tree; *Øllgaard et al. 35142* (AAU); *Brandbyge & Azanza 31443* (AAU)
Myrcia sp. 4
    Prov.: N; shrub; *Holm-Nielsen et al. 21203* (AAU)

Myrtaceae (cont.)

Myrcia sp. 5
> Prov.: N; shrub; *Jaramillo & Coello 2923* (AAU)

Myrcia sp. 6
> Prov.: N; tree; *Lawesson et al. 43412* (AAU)

Myrcia sp. 7
> Prov.: N; shrub, tree; *Jaramillo & Coello 2944* (AAU)

Myrcia sp. 8
> Prov.: P; tree; *Brandbyge & Azanza 31684* (AAU)

Myrcia sp. 9
> Prov.: N; tree; *Øllgaard et al. 35497* (AAU)

Myrcia sp. 10
> Prov.: N; tree; *Brandbyge et al. 33590* (AAU)

Myrcia sp. 11
> Prov.: N; tree; *Holm-Nielsen et al. 19667* (AAU)

Myrcia sp. 12
> Prov.: N; tree; *Brandbyge et al. 30524* (AAU)

Myrcia sp. 13
> Prov.: N; shrub; *Jaramillo 95* (AAU)

Myrciaria dubia (H.B.K.) McVaugh
> Prov.: N; shrub; *Azanza & Barfod 41105* (AAU)

Myrciaria floribunda (Willd.) Berg
> Prov.: P; tree; *Palacios & Neill 670* (AAU)

Myrciaria sp.
> Prov.: N; tree; *Foster 3770, 3752* (AAU, QCA)

Plinia pinnata L.
> Prov.: N; tree; *Brandbyge et al. 30548, 30517* (AAU)

Plinia sp.
> Prov.: N; shrub; *Brandbyge et al. 33887* (AAU)

Psidium acutangulum DC.
> Prov.: N; tree; *Vickers 156* (QCA); *Palacios 278* (ASU)

Psidium guajava L.
> Prov.: N; tree; *Brandbyge et al. 33418* (AAU); *Alarcón 71* (QCA)

Psidium sp.
> Prov.: N; tree; *Brandbyge & Azanza 32865* (AAU)

Syzygium jambos (L.) Alston
> Prov.: M-S; tree; *Cerón 455* (QAME n.v.)

Myrtaceae sp. 1
> Prov.: N; shrub; *Øllgaard et al. 39116* (AAU)

Myrtaceae sp. 2
> Prov.: P; tree; *Holm-Nielsen et al. 22407* (AAU)

Myrtaceae sp. 3
> Prov.: P; tree; *Jaramillo et al. 31186, 31700* (AAU)

Myrtaceae sp. 4
> Prov.: P; shrub; *Jaramillo et al. 30731* (AAU); *Jaramillo & Coello 4628* (AAU)

Myrtaceae sp. 5
> Prov.: N; tree; *Brandbyge et al. 33806, 36231* (AAU); *Holm-Nielsen 39840* (AAU)

Najadaceae
R. R. Haynes and L. B. Holm-Nielsen, Fl. Ecuador 26, 1986.

Najas arguta H.B.K.
Prov.: N; submerged herb; *Holm-Nielsen et al. 19993* (AAU)

Nyctaginaceae
P. Standley *in* J. F. Macbride, Fl. Peru 2(2), Publ. Field Mus. Nat. Hist., Bot. Ser. 13: 518–546. 1937.

Neea divaricata Poeppig & Endl.
Prov.: N; tree; *Korning & Thomsen 47455* (AAU); *Palacios 51* (QAME n.v.)
Neea laxa Poeppig & Endl.
Prov.: N; tree; *Lawesson et al. 39319* (AAU, QCA)
Neea macrophylla (Poeppig & Endl.) Gilg
Prov.: N; shrub; *Korning & Thomsen 58730* (AAU); *Irvine 488* (F, QCA)
Neea ovalifolia Spruce
Prov.: N; tree; *Zaruma et al. 82* (QAME n.v.)
Neea parviflora Poeppig & Endl.
Prov.: N; tree; *SEF 10304* (AAU); *Irvine 508* (F, QCA)
Neea spruceana Heimerl
Prov.: N; tree; *Korning & Thomsen 47416* (AAU); *Irvine 421* (F, QCA)
Neea cf. *tristis* Heimerl
Prov.: N; tree; *SEF 8621* (AAU); *Korning & Thomsen 47664* (AAU)
Neea verticillata Ruíz & Pavón
Prov.: N; tree; *Zaruma et al. 55, 73* (QAME n.v.)
Neea virens Poeppig ex Heimerl
Prov.: N; shrub; *Korning & Thomsen 58613* (AAU); *Irvine 1000* (F, QCA)

Ochnaceae
J. F. Macbride, Fl. Peru 3A(2), Publ. Field Mus. Nat. Hist., Bot. Ser. 13: 686–697. 1956.

Cespedesia macrophylla Seemann
Prov.: M-S; tree; *Neill 7422* (QAME n.v.).   Reaches 700 m alt. in M-S: *Little et al. 362* (US)
Cespedesia spathulata (Ruíz & Pavón) Planchon
Prov.: N, M-S; tree; *Pennington & Tenorio 10752* (QCA).   Reaches 700 m alt.
Ouratea aromatica J. F. Macbr.
Prov.: N; tree; *Neill & Palacios 6654* (QCA); *Holm-Nielsen 19315* (AAU)
Ouratea weberbaueri Sleumer
Prov.: M-S; tree; *Little et al. 384, 403* (US)
Sauvagesia erecta L.
Prov.: N, P; herb; *Løjtnant & Molau 13307* (AAU, QCA).   Reaches 1050 m alt.

Olacaceae
H. O. Sleumer, Fl. Neotropica 38. 1984.

Aptandra tubicina (Poeppig) Benth. ex Miers
Prov.: N; tree; *SEF 8670* (AAU, QCA); *Korning & Thomsen 47721* (AAU)

Olacaceae (cont.)

Dulacia candida (Poeppig) Kuntze
    Prov.: N; tree; *Gentry et al. 21787* (AAU); *Lawesson et al. 44250* (AAU)
Heisteria acuminata (Humb. & Bonpl.) Engl.
    Prov.: N, P, M-S; tree; *Øllgaard et al. 34687* (AAU, QCA); *Little & Campuzano 82* (US). Syn. *H. cyanocarpa* Poeppig
Heisteria barbata Cuatrec.
    Prov.: N; tree; *SEF 10338* (AAU, QCA)
Heisteria guianensis Aublet
    Prov.: N; tree; *Balslev 3029* (QCA)
Heisteria latifolia Standley
    Prov.: N; shrub, tree; *Gentry 9750* (S), *12568* (AAU)
Heisteria nitida Spruce ex Engl.
    Prov.: N; tree; *Palacios et al. 1037* (AAU); *SEF 8794* (AAU, QCA)
Heisteria scandens Ducke
    Prov.: N, P; shrub; *Brandbyge & Azanza 31765* (AAU, QCA)
Heisteria spruceana Engl.
    Prov.: M-S; tree; *Little et al. 502* (US)
Minquartia guianensis Aublet
    Prov.: N; tree; *Lawesson et al. 39684* (AAU); *Neill & Priest 6914* (AAU, QCA)

Oleaceae
J. F. Macbride, Fl. Peru 5(1), Publ. Field Mus. Nat. Hist., Bot. Ser. 13: 235–239. 1959.

Chionanthus sp.
    Prov.: N; tree; *Brandbyge et al. 33421* (AAU)

Onagraceae
P. A. Munz, Fl. Ecuador 3, 1974.

Ludwigia affinis (DC.) Hara
    Prov.: N, P; shrub; *Lugo 2826* (AAU, QCA); *Løjtnant & Molau 13261* (GB)
    Reaches 1000 m alt. in Pastaza: *Asplund 18487* (S)
Ludwigia decurrens Walt.
    Prov.: N, P; herb; *Lugo 2751* (AAU); *McElroy 368* (QCA); *Alarcón 19557* (QCA). Reaches ca. 800 m alt. in Napo: *Lugo 2360* (QCA)
Ludwigia hyssopifolia (G. Don) Exell
    Prov.: N, P; herb; *Lugo 3891* (AAU, QCA); *Balslev 2285* (QCA)
Ludwigia inclinata (L.f.) Gómez
    Prov.: N; herb; *Azanza & Barfod 41200* (AAU, QCA)
Ludwigia latifolia (Benth.) Hara
    Prov.: N; herb; *Lugo 2548* (AAU, QCA). Reaches 1600 m alt.

Opiliaceae
P. Standley *in* J. F. Macbride, Fl. Peru 2(2), Publ. Field Mus. Nat. Hist., Bot. Ser. 13(2): 420–421. 1937.

Agonandra silvatica Ducke
    Prov.: N; tree; *Palacios 962* (QAME n.v.)

Orchidaceae

prepared by D. E. Christensen

L. A. Garay: Fl. Ecuador 9, 1978. C. Schweinfurth in J. F. Macbride, Fl. Peru 30(1), Publ. Field Mus. Nat. Hist., Bot. Ser. 13: 1–260,1958; 30(2), 261–531,1959; 30(3), 533–786. 1960; 30(4), 787–1005, 1961; 33, suppl., 1–80, 1970. G. C. K. Dunsterville & L. A. Garay: Venezuelan Orchids, vols. 1–6, 1959–1976 and supplement in Lindleyana 1(4), 1986. C. A. Luer: Selbyana vols. 1, 2, 3, 5 and 7, 1975–1982; Phytologia 54, 1983. C. H. Dodson & P. M. Dodson: Icones Plantarum Tropicarum, Ecuador, vols. 1–5, 10, 1978–1984 and Icones Plantarum Tropicarum, series II, Ecuador, vols. 5–6, 1989.

Acostaea trilobata **Luer**
  Prov.: P; *Luer et al. 0465* (SEL). Ill. in Selbyana 1: 217, 1975.
Aspidogyne **sp. 1**
  Prov.: P; *Holm-Nielsen et al. 21665* (AAU)
Aspidogyne **sp. 2**
  Prov.: MS; *Brandbyge et al. 32018* (AAU)
Baskervillea auriculata **Garay**
  Prov.: N; *Dodson et al. 3764* (SEL). Ill. in Fl. Ecuador 9: 209,1978. Ic. Pl. Trop. 10: t. 905, 1984.
Beloglottis bicaudata **(Ames) Garay**
  Prov.: N; *Suárez 078* (RPSC). Ill. in Fl. Ecuador 9: 254, 1978. Ic. Pl. Trop. ser. II, 5: t. 405, 1989.
Bletia stenophylla **Schltr.**
  Prov.: N; *Øllgaard et al. 57168* (AAU)
Brassia arcuigera **Reichb. f.**
  Prov.: *N; Weinhold s.n.* (SEL, QCA); *Ackerman s.n.* (SEL, QCA). Ill. in Venez. Orch. Ill. 3: 46, 1965. Ic. Pl. Trop. 1: t. 010, 1980.
Brassia caudata **(L.) Lindl.**
  Prov.: N; *Palacios et al. 1038* (MO, NY, QAME n.v., QCA). Ill. in Venez. Orch. Ill. 4: 36, 1966. Ic. Pl. Trop. 6: t. 509, 1982.
Brassia lanceana **Lindl.**
  Prov.: N; *Dalstrøm 0467* (QCNE)
Brassia lawrenciana **Lindl.**
  Prov.: N; *Weinhold s.n.* (SEL)
Brassia neglecta **Reichb. f.**
  Prov.: N; *Suárez 090* (RPSC). Ill. in Venez. Orch. Ill. 5: 34, 1966. Ic. Pl. Trop. 6: t. 510, 1982.
Buchtiena ecuadorensis **Garay**
  Prov.: N; *Asplund 9358* (S). Ill. in Fl. Ecuador 9: 235, 1978.
Caluera vulpina **Dodson & Determann**
  Prov.: N; *J. Kuhn s.n. = O.I.C. 0014* (SEL); *Suárez 143* (RPSC). Ill. in Amer. Orchid Soc. Bull. 52: 376, 1983. Ic. Pl. Trop. 10: t. 908, 1984.
Caluera **sp.**
  Prov.: N; *Christensen 88115* (AAU); *Suárez 204* (RPSC). Ill. based on *C. Lindberg & A. Suárez no.143,* deposited at AAU. A new species
Campylocentrum fasciola **(Lindl.) Cogn.**
  Prov.: N; *Nielsen 76078* (AAU). Ill. in Ic. Pl. Trop. 1: t. 014, 1980.

Orchidaceae (cont.)

Campylocentrum mattogrossense Hoehne
Prov. N, M-S; *Cerón 1631: Suárez 127; Dodson 16470* (RPSC, MO)
Catasetum microglossum Rolfe
Prov.: N; *Gann s.n.* (SEL). Ill. in Ic. Pl. Trop. 5: t. 406, 1982.
Catasetum napoense Dodson
Prov.: N; *Dodson 5199* (SEL). Ill. in Selbyana 2: 156, 1978.
Catasetum tuberculatum Dodson
Prov.: N; *Besse et al. s.n.* (SEL). Ill. in Ic. Pl. Trop. 5: t. 410, 1982.
Cattleya iricolor Reichb. f.
Prov.: N; *Suárez 083* (RPSC). Ill. in Ic. Pl. Trop. 5: t. 411, 1982.
Cattleya violaceae (HBK) Lindl.
Prov.: N; *Balslev et al. 84708* (AAU), *Brucculeri 40991* (AAU)
Chaubardia surinamensis Rolfe
Prov.: N; *Christensen 88108* (AAU); *Suárez 040* (RPSC). Ill. in Venez. Orch.
Ill. 4: 50, 1966. Ic. Pl. Trop. 6: t. 516, 1982. Ic. Pl. Trop. ser II, 5: 411, 1989.
Chondrorhyncha suarezii Dodson
Prov.: N; *Suárez 195* (RPSC); *Dodson 16999c* (QCNE, RPSC). Ill. in Ic. Pl.
Trop. ser. II, 2: t. 181, 1989 and 5: 418, 1989.
Chondrorhyncha viridisepala Senghas
Prov.: N; *Christensen 88088* (AAU). Ill. based on *A. Suárez no. 213* deposited at
AAU.
Cischweinfia suarezii Dodson
Prov.: N; *Suárez 104* (SEL). Ill. in Ic. Pl. Trop. ser. II, 5, t. 420, 1989.
Cochleanthes amazonica (Reichb. f. & Warsc.) Schultes & Garay
Prov.: N, P; *Nielsen 76090* (AAU); *Lawesson et al. 43434* (AAU), *Suárez 194*
(RPSC); *Cerón 4372* (MO). Ill. in Ic. Pl. Trop. 10: t. 913, 1984.
Cochleanthes sp.
Prov.: N; *Christensen 88078* (AAU). Probably a new species. Ill. based on *A.*
Suárez no. 226 deposited at AAU.
Cranichis muscosa Sw.
Prov.: N; *Holm-Nielsen & Jeppesen 920* (AAU, QCA). Ill. in Venez. Orch. Ill.
4: 61, 1966. Ic. Pl. Trop. 4: t. 367, 1980.
Cryptarrhena acrensis Schltr.
Prov.: N; *Suárez 190* (RPSC); *Cerón 0935* (MO). Ill. in Venez. Orch. Ill. 3: 69,
1965. Ic. Pl. Trop. ser II, 5: 425, 1989.
Cryptocentrum hopii Schltr.
Prov.: N; *Luer & Hirtz 6921* (SEL). Ill. in Ic. Pl. Trop. 10: t. 914, 1983.
Cryptocentrum jamesonii Benth.
Prov.: N; *Suárez 057* (RPSC); *Dodson et al. 3767* (SEL). Ill. in Ic. Pl. Trop. 1;
t. 031, 1980.
Cryptocentrum pseudobulbosum C. Schweinf.
Prov.: P; *Hirtz 1303* (SEL)
Cycnoches hagii Barb. Rodr.
Prov.: N; *Holm-Nielsen et al. 20283* (AAU); *Suárez 035* (RPSC). Ill. in Venez.
Orch. Ill. 4: 63, 1966.
Cycnoches peruviana Rolfe
Prov. N; *Weinhold s.n.* (SEL). Ill. in Ic. Pl. Trop. 5: t. 420, 1982.
Cycnoches suarezii Dodson
Prov.: N; *Suárez 200* (RPSC). Ill. in Ic. Pl. Trop. ser. II, 5: 431, 1989.

Orchidaceae   (cont.)

Cycnoches thurnstonorum Dodson
Prov.: N; *Suárez 147* (RPSC); *Dodson & Chase 17249* (RPSC); *W. & M. Thurston s.n.* (SEL, DBG).   Ill. in Ic. Pl. Trop. ser. II, 5: 432, 1989.

Diadenum barkeri (Lindl.) Benth. & Hook. ex Jacks.
Prov.:N; *Hirtz 3918* (MO)

Diadenum micranthum Poeppig & Endl.
Prov.: N; *Holm-Nielsen et al. 21546* (AAU); *Suárez 026* (RPSC).   Ill. in Ic. Pl. Trop. 10: 915, 1984. Ic. Pl. Trop. ser II, 5: 433, 1989.

Dichaea ancoraelabia C. Schweinf.
Prov.: N; *Lawesson et al. 43375* (AAU, QCA);   *Cerón 2156 , 3656, 4933* (MO, QCA).   Ill. in Venez. Orch. Ill. 5: 65, 1966.

Dichaea brachypoda Reichb. f.
Prov.: N; *Suárez 140* (RPSC).   Ill. in Venez. Orch. Ill. 3: 73, 1965. Ic. Pl. Trop. 7: 650, 1982. Ic. Pl. Trop. ser II, 5: 434, 1989.

Dichaea campanulata C. Schweinf.
Prov.: N; *Christensen 88104* (AAU); *Lawesson et al. 43323* (AAU); *Dodson & Chase 17247* (RPSC).   Ill. in Ic. Pl. Trop. 6: t. 524, 1982.

Dichaea histrio Reichb. f.
Prov.: N; *Suárez 161* (RPSC).   Ill. in Venez. Orch. Ill. 5: 67, 1966.

Dichaea kegelii Reichb. f.
Prov.: N, P; *Suárez 100* (SEL, RPSC); *Luer et al. 505* (SEL).   Ill. in Venez. Orch. Ill. 4: 67, 1966. Ic. Pl. Trop. ser II, 5: 438, 1989.

Dichaea muricata (Sw.) Lindl.
Prov.: N; *Pinkley 526* (S); *Cerón & Coello 3208* (MO, QCA); *Cerón et al. 2298* (MO, QCA).   Ill. in Venez. Orch. Ill. 2: 89, 1961. Ic. Pl. Trop. 1: 044, 1980.

Dichaea pendula (Aublet) Cogn. vel sp. aff.
Prov.: N; *Azanza & Barfod 41219* (AAU);   *Cerón 1006, 1247* (MO).   Ill. in Lasser's Fl. Venezuela 15 (4): 466, 1970.

Dichaea suarezii Dodson
Prov.: N; *Suárez 178* (RPSC).   Ill. in Ic. Pl. Trop. ser. II, 5: t. 441, 1989.

Dichaea trinitensis Gleason
Prov.: N; *Brandbyge et al. 33932* (AAU); *Foster 3777* (AAU); *Suárez 156* (RPSC).   Ill. in Venez. Orch. Ill. 6: 105, 1976. Ic. Pl. Trop. ser II, 5: 443, 1989.

Dichaea trulla Reichb. f.
Prov.: N, P; *Lawesson et al. 44393* (AAU, QCNE); *Dodson & Thien 2314* (SEL); *Cerón 3338* (MO).   Ill. in Ic. Pl. Trop. 1: t. 050, 1980 and 7: t. 660, 1984.

Dichaea sp. 1
Prov.: N; *Christensen 88099* (AAU)

Dichaea sp. 2
Prov.: N; *Christensen 88104* (AAU)

Dimeranda stenopetala (Hook.) Schltr.
Prov.: N; *Lawesson et al. 39359* (AAU); *Suárez 095* (MO).   Ill. in Ic. Pl. Trop. 1: t. 051, 1980.   Syn. *Epidendrum stenopetalum* Hook.

Dryadella gnoma (Luer) Luer
Prov.: N; *Christensen 88066* (AAU, QCA); *Luer 0591, 6914* (SEL); *Suárez 158* (RPSC).   Ill. in Selbyana 3: 110, 1976.   Syn. *Pleurothallis gnoma* Luer

Dryadella sp. 1
Prov.: N; *Suárez 173* (RPSC).   Ill. based on *A. Suárez no. 173* deposited at AAU.

Dryadella sp. 2
Prov.: N; *Christensen 88121* (AAU); *Suárez 188* (RPSC).   Ill. based on *A. Suárez no. 188* deposited at AAU.

Orchidaceae (cont.)

Dryadella sp. 3
Prov.: N; *Christensen 88105* (AAU). Ill. based on *A. Suarez no. 214* deposited at AAU.

Elleanthus capitatus (Poeppig & Endl.) Reichb.f.
Prov.: N; *Cerón 4195* (MO). Ill. in Fl. Ecuador 9: 75, 1978.

Elleanthus caravata (Aublet) Reichb. f.
Prov.: N; *Dodson & Chase 17227* (MO, RPSC); *Suárez 196* (RPSC). Ill. in Venez, Orch. Ill. 5: 73, 1966. Fl. Ecuador 9: 73, 1978. Ic. Pl. Trop. ser II, 5: 446, 1989.

Elleanthus graminifolius (Barb. Rodr.) Løjtnant
Prov.: N; *Mexia 7103* (SEL). Ill. in Bot. Notiser 129: 447, 1977. Fl. Ecuador 9: 82, 1978.

Elleanthus hallii (Reichb. f.) Reichb. f.
Prov.: N; *Suárez 180* (RPSC). Ill. in Fl. Ecuador 9: 87, 1978. Ic. Pl. Trop. ser II, 5: 450, 1989.

Elleanthus hymenophorus (Reichb. f.) Reichb. f.
Prov.: N; *Korning & Thomsen 47356* (AAU). Ill. in Ic. Pl. Trop. 7: t. 675, 1984.

Elleanthus ruizii (Reichb. f.) Reichb. f.
Prov.: N; *Suárez 176* (RPSC). Ill. in Ic. Pl. Trop. 1: t. 062, 1980. Ic. Pl. Trop. ser II, 5: 453, 1989.

Elleanthus sphaerocephalus Schltr.
Prov.: N; *Cerón 1420* (MO); *Dodson et al. 3770* (SEL, QCA). Ill. in Fl. Ecuador 9: 103, 1978.

Elleanthus zamorensis Garay
Prov.: N; *Dodson et al. 3769* (SEL, QCA). Ill. in Fl. Ecuador 9: 106, 1978. Ic. Pl. Trop. 1: t. 063, 1980.

Eloyella panamensis (Dressler) Dodson
Prov.: N; *Suárez 208* (RPSC). Ill. in Ic. Pl. Trop. ser. II, 5: t. 455, 1989. Syn. *Phymatidium panamense* Dressler.

Eltroplectris roseo-alba (Reichb. f.) Hamer & Garay
Prov.: N; *Lawesson et al. 43534* (AAU)

Encyclia abbreviata (Schltr.) Dressler
Prov.: N; *Suárez 193* (RPSC); *Dodson & Chase 17224* (MO,QCNE, RPSC). Ill. in Ic. Pl. Trop. 7: t. 678, 1982. Ic. Pl. Trop. ser II, 5: 456, 1989.

Encyclia sp.
Prov.: N; *Balslev et al. 84698* (AAU); *Nielsen 76131* (AAU, QCNE); *Jaramillo & Coello 2886* (QCA, AAU). Syn. *E. fragrans* (Sw.) Lemée

Encyclia pygmea (Hook.) Dressler
Prov.: N; *Suárez 167* (RPSC); *Luer 6883* (SEL). Ill. in Ic. Pl. Trop. 1: t. 070, 1980. Syn. *Epidendrum pygmaeum* Hook.

Encyclia thienii Dodson
Prov.: N; *Suárez 148* (RPSC). Ill. in Ic. Pl. Trop. ser. II, 5: 841, 1989.

Encyclia venezuelana (Schltr.) Dressler
Prov.: N; *Suárez 166* (RPSC). Ill. in Ic. Pl. Trop. ser II, 5: 459, 1989. Syn. *Epidendrum venezuelanum* Schltr.

Encyclia vespa (Vell.) Dressler
Prov.: N; *Dodson & Thien 0693, 0883, 0886, 2045* (SEL). Ill. in Ic. Pl. Trop. 1: t. 071, 1980. Syn. *Epidendrum vespa* Vell.

Epidendrum agathosmicum Reichb. f.
Prov.: N; *Suárez 170* (RPSC). Ill. in Venez. Orch. Ill. 2: 103, 1965.

Orchidaceae   (cont.)

Epidendrum anceps Jacq.
> Prov.: N; *Suárez 181* (RPSC).   Ill. in Ic. Pl. Trop. 1: t. 072, 1980.

Epidendrum angustifolium (Schltr.)
> Prov.: N; *Suárez 201* (RPSC).   (fide Dodson)

Epidendrum baumannianum Schltr.
> Prov.: N; *Cerón 5582* (MO).   Ill. in Ic. Pl. Trop. 1: t. 074, 1980.

Epidendrum bifalce Schltr.
> Prov.: N; *Christensen 88092, 88130* (AAU); *Jaramillo & Coello 3790* (QCA).   Ill. in Ic. Pl. Trop. 4: t. 382, 1980. Ic. Pl. Trop. ser II, 5: 462, 1989.

Epidendrum compressum Griseb.
> Prov.: N, P; *Nielsen 76181* (AAU, QCNE); *Dodson 16469*(SEL); *McElroy 287* (QCA).   Ill. in Venez. Orch. Ill. 2: 111, 1961. Ic. Pl. Trop. 6: t. 529, 1982.

Epidendrum coronatum Ruíz & Pavón
> Prov.: N, M-S; *Dodson 17316* (MO, RPSC), *Weinhold s.n.* (SEL); *Suárez 170* (RPSC).   Ill. in Venez. Orch. Ill. 3: 99, 1965. Ic. Pl. Trop. ser II, 5: 465, 1989.

Epidendrum criniferum Reichb. f.
> Prov.: N; *Suárez 038* (RPSC).   Ill. in Ic. Pl. Trop. 8: t. 713, 1983.

Epidendrum cristatum Ruíz & Pavón
> Prov.: N; *Cerón 2113* (MO), *Dodson 17314* (MO, RPSC).   Ill. in Venez. Orch. Ill. 3: 101, 1965. Ic. Pl. Trop. 1: t. 077, 1980.

Epidendrum difforme Jacq.
> Prov.: N; *Suárez 088* (RPSC).   Ill. in Venez. Orch. Ill. 2: 115, 1961. Ic. Pl. Trop. 1: t. 078, 1980.   Syn. *Neolehmania difformis* (Jacq.) Pabst

Epidendrum fimbriatum HBK
> Prov.: N; *Suárez 197* (RPSC).   Ill. in Ic. Pl. Trop. 4; t. 378, 1980.

Epidendrum imatophyllum Lindl.
> Prov.: N; *Azanza & Barfod 41103* (AAU).   Ill. in Venez. Orch. Ill. 4: 91, 1966. Ic. Pl. Trop. 1: t. 082, 1980.

Epidendrum longicolle Lindl.
> Prov.: N; *Azanza & Barfod 41142, 41166* (AAU); *Balslev et al. 84457, 84691, 84863, 84584* (AAU, QCA); *Nielsen 76088, 76593* (AAU); *Luer et al. 0436* (SEL)

Epidendrum microphyllum Lindl.
> Prov.: N; *Nielsen 76592; Azanza & Barfod 41140, 41162* (all AAU); *Suárez 93* (RPSC), *Christensen 93439* (AAU).   Ill. in Ic. Pl. Trop. 6; t. 538, 1982. Ic. Pl. Trop. ser II, 5: 474, 1989.   Syn. *Lanium microphyllum* Lindl. ex Benth.

Epidendrum prostratum (Lindl.) Reichb. f.
> Prov.: N; *Suárez 076* (RPSC).   Ill. in Bradea 2 (34): 238, 1978. Ic. Pl. Trop. ser. II, 5: t. 482, 1989.   Syn. *Physinga prostrata* Lindl.

Epidendrum ramosum Jacq.
> Prov.: N; *Cerón 3746* (MO); *Suárez 186* (RPSC).   Ill. in Venez. Orch. Ill. 4: 94, 1966. Ic. Pl. Trop. 1: t. 093, 1980.

Epidendrum rectopedunculata C. Schweinf.
> Prov.: N; *Lawesson et al. 44306* (AAU, QCNE).   Ill. in Bot. Mus. Leafl. Harvard Univ. 11: 110, 1943

Epidendrum rigidum Jacq.
> Prov.: N; *Cerón 1327* (MO); *Christensen 88062* (AAU); *Luer et al. 0431* (SEL). Ill. in Venez. Orch. Ill. 4: 100, 1966. Ic. Pl. Trop. 1: t. 095, 1980.

Epidendrum schomburgkii Lindl.
> Prov.: N; *Jaramillo & Coello 4461* (QCA).   Ill. in Venez. Orch. Ill. 2: 130, 1961.

Epidendrum sculptum Reichb. f.
> Prov.: N; *Suárez 164* (RPSC), *Dodson & Dodson 16478* (QCNE, RPSC).   Ill. in Ic. Pl. Trop. 9: t. 810, 1983. Ic. Pl. Trop. ser II, 5: 486, 1989.

Orchidaceae (cont.)

Epidendrum secundum Jacq.
Prov.: N; *Suárez 082* (RPSC). Ill. in Ic. Pl. Trop. 1: t. 096, 1980. Syn. *E. elongatum* Jacq.

Epidendrum smaragdinum Lindl.
Prov.: N; *Suárez 129* (RPSC). Ill. in Venez. Orch. Ill. 5: 104, 1966; Ic. Pl. Trop., ser. II, 5: t. 488, 1989.

Epidendrum stiliferum Dressler
Prov.: N; *Suárez 174* (RPSC). Ill. in Brittonia 19: 242,1967; Ic. Pl. Trop., ser. II, 5: t. 489, 1989.

Epidendrum strobiliferum Reichb. f.
Prov.: N; *Azanza & Barfod 41190* (AAU); *Dodson 16471* (RPSC). Ill. in Venez. Orch. Ill. 4: 102, 1966. Ic. Pl. Trop. 4: t. 104, 1983.

Epidendrum strobiloides Garay & Dunsterville
Prov.: N; *Dodson 17217* (RPSC). Ill. in Venez. Orch. Ill. 4: 104, 1966.

Epidendrum viviparum Lindl.
Prov.: N; *Suárez 041* (RPSC). Ill. in Ic. Pl. Trop., ser. II, 5: t. 49, 1989.

Epidendrum sp. 1
Prov.: N; *Christensen 88113* (AAU)

Epidendrum sp. 2
Prov.: N; *Suárez 73* (RPSC). A new species

Eriopsis sceptrum Reichb. f.
Prov.: N; *Balslev et al. 84855* (AAU, QCA); *Nielsen 76166* (AAU); *Lawesson et al. 44283* (AAU); *Jaramillo & Coello 2873* (QCA)

Erythrodes major (Presl) Ames
Prov.: P; *Luer et al. 1806* (SEL). Ill. in Ic. Pl. Trop. 2: 101, 1980.

Erythrodes multifoliata C. Schweinf.
Prov.: N; *Holm-Nielsen et al. 19736* (AAU). Ill. in Bot. Mus. Leafl. Harvard Univ. 9: 234, 1941.

Erythrodes mystacina (Reichb. f.) Ames
Prov.: N; *Cerón 2180* (MO, QCA); *Suárez 086* (RPSC)

Erythrodes roseus (Lindl.) Ames
Prov.: N; *Harling & Andersson 11988* (GB); *Lugo 3043* (AMES, GB). Ill. in Fl. Ecuador 9: 275, 1978. Syn. *Ligeophila rosea* (Lindl.) Garay

Erythrodes sp.
Prov. N; *Besse et al. 023* (QCA, SEL)

Eulophia alta (L.) Fawc. & Rendle
Prov.: N; *Holm-Nielsen et al. 19607* (AAU); *Løjtnant et al 14510* (AAU). Ill. in Venez. Orch. Ill. 1: 150, 1959. Ic. Pl. Trop. 2: t. 105, 1980.

Galeandra stangeana Reichb. f.
Prov.: N; *Poulsen 80725* (AAU)

Galeandra sp.
Prov.: N; *Jaramillo & Coello 2912* (QCA)

Gomphicis crassilabia Garay
Prov.: N; *Prescott 548* (NY). Ill. in Fl. Ecuador 9; 156, 1978; Ic. Pl. Trop., ser. II, 5: t. 498, 1989.

Gongora aromatica Reichb. f.
Prov.: N; *Suárez 008* (SEL). Ill. in Ic. Pl. Trop., ser. II, 5: t. 499, 1989.

Orchidaceae   (cont.)

Gongora gracilis Jenny
> Prov.: N; *Suárez 012* (SEL); *Dodson & Chase 17251* (RPSC, MO); *Univ. Fl. 87118, 87119, 87123* (UF). Ill. based on *C. Lindberg & A. Suárez no. 012* deposited at AAU.

Gongora pardina Jenny
> Prov.: N, M-S; *Dodson & Chase 17251* (RPSC, MO); *Dodson 18024* (RPSC, MO); *Univ. Fl. 87115, 87175, 87180* (UF); *Whitten et al. 952, 954, 997* (MO)

Gongora pleiochroma Reichb. f.
> Prov.: N, M-S; *Whitten et al. 951* (MO); *Whitten et al 953, 956, 998* (MO)

Gongora quinquenervis Ruíz & Pavón vel sp. aff.
> Prov.: N; *Whitten et al. s.n.* (MO). Ill. in Ic. Pl. Trop. 8: 748, 1984.

Gongora scaphephorus Reichb. f. & Warsc.
> Prov.: MS; *Univ. FL. 87481?* (UF). Ill. in Ic. Pl. Trop. 5: 438, 1982.

Habenaria monorhiza (Sw.) Reichb. f.
> Prov.: N; *Korning & Thomsen 47054, 47198* (AAU). Ill. in Venez. Orch. Ill. 2: 170, 1965. Fl. Ecuador 9: 35, 1978. Ic. Pl. Trop. 2: t. 111, 1980. Reaches 1050 m alt.

Habenaria repens Nutt.
> Prov.: N; *Dodson 17329* (RPSC, MO). Ill. in Ic. Pl. Trop. 2: 113, 1980.

Habenaria sp.
> Prov.: N; *Korning & Thomsen 47198* (AAU)

Ionopsis satyroides (Sw.) Reichb. f.
> Prov.: N; *Christensen 88062* (AAU); *Palacios 340* (QCA, QCNE, MO). Ill. in Venez. Orch. Ill. 1: 176, 1959. Ic. Pl. Trop. 2: t. 117, 1980.

Jacquiniella globosa (Jacq.) R. Br.
> Prov.: N; *Christensen 88129* (AAU); *Dodson 14057* (RPSC, MO) Ill. in Venez. Orch. Ill. 1: 180, 1959. Ic. Pl. Trop. 8: t. 791, 1983.

Koellensteinia graminea (Lindl.) Reichb. f.
> Prov.: N; *Lawesson et al. 44286, 44494; Balslev et al. 84826, 84587; Nielsen 76151* (AAU). Ill. in Venez. Orch. Ill. 1: 186, 1959. Ic. Pl. Trop. ser II, 6: 507, 1989.

Lepanthes embreei Luer & Hirtz
> Prov.: N; *Luer et al. 11752* (MO)

Lepanthes helicophylla Reichb. f.
> Prov.: N; *Christensen 88071* (AAU). Ill. in Venez. Orch. Ill. 5: 142, 1966.

Lepanthes iricolor Luer
> Prov.: N; *Luer & Hirtz 6895* (SEL)

Lepanthes nontecta Luer
> Prov.: N; *Luer & Hirtz 6887* (SEL)

Lepanthes ximenae Luer
> Prov.: N; *Luer & Hirtz 6915* (SEL)

Lepanthes sp. 1
> Prov.: N; *Dodson 15005* (RPSC)

Lepanthes sp. 2
> Prov.: N; *Christensen 88082* (AAU). Ill. based on *A. Suárez no. 211* deposited at AAU.

Lepanthes sp. 3
> Prov.: N; *Christensen 88096* (AAU). Ill. based on *A. Suárez no. 223* deposited at AAU.

Lepanthes sp. 4
> Prov.: N; *Christensen 88102* (AAU). Ill.based on *A. Suárez no. 219* deposited at AAU.

Orchidaceae (cont.)

Lepanthes sp. 5
Prov.: N; *Christensen 88103* (AAU)
Lepanthes sp. 6
Prov.: N; *Suárez 077* (RPSC); *Christensen 88081* (AAU). Probably sp. nov.
Ill. based on *C. Lindberg & A. Suárez no. 077*deposited at AAU.
Lycaste macrophylla (Poeppig & Endl.) Lindl.
Prov.: N; *Suárez 034* (SEL). Ill. in Venez. Orch. Ill. 1: 204, 1959. Ic. Pl. Trop.
10: t. 936, 1984.
Lycaste sp. 1
Prov.: N; *Christensen 88141* (AAU); *Lindberg & Suarez 106* (RPSC). May be *L.
rossey* (fide Dodson). Ill. based on *C. Lindberg & A. Suárez no. 106* deposited
at AAU.
Lycaste sp. 2
Prov.: N; *Christensen 88128* (AAU)
Macradenia lutescens Lindl.
Prov.: N; *Suárez 207* (RPSC). Ill. in Venez. Orch. Ill. 2: 190, 1961. Ic. Pl. Trop.
ser II, 6: 513, 1989.
Macroclinium dalstroemii Dodson
Prov.: N; *Christensen 88135* (AAU); *Dodson et al. 14055* (MO, RPSC); *Cerón &
Iguago 5577* (MO). Ill. in Ic. Pl. Trop. 10: t. 938, 1984.
Macroclinium hirtzii Dodson
Prov.: N; *Suárez 019* (RPSC); *Dodson et al. 14054* (MO, RPSC). Ill. in Ic. Pl.
Trop. 10: t. 939, 1984.
Masdevallia sanchezii Luer & Andreetta
Prov.: P; *Øllgaard et al. 34567* (AAU)
Masdevallia wendlandiana Reichb. f.
Prov.: N; *Brandbyge & Azanza 30585* (AAU). Ill. in Venez. Orch. Ill. 4: 134,
1966.
Masdevallia sp. 1
Prov.: N; *Christensen 88076* (AAU). Ill. based on *A. Suárez no. 209* deposited
at AAU.
Masdevallia sp. 2
Prov.: N; *Cerón 4940* (MO)
Maxillaria acuminata Lindl.
Prov.: N; *Suárez 079* (RPSC). Ill. in Ic. Pl. Trop., ser. II, 6: t. 529, 1989.
Maxillaria acutifolia Lindl.
Prov.: N, P, M-S; *Lawesson et al. 44300, 44419* (AAU, QCA), *Balslev et al. 84872*
(AAU); *Palacios et al. 0482* (QCNE). Ill. in Ic. Pl. Trop. 2: t. 162, 1980.
Maxillaria alba (Hook.) Lindl.
Prov.: N; *Christensen 88123* (AAU). Ill. in Venez, Orch. Ill. 2: 196, 1961. Ic. Pl.
Trop. 2: t. 144, 1980.
Maxillaria attenuata Ames & C. Schweinf.
Prov.: N; *Dodson 16485* (RPSC)
Maxillaria brunnea Linden & Reichb. f.
Prov.: N; *Christensen 88094* (AAU); *Dodson & Thien 2319* (SEL); *Cerón 6330*
(MO). Ill. in Venez. Orch. Ill. 2: 220, 1959. Ic. Pl. Trop. 2: t. 147, 1980.
Maxillaria caespitifica Reichb. f.
Prov.: N; *Christensen 88098* (AAU); *Cerón 3891* (MO). Ill. in Venez, Orch. Ill.
4: 138, 1966. Ic. Pl. Trop. 9: t. 845, 1983.

Orchidaceae   (cont.)

Maxillaria camaridii Reichb. f.
Prov.: N; *Nielsen 76594* (AAU); *Balslev et al. 84870* (AAU); *Brucculeri 40928, 40934,* (AAU). Ill. in Venez. Orch. Ill. 3: 182, 1961. Ic. Pl. Trop. 6: t. 552, 1982.

Maxillaria chacoensis Dodson
Prov.: N; *Lawesson et al. 43339* (AAU, QCA); *Cerón 2154* (MO, QCA). Ill. in Ic. Pl. Trop. ser. II, 6: t. 531, 1989.

Maxillaria conferta (Griseb.) C. Schweinf. ex Léon
Prov.: N, P, M-S; *Korning & Thomsen 47147* (AAU, QCA); *Cerón & Hurtado 4244* (MO). Ill. in Venez. Orch. Ill. 1; 234, 1959. Ic. Pl. Trop. 2: t. 149, 1980.

Maxillaria crassifolia (Lindl.) Reichb. f.
Prov.: N; *Suárez 039* (RPSC). Ill. in Venez. Orch. Ill. 4: 140, 1966. Ic. Pl. Trop. 2: t. 150, 1980.

Maxillaria cuencana Garay
Prov.: N; *Suárez 035* (RPSC). Ill. in Canad. J. Bot. 34: 257, 1956.

Maxillaria densiflora Hook.
Prov.: N; *Cerón 1411* (MO, QCA). Ill. in Ic. Pl. Trop. 2: t. 151, 1980.

Maxillaria desvauxiana Reichb. f.
Prov.: N; *Suárez 071* (RPSC). Ill. in Venez. Orch. Ill. 5: 180, 1966. Ic. Pl. Trop. ser II, 6: 532, 1989.

Maxillaria discolor (Lodd.) Lindl. vel sp. aff.
Prov.: N; *Cerón 1629* (MO); *Cerón et al. 2310* (MO, QCA). Ill. in Venez. Orch. Ill. 1: 222, 1959. Ic. Pl. Trop. 4: t. 395, 1980.

Maxillaria fletcheriana Rolfe
Prov.: P; *Luer et al. 405, 466* (SEL). Ill. in Ic. Pl. Trop. 5: t. 452, 1982.

Maxillaria guareimensis Reichb. f.
Prov.: N; *Lindberg & Suárez 17* (RPSC). Ill. in Ic. Pl. Trop., ser. II, 6: t. 535, 1989.

Maxillaria juergensii Schltr.
Prov.: N; *Suárez 007* (RPSC). Ill. in Ic. Pl. Trop. 6: t. 544, 1982.

Maxillaria melina Lindl.
Prov.: N; *Christensen 88095* (AAU); *Suárez 48* (RPSC). Ill. in Venez. Orch. Ill. 1: 228, 1959 and 2: 204, 1961; Ic. Pl. Trop., ser. II, 6: t. 539, 1989.

Maxillaria microtricha Schltr.
Prov.: N; *Suárez 094* (RPSC). Ill. based on *C. Lindberg & A. Suárez no. 094* deposited at AAU.

Maxillaria napoënsis Dodson
Prov.: N; *Suárez 183* (RPSC). Ill. in Ic. Pl. Trop. ser. II, 6: t. 540, 1989.

Maxillaria nasuta Reichb. f.
Prov.: N; *Christensen 88120* (AAU); *Azanza & Barfod 41127* (AAU, QCA). Ill. in Venez, Orch. Ill. 1: 230, 1959. Ic. Pl. Trop. 2: t. 158, 1980.

Maxillaria ochroleuca Lodd ex Lindl.
Prov.: N; *Cerón 3334* (MO)

Maxillaria poneranthera Reichb. f.
Prov.: N; *Nielsen 76149* (AAU); *Cerón 1627* (MO, QCA). Ill. in Venez, Orch. Ill. 2: 212, 1961. Ic. Pl. Trop. 5: t. 451, 1982. Ic. Pl. Trop. ser II, 6: 542, 1989.

Maxillaria ramosa Ruíz & Pavón
Prov.: N; *Christensen 88138* (AAU); *Suárez 044* (RPSC). Ill. in Venez. Orch. Ill. 1: 242, 1959. Ic. Pl. Trop. 2: t. 161, 1980.

Maxillaria rufescens Lindl.
Prov.: N; *Brucculeri 40993* (AAU); *Suárez 014 ,* (RPSC); *Jaramillo & Coello 2893* (QCA). Ill. in Venez. Orch. Ill. 2: 160, 1959. Ic. Pl. Trop. 6: t. 557, 1983.

Orchidaceae   (cont.)

Maxillaria santanae Carnevali & Ramirez
 Prov.: N; *Lindberg & Suárez 39* (RPSC).   Ill. in Ic. Pl. Trop., ser. II, 6: t. 544,
 1989.
Maxillaria scorpioidea Kränzlin
 Prov.: N; *Christensen 88087* (AAU); *Dodson & Chase 16234* (QCNE, RPSC);
 Cerón et al. 1985, 2004 (MO).   Ill. in Ic. Pl. Trop. ser. II, 6: t. 545, 1989.
Maxillaria splendens Poeppig & Endl.
 Prov.: N; *Brucculeri 40912* (AAU); *Christensen 88118* (AAU); *Oldeman et al.*
 016 (QCA).   Ill. in Venez. Orch. Ill. 6: 270, 1976. Ic. Pl. Trop. ser II, 6: 546, 1989.
Maxillaria suarezorum Dodson
 Prov.: N; *Christensen 88118* (AAU); *Suárez 004* (QCNE, RPSC); *Dodson et al.*
 151189 (RPSC).   Ill. in Ic. Pl. Trop. ser. II, 6: t. 547, 1989.
Maxillaria subulifolia Schltr.
 Prov.: N; *Dodson & Chase 17255* (RPSC)
Maxillaria superflua Reichb. f.
 Prov.: N; *Nielsen 76132* (AAU);   *Cerón & Hurtado 3870, 3889, 4129, 4947* (MO)
Maxillaria tarumaënsis Hoehne
 Prov.: N; *Suárez 122* (RPSC).   Ill. in Venez. Orch. Ill. 2: 220, 1961. Ic. Pl. Trop.
 ser II, 6: 548, 1989.
Maxillaria uncata Lindl.
 Prov.: N, P; *Christensen 88139* (AAU); *Holm-Nilsen et al. 19888B, 19909* (AAU)
 Ill. in Venez. Orch. Ill. 2: 224, 1961. Ic. Pl. Trop. 2: t. 163, 1980.
Maxillaria valenzuelana (A. Rich.) Nash
 Prov.: N; *Suárez 175* (RPSC).   Ill. in Venez. Orch. Ill. 2: 228, 1961. Ic. Pl.
 Trop. 6: t. 558, 1982. Ic. Pl. Trop. ser II, 6: 549, 1989.
Maxillaria villosa (Barb. Rodr.) Cogn.
 Prov.: N; *Brucculeri 40918, 40956* (AAU); *Dodson 17372A* (MO, RPSC)
Maxillaria violaceopunctata Reichb. f.
 Prov.: N; *Azanza & Barfod 30599, 41217* (AAU).   Ill. in Venez. Orch. Ill. 2:
 228, 1961. Ic. Pl. Trop. 6: t. 558, 1982. Ic. Pl. Trop. ser II, 6: 550, 1989.
Maxillaria xylobiiflora Schltr.
 Prov.: N; *Dodson 14061A* (RPSC).   Ill. in Ic. Pl. Trop. 2; 164, 1980.
Maxillaria sp. 1
 Prov.: N; *Cerón 1480* (MO)
Maxillaria sp. 2
 Prov.: N; *Hurtado & Neill 1526* (MO)
Maxillaria sp. 3
 Prov.: N; *Dodson 17339* (RPSC); *Cerón 3893* (MO).   A new species
Mesadenella angustisegmenta Garay
 Prov.: N; *Palacios 1618* (MO).   Ill. in Bot. Mus. Leafl. Harvard Univ. 28 (4):
 285, 1980 (publ. 1982.)
Mesospinidium incantans Reichb. f.
 Prov.: N; *Cerón 0725* (MO).   Ill. in Ic. Pl. Trop. 2: 166, 1980.
Miltoniopsis roezlii (Reichb. f.) Godef.-Leb.
 Prov.: N; *Dodson 4459* (SEL).   Ill. in Venez. Orch. Ill. 6: 278, 1976. Ic. Pl. Trop.
 2: t. 167, 1980 and 10: 942, 1984. Ic. Pl. Trop. ser II, 6: 554, 1989.
Mormodes andreettae Dodson
 Prov. N; *Dodson et al. 3371* (SEL, QCA); *Suárez 192* (RPSC).   Ill. in Ic. Pl.
 Trop. 5: t. 462, 1982.

Orchidaceae   (cont.)

Mormolyca gracilipes (Schltr.) Garay & Wirth
Prov.: N; *Suárez 130* (RPSC).   Ill. in Venez. Orch. Ill. 6: 280, 1976.   Ic. Pl.
Trop. 2: t. 172, 1980.
Myoxanthus affinis (Lindl.) Luer
Prov.: N, P; *Christensen 88110* (AAU); *Luer et al. 0482* (SEL).   Ill. in Selbyana
1: 227, 1975.   Ic. Pl . Trop. 2: t. 172, 1980.   Syn. *Pleurothallis affinis* Lindl.
Myoxanthus ephelis (Luer) Luer
Prov.: P; *Luer et al. 0479* (SEL).   Ill. in Selbyana 1: 417, 1975.   Syn.
Pleurothallis ephelis Luer
Myoxanthus pastacensis (Luer) Luer
Prov.: P; *Luer et al. 949* (SEL).   Ill. in Selbyana 3: 157, 1976.   Syn. *Pleurothallis
pastacensis* Luer
Myoxanthus sarcodactylae (Luer) Luer
Prov.: N; *Luer et al. 621* (SEL).   Ill. in Selbyana 1: 423, 1975.   Syn.
Pleurothallis sarcodactylae Luer
Myoxanthus scandens (Ames) Luer
Observed in Napo by A. Suárez.   Ill. in Selbyana 3: 157, 1976.   Syn. *Pleurothallis
scandens* Luer
Myoxanthus trachyclamys (Schltr.) Luer
Prov.: P; *Fuchs, Jr. s.n.* (SEL).   Ill. in Venez. Orch. Ill. 4: 247, 1966.   Selbyana 3:
192, 1976.   Ic. Pl. Trop. 3: 264, 1980.   Syn. *Plerothallis trachyclamys* Luer
Myoxanthus sp. 1
Prov.: N; *Christensen 88085* (AAU)
Myoxanthus sp. 2
Prov.: N; *Christensen 88116* (AAU)
Nidema ottonis (Reichb. f.) Britton & Millsp.
Prov.: N; *Suárez 118* (RPSC).   Ill. in Venez. Orch. Ill. 4: 92, 1966.   Ic. Pl. Trop.
9: t. 885, 1983.   Syn. *Epidendrum ottonis* Reichb. f.
Notylia bungerothii Reichb. f.
Prov.: N, M-S; *Suárez 136* (RPSC); *Lindberg & Suárez 3* (RPSC).   Ill. in
Venez. Orch. Ill. 1: 250, 1959;   Ic. Pl. Trop., ser. II, 6: t. 555, 1989.
Notylia ecuadoriensis Schltr.
Prov.: N; *Lawesson et al. 43379* (AAU);   *Whitten et al 0955* (MO)
Notylia laxa Reichb. f.
Prov.: N; *Suárez 137* (RPSC).   Ill. in Venez. Orch. Ill. 5: 192, 1966;   Ic. Pl.
Trop., ser. II, 6: t. 556, 1989.
Notylia peruviana (Schltr.) C. Schweinf.
Prov.: N; *Suárez 120* (MO, RPSC), *Dodson & Dodson 16468* (RPSC).   Ill. in
Venez. Orch. Ill. 3: 198, 1965;   Ic. Pl. Trop., ser. II, 6: t. 557, 1989.
Notylia trullulifera Brade
Prov.: N; *Palacios 1508* (MO)
Octomeria sp.
Prov.: N; *Brucculeri 40973* (AAU);   *Cerón 2092, 3336* (MO)
Oncidium baueri Lindl.
Prov.: N; *Suárez 134* (RPSC).   Ill. in Venez. Orch. Ill. 5: 216, 1966.
Oncidium dactyliferum Garay & Dunsterville
Prov.: N; *Croat 50424* (MO?);   *Christensen 88133* (AAU); *Suárez 084* (RPSC)
Ill. in Venez. Orch. Ill. 5: 224, 1966;   Ic. Pl. Trop., ser. II, 6: t. 559, 1989.
Oncidium fuscatum Reichb. f.
Prov.: N; *Dodson & Thien 2313* (SEL).   Ill. in Ic. Pl. Trop. 5: t. 475, 1982.
Considered a synonym of *Miltonia warscewiczii* Reichb. f. in Fl. Peru.

Orchidaceae (cont.)

Oncidium nanum Lindl.
Prov.: N; *Cerón 3708* (MO); *Cerón & Iguago 5971* (MO); *Suárez 013* (RPSC)
Ill. in Venez. Orch. Ill. 1: 272, 1959. Ic. Pl. Trop. 6: t. 569, 1982.
Orleanesia pleurostachys (Linden & Reichb. f.) Garay & Dunsterv.
Prov.: N; *Dodson 17239* (RPSC). Ill. in Venez. Orch. Ill. 3: 228, 1965.
Ornithocephalus falcatus Focke
Prov.: N; *Dodson & Dodson 16458* (QCNE, RPSC). Ill. in Venez. Orch. Ill. 3:
230, 1965. Ic. Pl. Trop. 11: t. 1065, 1984. Ic. Pl. Trop. ser II, 6: 564, 1989.
Ornithocephalus suarezii Dodson
Prov.: N; *Suárez 150* (MO); *Cerón 0697* (MO); *Dodson 16457* (RPSC). Ill. in
Ic. Pl. Trop. ser. II, 6: t. 564, 1989.
Palmorchis lobulata (Mansf.) C. Schweinf. & Correl
Prov.: N; *Harling & Andersson 11789* (GB); *B. Stein 3058* (MO). Ill. in Ic. Pl.
Trop. 2: t. 196, 1980.
Palmorchis silvicola L. O. Williams
Prov.: N; *Lugo 2729* (GB). Ill. in Ic. Pl. Trop. 11: t. 1070, 1984.
Palmorchis sobraloides Barb. Rodr.
Prov.: N; *Lawesson et al. 43445* (AAU)
Palmorchis sp.
Prov.: N; *Balslev et al. 60542* (AAU)
Phragmipedium ecuadorense Garay
Prov.: N; *Harling 3624* (S). Ill. in Fl. Ecuador 9: 17, 1978.
Phragmipedium pearcei (Reichb. f.) Pank. & Senghas
Prov.: N; *Pinkley 0553* (SEL); *Suárez 182* (MO); *Dodson et al. 17055* (MO,
RPSC). Ill. in Ic. Pl. Trop., ser. II, 6: t. 569, 1989..
Platystele brenneri Luer
Prov.: N; *Brenner 021* (SEL) ; *Luer et al. 0471* (SEL). Ill. in Selbyana 2: 25,
1976. Ic. Pl. Trop. 3: t. 204, 1980.
Platystele ornata Garay
Prov.: N; *Christensen 88084* (AAU). Ill. in Venez. Orch. Ill. 1: 300, 1959.
Platystele stenostachya (Reichb. f.) Garay
Prov.: N; *Suárez 045* (RPSC). Ill. in Venez. Orch. Ill. 3: 244, 1965. Ic. Pl.
Trop. 11: t. 1079, 1984.
Plectrophora cultrifolia (Barb. Rodr.) Cogn.
Prov.: N; *Suárez 046* (RPSC). Ill. in Venez. Orch. Ill. 1: 302, 1959. Ic. Pl.
Trop. 6: t. 574, 1982.
Plectrophora suarezii Dodson & Chase
Prov.: N; *Suárez 105* (RPSC); *Christensen 88080* (AAU). Ill. in Ic. Pl. Trop.
ser. II, 6: 570, 1989.
Pleurothallis acanthodes Luer
Prov.: N; *Christensen 88068* (AAU) ; *Luer et al. 0475* (SEL). Ill. in Selbyana 1:
123, 1975.
Pleurothallis agathophylla Reichb. f.
Prov.: N; *Suárez 187* (RPSC). Ill. in Ic. Pl. Trop. 6: 575, 1984.
Pleurothallis alveolata Luer
Prov.: P; *Luer et al. 0497* (SEL). Ill. in Selbyana 3: 49, 1976.
Pleurothallis aristata Hook.
Prov.: N; *Suárez 087* (RPSC). Ill. in Selbyana 1: 173, 1975.
Pleurothallis barbulata Lindl.
Prov.: N; *Dodson & Thien 2316* (SEL). Ill. in Venez. Orch. Ill. 1: 306, 1959.
Selbyana 1: 61, 1975. Ic. Pl. Trop. 3: t. 213, 1980.

Orchidaceae   (cont.)

Pleurothallis breviscapa C. Schweinf.
   Prov.: N; *Christensen 88131* (AAU); *Suárez 064* (RPSC).   Ill. in Venez. Orch.
   Ill. 1: 308, 1959. Selbyana 1: 177, 1975.
Pleurothallis cordifolia Reichb. f. & Wegener
   Prov.: N; *Luer et al. 0649* (SEL).   Ill. in Venez. Orch. Ill. 6: 334, 1976.   Selbyana
   3: 85, 1976.
Pleurothallis corralensis Garay
   Prov.: N; *Luer et al. 0516* (SEL).   Ill. in Selbyana 3: 277, 1976.
Pleurothallis cypripediodes Luer
   Prov.: N; *Fuchs s.n.* (SEL).   Ill. in Selbyana 1: 71, 1975.
Pleurothallis erythrium Luer
   Prov.: N; *Luer et al. 0517* (SEL)
Pleurothallis fastidiosa Luer
   Prov.: N, P; *Luer et al. 0670* (SEL);   *Luer et al.1266* (SEL).   Ill. in Selbyana 3:
   301, 1977.
Pleurothallis flexuosa (Poeppig & Endl.) Lindl.
   Prov.: N; *Luer et al. 0510, 11773* (SEL).   Ill. in Selbyana 1: 183, 1975.
Pleurothallis floribunda Poeppig & Endl.
   Prov.: N; *Gentry & Miller 54955* (MO?)
Pleurothallis fuchsii Luer
   Prov.: N; *Christensen 88074* (AAU).   Ill. in Selbyana 1: 245, 1975.
Pleurothallis grobyii Batem. ex Lindl.
   Prov.: N; *Brandbyge & Azanza 30595* (AAU).   Ill. in Ic. Pl. Trop. 3: 232, 1980.
Pleurothallis hitchcockii Ames
   Prov.: N; *Suárez 06* (SEL); *Christensen 88064* (AAU).   Ill. in Venez. Orch. Ill.
   1: 328, 1959.
Pleurothallis imraei Lindl.
   Prov.: P; *Luer et al. 0475* (SEL).   Ill. in Selbyana 1: 188, 1975. Ic. Pl. Trop. 3: t.
   237, 1980.
Pleurothallis intricata Luer
   Prov.: P; *Luer et al. 0659* (SEL).   Ill. in Selbyana 3: 127, 1976.
Pleurothallis lanceana Lodd.
   Prov.: N; *Suárez 001* (SEL); *Besse et al. 072* (QCA, SEL); *Dodson 14073*
   (RPSC).   Ill. in Venez. Orch. Ill. 4: 222, 1966. Ic. Pl. Trop. 3: t. 238, 1980.
Pleurothallis megalöephora Luer
   Prov.: N; *Luer et al. 6933* (SEL)
Pleurothallis mentosa Cogn.
   Prov.: N; *Jaramillo & Coello 2891* (MO); *Brandbyge et al. 33946* (AAU);
   Brandbyge & Azanza 30597 (AAU).   Ill. in Selbyana 3: 143, 1976.
Pleurothallis niveoglobula Luer
   Prov.: N; *Luer et al. 0519* (SEL).   Ill. in Selbyana 1: 259, 1975.
Pleurothallis obpyriformis Luer
   Prov.: N; *Luer et al. 0507* (SEL).   Ill. in Selbyana 3: 151, 1976.
Pleurothallis pennellia Luer
   Prov.: P; *Luer et al. 0687* (SEL).   Ill. in Selbyana 3: 161, 1976.
Pleurothallis perangusta Luer
   Prov.: N; *Brenner 14* (SEL).   Ill. in Selbyana 3: 163, 1976.
Pleurothallis pluriracemosa Garay
   Prov.: N; *Luer et al. 0521, 0522* (SEL).   Ill. in Venez. Orch. Ill. 2: 241, 1961.
   Selbyana 3: 151, 1976.

Orchidaceae (cont.)

Pleurothallis polygonoides Griseb.
Prov.: P; *Løjtnant & Molau 13373* (AAU). Ill. in Venez. Orch. Ill. 4: 232, 1966.
Selbyana 3: 369, 1977.
Pleurothallis praemorsa Luer
Prov.: P; *Luer et al. 01813* (SEL)
Pleurothallis pruinosa Luer
Prov.: N; *Christensen 88100* (AAU). Ill. in Venez. Orch. Ill. 2: 296, 1961.
Selbyana 3: 267, 1975. Ic. Pl. Trop. 3: t. 252, 1980.
Pleurothallis punicea Luer
Prov.: N; *Luer et al. 0519* (SEL). Ill. in Selbyana 1: 271, 1975.
Pleurothallis quadrata C. Schweinf.
Prov.: P; *Luer et al. 1292* (SEL). Ill. in Selbyana 3: 370, 1976.
Pleurothallis ruscifolia (Jacq.) R. Br.
Prov.: N; *Cerón 1452* (MO, QCA). Ill. in Venez. Orch. Ill. 1: 356, 1959.
Selbyana 1: 87, 1975. Ic. Pl. Trop. 3: t. 256, 1980.
Pleurothallis samacensis Ames
Prov.: N; *Luer et al. 0520* (SEL). Ill. in Venez. Orch. Ill. 4: 240, 1966. Selbyana
1: 279, 1975. Ic. Pl. Trop. 3: t. 257, 1980.
Pleurothallis schlerophylla Lindl.
Prov.: N; *Luer et al. 0906* (SEL, QCA). Ill. in Venez. Orch. Ill. 2: 300, 1965.
Pleurothallis smaragdina Luer
Prov.: N; *Luer et al. 0473* (SEL). Ill. in Selbyana 1: 291, 1975.
Pleurothallis sphaerantha Luer
Prov.: P; *Luer et al. 0486* (SEL) ; *Luer et al. 0904* (SEL, QCA). Ill. in Selbyana
1: 293, 1975.
Pleurothallis xanthella Luer
Prov.: N; *Christensen 88127* (AAU) ; *Suárez 189* (RPSC). Ill. in Selbyana 1:
301, 1975.
Pleurothallis sp. 1
Prov.: N; *Cerón 1454* (MO)
Pleurothallis sp. 2
Prov.: N; *Cerón 1052* (MO)
Pleurothallis sp. 3
Prov.: N; *Cerón 1071* (MO)
Pleurothallis sp. 4
Prov.: N; *Cerón 1272* (MO)
Pleurothallis sp. 5
Prov.: N; *Cerón 1408* (MO)
Pleurothallis sp. 6
Prov.: N; *Cerón 1410* (MO)
Pleurothallis sp. 7
Prov.: N; *Cerón 1997* (MO)
Pleurothallis sp. 8
Prov.: N; *Palacios 2003* (MO)
Pleurothallis sp. 9
Prov.: N; *Neill 8006* (MO)
Pleurothallis sp. 10
Prov.: N; *Suárez 018* (RPSC)
Pleurothallis sp. 11
Prov.: N; *Suárez 021* (RPSC)

Orchidaceae   (cont.)

***Pleurothallis* sp. 12**
  Prov.: N; *Suárez 027* (RPSC)
***Pleurothallis* sp. 13**
  Prov.: N; *Suárez 049* (RPSC)
***Pleurothallis* sp. 14**
  Prov.: N; *Suárez 058* (RPSC)
***Pleurothallis* sp. 15**
  Prov.: N; *Suárez 061* (RPSC)
***Pleurothallis* sp. 16**
  Prov.: N; *Christensen 88070* (AAU)
***Pleurothallis* sp. 17**
  Prov.: N; *Christensen 88097* (AAU)
***Pleurothallis* sp. 18**
  Prov.: N; *Christensen 88114* (AAU)
***Pleurothallis* sp. 19**
  Prov.: N; *Christensen 88086* (AAU)
***Pleurothallis* sp. 20**
  Prov.: N; *Suárez 121* (RPSC)
***Pleurothallis* sp. 21**
  Prov.: N; *Suárez 152* (RPSC)
***Pleurothallis* sp. 22**
  Prov.: N; *Suárez 151* (RPSC)
***Pleurothallis* sp. 23**
  Prov.: N; *Suárez 163* (RPSC)
***Pleurothallis* sp. 24**
  Prov.: N; *Suárez 169* (RPSC)
***Pleurothallis* sp. 25**
  Prov.: N; *Christensen 88114* (AAU)
***Pleurothallis* sp. 26**
  Prov.: N; *Suárez 011* (RPSC).   Ill. based on *C. Lindberg & A. Suárez no. 011* deposited at AAU. A new species.
***Pleurothallis* sp. 27**
  Prov.: N; *Christensen 88117* (AAU); *Suárez 113* (RPSC).   A new species.
***Polystachya amazonica* Schltr.**
  Prov.: N; *Lawesson et al. 44299* (AAU); *Brucculeri 40924* (AAU).   Ill. in Venez. Orch. Ill. 6: 376, 1976.   Considered a synonym of *P. foliosa* in Fl. Peru.
***Polystachya concreta* (Jacq.) Garay & Sweet**
  Prov.: N; *Cerón 3718* (MO).   Ill. in Ic. Pl. Trop. 3: 270, 1980.
***Polystachya foliosa* (Hook.) Reichb. f.**
  Prov.: N; *Suárez 036* (RPSC).   Ill. in Venez. Orch. Ill. 1: 360, 1959. Ic. Pl. Trop. 12: 1133, 1984.
***Polystachya nana* (Poeppig & Endl.) Reichb. f.**
  Prov.: N; *Lawesson et al. 44279* (AAU, QCA); *Jaramillo & Coello 2876* (QCA); *Dodson 15685* (MO, RPSC)
***Prescottia* sp.**
  Prov.: N; *Jaramillo & Coello 2858* (QCA)
***Psychopsis sanderae* (Rolfe) Lüeckel & Braem**
  Prov.: N; *Dodson 17737* (MO, RPSC).   Ill. in Ic. Pl. Trop. 6: t. 570, 1982.   Syn. *Oncidium sanderae* Rolfe

Orchidaceae   (cont.)

Psygmorchis glossomystax (Reichb. f.) Dodson & Dressler
Prov.: N; *Balslev & Madsen 10610* (AAU).   Ill. in Venez. Orch. Ill. 1: 268, 1959.
Ic. Pl. Trop. 3: 274, 1980.   Syn. *Oncidium glossomystax* Reichb. f.
Psygmorchis pusilla (L.) Dodson & Dressler
Prov.: N, P; *Azanza & Barfod 41216* (AAU).   Ill. in Venez. Orch. Ill. 1: 280,
1959. Ic. Pl. Trop. 3: 276, 1980.   Syn. *Oncidium pusillum* (L.) Reichb. f.
Psygmorchis zamorensis Dodson
Prov.: N; *Dodson 16475* (MO, RPSC).   Ill. in Ic. Pl. Trop. 5: 483, 1982.
Reichenbachanthus reflexus (Lindl.) Brade
Prov.: N; *Dodson 17223* (RPSC), *Suárez 205* (RPSC).   Ill. in Venez. Orch. Ill.
1: 372, 1959. Ic. Pl. Trop. 3: 277, 1980.
Rodriguezia batemanii Poeppig & Endl.
Prov.: N; *Dodson 16479* (MO, RPSC)
Rodriguezia carnea Lindley
Prov.: N; *Holm-Nielsen & Jeppesen 01018* (AAU)
Rodriguezia lanceolata Ruíz & Pavón
Prov.: N; *Suárez 081* (RPSC).   Ill. in Venez. Orch. Ill. 1: 376, 1959.
Rodriguezia leeana Reichb. f.
Prov.: N; *Dodson 16634* (MO, RPSC)
Rodriguezia sp. nov.
Prov.: N; *Dodson 17246* (MO, RPSC); *Cerón 3743* (MO); *Palacios 1546* (MO)
Rudolfiella aurantiaca (Lindl.) Hoehne
Prov.: N; *Cerón 4839* (MO)
Sarcoglottis sp.
Prov.: N; *Palacios 1665* (MO)
Scaphosepalum ovulare Luer
Prov.: N; *Luer et al. 0460* (SEL).   Ill. in Selbyana 3: 35, 1976.
Scaphosepalum rapax Luer
Prov.: P; *Luer et al. 0474* (SEL).   Ill. in Selbyana 3: 37, 1976.
Scaphyglottis amethystina (Reichb. f.) Schltr.
Prov.: N; *Dodson 17334* (RPSC)
Scaphyglottis boliviensis (Rolfe) B. Adams
Prov.: N; *Nielsen 76202, 76041* (AAU);   *Neill et al. 7362* (NY, QCNE)
Scaphyglottis huebneri Schltr.
Prov.: N; *Dodson 17334* (MO, RPSC).   Ill. in Selbyana 11, 745, 1990.
Scaphyglottis prolifera Cogn.
Prov.: N; *Holm-Nielsen et al. 7033* (AAU); *Suárez 172* (RPSC).   Ill. in Venez.
Orch. Ill. 6: 394, 1976. Ic. Pl. Trop. 3: t. 286, 1980.
Scaphyglottis punctulata (Reichb. f.) C. Schweinf.
Prov.: N; *Cerón 1074* (MO).   Ill. in Venez. Orch. Ill. 1: 382, 1959. Ic. Pl. Trop. 3:
t. 287, 1980.   Syn. *Helleriella punctulata* (Reichb. f.) Garay & Sweet
Scaphyglottis suarezii Dodson
Prov.: N; *Suárez 124* (MO).   Ill. in Ic. Pl. Trop. ser. II, 6: t. 579, 1989.
Scaphyglottis violacea Lindl.
Prov.: N; *Dodson 17256* (MO, RPSC).   Ill. in Venez. Orch. Ill. 1: 384, 1959.
Scaphyglottis sp. 1
Prov.: N; *Suárez 112* (RPSC)
Scaphyglottis sp. 2
Prov.: N; *Suárez 172* (RPSC)

Orchidaceae (cont.)

Scaphyglottis sp. 3
Prov.: N; *Christensen 88142* (AAU)
Scaphyglottis sp. 4
Prov.: N; *Jaramillo & Coello 2610 (MO)*
Scaphyglottis sp. 5
Prov.: N; *Cerón 603 (MO)*
Scelochilus williamsii Dodson
Prov.: M-S; *Dodson 17840* (RPSC). Ill. in Ic. Pl. Trop. ser. II, 6: t. 581, 1989.
Scelochilus sp.
Observed in Napo by D. E. Christensen.
Schomburgkia crispa Lindl.
Prov.: N; *Suárez 089* (RPSC)
Schomburgkia gloriosa Reichb. f.
Prov.: N; *Nielsen 76591* (AAU); *Dodson & Chase 17232* (MO, RPSC)
Selenipedium sp.
Prov.: N; *Davis & Yost 1048* (QCA)
Sievekingia sp.nov.
Prov.: N; *Dodson 16483* (MO, RPSC). This species is going to be described by Dodson as *S. marsupialis.*
Sigmatostalix amazonica Schltr.
Prov.: N; *Christensen 88107* (AAU); *Lawesson et al. 44266* (AAU). Ill. in Venez. Orch. Ill. 5: 274, 1966. Ic. Pl. Trop. 6: t. 586, 1982.
Sigmatostalix graminea (Poeppig & Endl.) Reichb. f.
Prov.: N; *Christensen 88109* (AAU); *Cerón 3625* (MO); *Suárez 037* (RPSC). Ill. in Ic. Pl. Trop. 6: t. 587, 1982.
Sobralia biflora Ruíz & Pavón
Prov.: N; *Suárez 126* (RPSC). Ill. in Fl. Ecuador 9: 129, 1978.
Sobralia fenzliana Reichbf.
Prov. N; *Grubb et al. 1501* (AMES, K, NY). Ill. in Fl. Ecuador 9: 119, 1978. Ic. Pl. Trop. 4: t. 306, 1980.
Sobralia fimbriata Poeppig & Endl.
Prov.: N; *Suárez 032* (RPSC). Ill. in Venez. Orch. Ill. 3: 288, 1965. Fl. Ecuador 9: 123, 1978.
Sobralia fragrans Lindl.
Prov.: N; *Brandbyge et al. 33851* (AAU); *Nielsen 76177* (AAU); *Cerón & Hurtado 3831* (MO). Ill. in Ic. Pl. Trop. 4: t. 307, 1980.
Sobralia macrophylla Lindl.
Prov.: N; *Korning & Thomsen 47050* (AAU); *Cerón 1072* (SEL, QCA) Ill. in Venez. Orch. Ill. 4: 274, 1966. Ic. Pl. Trop. 4: t. 310, 1980.
Sobralia pulcherrima Garay
Prov.: N; *Jaramillo 1109* (QCA). Ill. in Ic. Pl. Trop. 4: t. 313, 1980.
Sobralia rosea Poeppig & Endl.
Prov.: N; *Øllgaard et al 57158* (AAU); *Cerón 1302* (MO)
Sobralia violacea Linden ex Lindl.
Prov.: N; *Lawesson et al. 44422* (AAU, QCA); *Cerón 900* (MO); *Cerón & Iguago 5401* (MO)
Stanhopea anfracta Rolfe
Prov.: MS; *Univ. Florida 87210?* (MO). Ill. in Ic. Pl. Trop. 5: t. 491, 1982.
Stanhopea candida Barb. Rodr.
Prov.: N; *Lawesson et al. 43371* (AAU); *Cerón 1451* (MO); *Suárez 056* (RPSC). Ill. in Venez. Orch. Ill. 4: 286, 1966. Ic. Pl. Trop. 5: t. 492, 1982 and 6: t. 590, 1982.

Orchidaceae (cont.)

Stanhopea napoensis Dodson
Prov.: N; *Dodson & Thien 2398* (SEL). Ill. in Selbyana 1: 119, 1975. Ic. Pl.
Trop. 5: t. 494, 1982.
Stelis argentata Lindl.
Prov.: N; *Christensen 88132* (AAU); *Suárez 092* (RPSC). Ill. in Venez. Orch.
Ill. 1: 414, 1959. Ic. Pl. Trop. 4: t. 330, 1980.
Stelis garayi Dunsterville
Prov.: N; *Suárez 108* (RPSC). Ill. in Amer. Orchid. Soc. Bull. 46: 10, 1976.
Stelis santiagoensis Mansf.
Prov.: N; *Suárez 107* (RPSC); *Cerón 3649* (MO). Ill. in Venez. Orch. Ill. 4:
316, 1966.
Stelis tridactylon Luer
Prov.: N; *Luer et al. 0622* (SEL, QCA)
Stelis sp. nov.
Prov.: N; *Suárez 096* (RPSC); *Christensen 88126* (AAU). Ill. based on *C.
Lindberg & A. Suárez no. 096* deposited at AAU.
Stelis sp. 1
Prov.: N; *Cerón 0995* (SEL)
Stelis sp. 2
Prov.: N; *Cerón 1053* (SEL)
Stelis sp. 3
Prov.: N; *Cerón 1405* (SEL)
Stelis sp. 4
Prov.: N; *Cerón 1424* (SEL)
Stelis sp. 5
Prov.: N; *Cerón 1476* (SEL, QCA)
Stelis sp. 6
Prov.: N; *Cerón 2517* (SEL)
Stelis sp. 7
Prov.: N; *Christensen 88083* (AAU)
Stelis sp. 8
Prov.: N; *Suárez 159* (RPSC); *Christensen 88136* (AAU)
Stelis sp. 9
Prov.: N; *Dodson 15006* (MO, RPSC)
Stenia caudata (Ackerman) Dodson & Bennett
Prov.: N; *Christensen 88077* (AAU). Ill. in Selbyana 5: 299, 1981. Ic. Pl. Trop. 5:
t. 413, 1982.
Stenia pallida Lindl.
Prov.: N; *Suárez 149* (RPSC). Ill. in Venez. Orch. ill. 1: 422, 1959.
Stictophyllum pygmaeum (Cogn.) Dodson & Chase
Prov.: N; *Christensen 88093* (AAU). Ill. in Venez. Orch. Ill. 1: 370, 1959; Ic. Pl.
Trop., ser. II, 6: t. 584, 1989. Syn. *Quekettia pygmaea* Cogn.
Suarezia ecuadorana Dodson
Prov.: N; *Suárez 141* (RPSC), *Cerón 0983* (MO). Ill. in Ic. Pl. Trop., ser. II, 6:
t. 585, 1989.
Trichosalpinx acremona (Luer) Luer
Prov.: N; *Luer 0596* (SEL). Syn. *Pleurothallis acremona* Luer
Trichosalpinx blaisdellii (Watson) Luer
Prov.: N; *Suárez 102* (RPSC). Syn. *Pleurothallis blaisdellii* Watson.

Orchidaceae   (cont.)

Trichosalpinx chaetoglossa (Luer) Luer
   Prov.: P; *Luer et al. 1097* (SEL).   Syn. *Pleurothallis chaetoglossa* Luer
Trichosalpinx dirhamphis (Luer) Luer
   Prov.: P; *Luer et al. 0661* (SEL).   Ill. in Selbyana 3: 293, 1977.   Syn.
   Pleurothallis dirhamphis Luer
Trichosalpinx pumila (Luer) Luer
   Prov.: P; *Luer et al. 483* (SEL).   Ill. in Selbyana 1: 268, 1975.
Trichosalpinx sp. 1
   Prov.: N; *Dodson 16468A* (RPSC)
Trichosalpinx sp. 2
   Prov.: N; *Nielsen 76634* (AAU)
Trigonidium acuminatum Bateman
   Prov.: N; *Nielsen 76281* (AAU); *Suárez 116* (RPSC); *Dodson 17373* (QCNE,
   RPSC).   Ill. in Venez. Orch. Ill. 2: 340, 1961; Ic. Pl. Trop., ser. II, 6: t. 598, 1989.
Trigonidium grande Garay
   Prov.: MS; *D'Alessandro 327* (MO).   Ill. in Ic. Pl. Trop. 5; t. 499, 1982.
Trizeuxis falcata Lindl.
   Prov.: N; *Luer et al. 0467, 0512* (SEL); *Suárez 030* (RPSC).   Ill. in Venez.
   Orch. Ill. 1: 430, 1959.   Ic. Pl. Trop. 4; t. 350, 1980.
Vanilla odorata Presl
   Prov.: N; *Felton s.n.* (AMES).   Ill. in Fl. Ecuador 9: 50, 1978.   Ic. Pl. Trop. 4; t.
   353, 1980.
Vanilla palmarum Lindl.
   Prov.: N; *Cerón 2467* (MO)
Vanilla planifolia G. Jackson
   Prov.: N; *Balslev & Alarcón 2958* (QCA); *Irvine 400* (F, QCA).   Ill. in Fl.
   Ecuador 9: 51, 1978.   Ic. Pl. Trop. 4; t. 354, 1980.
Vanilla pompona Scheide
   Prov.: N; *Felton s.n.* (AMES).   Ill. in Venez. Orch. Ill. 1: 434, 1959.   Fl. Ecuador
   9: 53, 1978.   Ic. Pl. Trop. 12; t. 1195, 1984.
Vanilla sp.
   Prov.: N; *Cerón 48601* (MO)
Wullschlaegelia calcarata Benth.
   Prov.: N; saprophytic herb; *Holm-Nielsen & Jeppesen 651* (AAU).   Ill. in Fl.
   Ecuador 9: 232, 1978.
Xylobium bractescens (Lindl.) Kränzlin
   Prov.: N; *Cerón 1460B* (MO).   Ill. in Ic. Pl. Trop. 10; t. 999, 1984.
Xylobium colleyii (Bateman ex Lindl.) Rolfe
   Prov.: N; *Suárez 016 , 047* (RPSC); *Christensen 88091* (AAU).   Ill. in Venez.
   Orch. Ill. 3: 330, 1965; Ic. Pl. Trop., ser. II, 6: t. 600, 1989.
Xylobium foveatum (Lindl.) Nichols.
   Prov.: N; *Christensen 88125* (AAU).   Ill. in Venez. Orch. Ill. 6: 440, 1976. Ic. Pl.
   Trop. 4; t. 356, 1984.
Xylobium latilabium C. Schweinf.
   Prov.: N; *Dodson 17000* (MO, RPSC)
Xylobium variegatum (Ruíz & Pavón) Garay & Dunsterville
   Prov.: N; *Suárez 160* (RPSC); *Cerón 2062* (MO, QCA).   Ill. in Venez. Orch. Ill.
   2: 342, 1961.
Zootrophion griffin Luer
   Prov.: N; *Luer et al. 6893* (SEL).   Ill. in Selbyana 7: 83, 1982.

Oxalidaceae
J. F. Macbride, Fl. Peru 3(2), Publ. Field Mus. Nat., Bot. Ser. 13: 544–608. 1949. Identifications by A. Lourteig, P.

Biophytum dendroides (H.B.K.) DC.
Prov.: N; shrub; *Øllgaard et al. 39207* (AAU)
Oxalis barrelieri L.
Prov.: N, P; herb; *Løjtnant & Molau 13422* (AAU)
Oxalis caucensis Kunth
Prov.: M-S; shrub; *Lugo 3793* (GB)
Oxalis ortgiesii Regel
Prov.: N; herb; *Brandbyge & Azanza 30324* (AAU).   Reaches 750 m alt. in Napo: *Asplund 9402* (S)
Oxalis zamorana Lourteig
Prov.: M-S; shrub; *Løjtnant & Molau 14556* (AAU)
Oxalis sp.
Prov.: N; herb; *Jaramillo & Coello 3970* (AAU)

Passifloraceae
L. B. Holm-Nielsen, P. Møller Jørgensen, and J. E. Lawesson, Fl. Ecuador 31, 1988.

Dilkea parviflora Killip
Prov.: N, P; shrub; *Brandbyge et al. 36097* (AAU)
Dilkea retusa Masters
Prov.: N, P; shrub, tree; *Lawesson et al. 39785* (AAU)
Passiflora ambigua Hemsley
Prov.: N; vine; *Lugo 2818* (AAU)
Passiflora auriculata H.B.K.
Prov.: N; vine; *Cerón 1473* (QAME n.v.)
Passiflora edulis Sims
Prov.: N; vine; *Holm-Nielsen et al. 19733* (AAU)
Passiflora foetida L.
Prov.: N; vine; *Neill et al. 6050* (QCA); *Pinkley 554* (ECON)
Passiflora menispermifolia H.B.K.
Prov.: N; vine; *Harling & Andersson 11765* (AAU)
Passiflora micropetala Masters ex C. Martius
Prov.: N, P; vine; *Holm-Nielsen et al. 22473* (AAU)
Passiflora pyrrhantha Harms
Prov.: N; vine; *Neill 6910* (QAME n.v.)
Passiflora quadrangularis L.
Prov.: N; vine; *Vickers 102* (F)
Passiflora quadriglandulosa Rodsch.
Prov.: N; vine; *Holm-Nielsen et al. 19843* (AAU)
Passiflora riparia C. Martius
Prov.: N; vine; *Holm-Nielsen & Jeppesen 1040* (AAU); *Pinkley 208* (S)
Passiflora serrato-digitata L.
Prov.: N, P; vine; *Jaramillo & Coello 3419* (AAU); *Cerón 1260* (QAME n.v.)
Passiflora spinosa (Poeppig & Endl.) Masters
Prov.: N; vine; *Holm-Nielsen et al. 19932* (AAU)
Passiflora trifasciata Lam.
Prov.: N; vine; *Holm-Nielsen 19148* (AAU)

Passifloraceae   (cont.)

Passiflora vespertilio L.
    Prov.: N; vine; *Lawesson et al. 44246* (AAU)
Passiflora vestita Killip
    Prov.: N; vine; *Andrade 33111* (AAU)
Passiflora vitifolia H.B.K.
    Prov.: N, P, M-S; vine; *Løjtnant & Molau 13355* (AAU); *Alarcón 132* (QCA);
    Vickers 52 (F).   Reaches 1050 m alt.

Phytolaccaceae
J. F. Macbride, Fl. Peru 2(2), Publ. Field Mus. Nat. Hist., Bot. Ser. 13:
546–558. 1937. Identifications by U. Eliasson, GB.

Hilleria latifolia (Lam.) H. Walter
    Prov.: N; herb; *Jaramillo & Coello 3723* (AAU)
Microtea debilis Sw.
    Prov.: N, P; herb; *Holm-Nielsen & Jeppesen 937* (AAU)
Petiveria alliacea L.
    Prov.: N; herb; *Alarcón 103* (QCA); *Balslev & Santos Dea 2899* (QCA)
Phytolacca rivinoides Kunth & Bouché
    Prov.: N, P, M-S; herb; *Holm-Nielsen & Jeppesen 720* (AAU); *Irvine 361* (QCA);
    Alarcón 19516 (QCA); *Vickers 39* (F); *Pinkley 5* (ECON).   Reaches 1050 m alt.
Trichostigma octandrum (L.) H. Walter
    Prov.: N; shrub; *Andrade 33123* (AAU)
Trichostigma peruvianum (Moq.) H. Walter
    Prov.: N, P, M-S; herb; *Holm-Nielsen et al. 22679* (AAU)

Piperaceae
M. C. Tebbs, Bull. Br. Mus. Nat. Hist. (Bot.) 19: 117–158.   1989.   This
listing checked by R. Callejas, Jan 1989.

Peperomia alata Ruíz & Pavón
    Prov.: N; epiphytic herb; *Balslev & Madsen 10639B* (AAU)
Peperomia elongata H.B.K.
    Prov.: N; herb; *Luteyn et al. 9013* (AAU)
Peperomia glabella (Sw.) A. Dietr.
    Prov.: N, P, M-S; epiphytic herb; *Brandbyge & Azanza 30571* (AAU).   Reaches
    1600 m alt.
Peperomia hoffmanii C. DC.
    Prov.: P, M-S; epiphytic herb; *Øllgaard et al. 35237* (AAU)
Peperomia jamesoniana C. DC.
    Prov.: N; epiphytic herb; *Balslev & Madsen 10639A* (AAU)
Peperomia laxiflora H.B.K.
    Prov.: N, P; herb; *Luteyn et al. 8497* (AAU)
Peperomia macrostachya (Vahl) A. Dietr.
    Prov.: N, P, M-S; epiphytic herb; *Brandbyge et al. 33701* (AAU); *Gentry 9806* (S)
Peperomia obtusifolia (L.) A. Dietr.
    Prov.: N; epiphytic herb; *Brandbyge & Azanza 30618* (AAU)

Piperaceae (cont.)

Peperomia omnicola C. DC.
Prov.: N, P, M-S; epiphytic herb; *Løjtnant & Molau 14529* (AAU). Usually above 600 m alt.

Peperomia panamensis C. DC. ex Schroeder
Prov.: N; epiphytic herb; *Holm-Nielsen & Jeppesen 923* (AAU)

Peperomia perlongipes C. DC.
Prov.: P; epiphytic herb; *Jaramillo & Coello 3575* (AAU)

Peperomia pseudorynchophora C. DC.
Prov.: N; epiphytic herb; *Palacios et al. 396* (AAU)

Peperomia quaesita Trel.
Prov.: M-S; epiphytic herb; *Asdall 83–27* (QCA); *Renner 69074* (AAU, QCA)

Peperomia rotundifolia (L.) Dahlst.
Prov.: P; epiphytic herb; *Holm-Nielsen & Jeppesen 986* (AAU)

Peperomia sachatzinzumba Trel. & Yuncker
Prov.: N, P, M-S; epiphytic herb; *Holm-Nielsen & Jeppesen 980* (AAU); *Balslev & Madsen 10633* (AAU). Reaches 1400 m alt.

Peperomia serpens (Sw.) Loud.
Prov.: N, P, M-S; epiphytic herb; *Brandbyge & Azanza 32345* (AAU); *Gentry 12561* (GB). Reaches 1200 m alt.

Peperomia sp.
Prov.: N; herb; *Holm-Nielsen & Jeppesen 746* (AAU)

Piper aduncum L.
Prov.: N, P, M-S; shrub; *Øllgaard et al. 34953* (AAU); *Foster 3848* (AAU, F)

Piper aequale Vahl
Prov.: N, P; shrub; *Luteyn et al. 9080* (AAU); *Irvine 689* (F, QCA)

Piper albert-smithii Trel. & Yuncker
Prov.: N; shrub; *Balslev & Alarcón 2916* (QCA)

Piper aquadulcense Trel. & Yuncker
Prov.: N; shrub; *Balslev & Santos Dea 2853* (QCA)

Piper arboreum Aublet ssp. tuberculatum (Jacq.) Tebbs
Prov.: N, P; shrub, tree; *Brandbyge & Azanza 30076* (AAU); *Irvine 147* (F, QCA). Syn. *P. tuberculatum* Jacq.

Piper armatum Trel. & Yuncker
Prov.: N, P; shrub; *Holm-Nielsen & Jeppesen 983* (AAU)

Piper augustum Rudge
Prov.: N, P, M-S; shrub; *Jaramillo et al. 31113* (AAU); *Foster 3666* (AAU, F); *Davis & Yost 938* (QCA). Reaches 800 m alt.

Piper bellidifolium Yuncker
Prov.: N, P; shrub; *Brandbyge et al. 33693* (AAU); *Irvine 977* (F, QCA)

Piper callosum Ruíz & Pavón
Prov.: P; shrub; *Øllgaard et al. 35163* (AAU)

Piper cernuum Vell.
Prov.: N, P; shrub; *Brandbyge & Azanza 31442* (AAU)

Piper cingens C. DC.
Prov.: N; shrub; *Luteyn et al. 9078* (AAU)

Piper coruscans H.B.K.
Prov.: N, P; herb; *Holm-Nielsen et al. 21416* (AAU); *Harling 3595* (S); *Vickers 257* (F). Syn. *P. amazonicum* (Miq.) C. DC.

Piper crassinervium H.B.K.
Prov.: N, P, M-S; shrub; *Øllgaard et al. 34632* (AAU); *Irvine 510* (F, QCA). Reaches 1050 m alt.

Piper cryptocarpum Trel. & Yuncker
Prov.: N; shrub; *Asplund 8846* (S). Collected at 800 m alt.

Piperaceae (cont.)

Piper cuniculorum Trel. & Yuncker
  Prov.: N; shrub; *Irvine 439* (F, QCA)
Piper demeraranum (Miq.) C. DC.
  Prov.: P; shrub; *Jaramillo et al. 30971* (AAU)
Piper divaricatum Meyer
  Prov.: N; shrub; *Neill & Gómez 6421* (AAU)
Piper eruckea (Miq.) C. DC. vel sp. aff.
  Prov.: N; herb; *Asplund 10240* (S); *Pennington 10649* (MO)
Piper guianense (Klotzsch) C. DC.
  Prov.: N; shrub; *Vickers 18* (F)
Piper heterophyllum Ruíz & Pavón
  Prov.: P; shrub; *Jaramillo et al. 31399* (AAU)
Piper hispidum Sw.
  Prov.: N, P, M-S; shrub; *Brandbyge & Azanza 31675* (AAU); *Irvine 511* (QCA)
Piper immutatum Trel.
  Prov.: N, P, M-S; shrub; *Holm-Nielsen et al. 21068* (AAU)
Piper laevigatum Kunth
  Prov.: P; shrub; *Øllgaard et al. 34633* (AAU)
Piper leticianum C. DC.
  Prov.: N, P; shrub; *Holm-Nielsen & Jeppesen 977* (AAU); *Davis & Yost 939*
  (QCA); *Palacios et al. 232* (AAU). Syn. *P. conejoense* Trel. & Yuncker
Piper lineatum Ruíz & Pavón
  Prov.: N, P, M-S; shrub; *Brandbyge & Azanza 32282* (AAU)
Piper longifolium Ruíz & Pavón
  Prov.: N, M-S; shrub; *Brandbyge & Azanza 32699* (AAU)
Piper longipilosum C. DC.
  Prov.: N; shrub; *Irvine 294* (F, QCA)
Piper macerispicum Trel. & Yuncker
  Prov.: P; shrub; *Øllgaard et al. 35470* (AAU); *Irvine 594* (F, QCA)
Piper macrotrichum C. DC.
  Prov.: N, P; shrub; *Brandbyge & Azanza 30665* (AAU); *Irvine 708* (F, QCA)
  Reaches 700 m alt.
Piper maranyonense Trel.
  Prov.: N, P; shrub; *Brandbyge et al. 32541* (AAU); *Holm-Nielsen & Jeppesen*
  978 (AAU). Syn. *P. rotundistipulum* Trel. & Yuncker
Piper marsupiatum Trel. & Yuncker
  Prov.: N; shrub; *Irvine 978* (F, QCA
Piper nudilimbum C. DC.
  Prov.: N, P; shrub; *Brandbyge & Azanza 32711* (AAU); *Luteyn et al. 9001*
  (AAU); *Vickers 252* (F)
Piper obliquum Ruíz & Pavón
  Prov.: N, P, M-S; shrub; *Jaramillo et al. 31556* (AAU); *Baslev & Santos Dea*
  2837 (QCA); *Foster 3630* (AAU, F)
Piper obtusilimbum C. DC.
  Prov.: M-S; shrub; *Brandbyge & Azanza 31829* (AAU); *Balslev & Santos Dea*
  2967 (QCA)
Piper ottoniaefolium C. DC.
  Prov.: N; shrub; *Cerón 673* (QAME n.v.)
Piper phytolaccaefolium Opiz ex Presl
  Prov.: N, P; shrub; *Øllgaard et al. 34929* (AAU)

Piperaceae (cont.)

Piper reticulatum L.
Prov.: N, P; shrub, tree; *Holm-Nielsen & Jeppesen 726* (AAU); *Palacios et al. 287* (AAU); *Irvine 480* (F, QCA)

Piper sancti-felicis Trel.
Prov.: P; shrub; *Løjtnant & Molau 13306* (AAU)

Piper scutilimbum C. DC.
Prov.: N; shrub; *Cerón 638* (QAME n.v.); *Irvine 1125* (F, QCA)

Piper sipenanum Trel. & Yuncker
Prov.: N, P; shrub; *Andrade 33171* (AAU); *Brandbyge et al. 36213* (AAU)

Piper soledadense Trel.
Prov.: N, P; shrub; *Brandbyge & Azanza 30892* (AAU)

Piper tortivenulosum Yuncker
Prov.: N; shrub; *Luteyn et al. 9055* (AAU)

Piper umbriense Trel. & Yuncker
Prov.: N; shrub; *Irvine 685* (F, QCA)

Pothomorphe peltata (L.) Miq.
Prov.: N, P; shrub; *Holm-Nielsen & Jeppesen 711* (AAU); *Alarcón 19118* (QCA); *Vickers 30* (F); *Irvine 712* (F, QCA)

Pothomorphe umbellata (L.) Miq.
Prov.: N, P, M-S; shrub; *Brandbyge & Azanza 31984* (AAU); *Pinkley 421* (S)
Reaches 1050 m alt.

Sarcorhachis sydowii Trel.
Prov.: N; shrub; *Brandbyge et al. 32648* (AAU). Reaches 1000 m alt.

Poaceae

A. S. Hitchcock, 1927, The Grasses of Ecuador, Peru, and Bolivia. Contr. U.S. Natl. Herb. 24(8): 291–556. Identifications mostly by S. Lægaard, AAU; herbaceous bamboos by E. Judziewicz, US.

Acroceras zizanioides (H.B.K.) Dandy
Prov.: N, P; herb; *Holm-Nielsen et al. 20004* (AAU); *Harling & Andersson 17657* (AAU); *Molau & Öhman 1584* (GB, QCA). Syn. *A. oryzoides* Stapf.

Andropogon bicornis L.
Prov.: N, P; herb; *Holm-Nielsen & Jeppesen 1009* (AAU); *Palacios et al. 72* (QCA)

Aristida adscensionis L.
Prov.: P; herb; *Harling & Andersson 18197* (AAU, GB)

Arthrostylidium simpliciusculum (Pilger) McClure
Prov.: N; herb; *Young 24* (AAU, QCA)

Arundinella berteroniana (Schultes) Hitchc. & Chase
Prov.: N, P; herb; *Øllgaard et al. 34993* (AAU). Considered a synonym of *S. cuneata* Schltr. in Fl. Peru.

Arundo donax L.
Prov.: N; herb; *Balslev 4881* (AAU, QCA); *Vickers 99* (F)

Axonopus compressus (Sw.) P. Beauv.
Prov.: P; herb; *Løjtnant & Molau 13322* (AAU, GB)

Axonopus scoparius (Flügge) Hitchc.
Prov.: N; herb; *Vickers 199* (F)

Bambusa guadua Humb. & Bonpl.
Prov.: N; herb; *Lægaard 51554* (AAU)

Poaceae (cont.)

***Bambusa vulgaris* Schrad. ex Wendl.**
    Prov.: N; herb; *Young 102* (AAU); *Davis & Yost 1027* (QCA)
***Chloris radiata* (L.) Sw.**
    Prov.: N; herb; *Holm-Nielsen et al. 20285* (AAU)
***Coix lacryma-jobi* L.**
    Prov.: N; herb *Jaramillo & Coello 4504* (AAU, QCA); *Alarcón 140* (QCA);
    Vickers 100 (F); *Pinkley 371* (ECON); *Balslev 4879* (QCA). Reaches 750 m alt.
***Cryptochloa unispiculata* Soderstrom**
    Prov.: N; herb; *Madison et al. 5303* (AAU, QCA, SEL); *Lægaard 55815* (AAU)
***Cymbopogon citratus* (DC.) Stapf**
    Prov.: N; herb; *Vickers 11* (F); *Brandbyge & Azanza 32846* (AAU)
***Digitaria* sp.**
    Prov.: N; herb; *Jaramillo 6954* (QCA)
***Echinochloa colonum* (L.) Link**
    Prov.: M-S; herb *Brandbyge & Azanza 32255* (AAU, QCA)
***Echinochloa polystachya* (H.B.K.) Hitchc.**
    Prov.: N; herb; *Cerón 1027* (QAME n.v.)
***Eleusine indica* (L.) Gaertn.**
    Prov.: N; herb; *Vickers 31* (F); *Irvine 561* (F, QCA)
***Eragrostis acutiflora* (Kunth) Nees**
    Prov.: N; herb; *Lægaard 52010* (AAU)
***Eragrostis* cf. *bahiensis* Schrad.**
    Prov.: N; herb; *Lægaard 51420* (AAU)
***Eragrostis pectinacea* (Michx.) Nees**
    Prov.: N; herb; *Lægaard 51421* (AAU)
***Gynerium sagittatum* (Aublet) P. Beauv.**
    Prov.: N; herb; *Vickers 16* (F)
***Hymenachne amplexicaulis* Nees**
    Prov.: N; herb; *Luteyn & Mori 8528* (QCA)
***Hymenachne donacifolia* (Raddi) Chase**
    Prov.: N; herb; *Lawesson et al. 44488* (AAU, QCA)
***Ichnanthus pallens* (Sw.) Munro ex Benth.**
    Prov.: N, P; herb; *Harling & Andersson 11756* (GB); *Løjtnant & Molau 13284*
    (GB); *Cerón 2074* (QAME n.v.)
***Lasiacis divaricata* (L.) Hitchc.**
    Prov.: P, M-S; herb; *Løjtnant & Molau 13374* (AAU, GB, QCA). Reaches 1100 m
***Lasiacis ligulata* Hitchc. & Chase**
    Prov.: N, P, M-S; herb; *Vickers 243* (F); *Lægaard 11837* (AAU)
***Lasiacis sorghoidea* (Desv.) Hitchc. & Chase**
    Prov.: N, P, M-S; herb; *Balslev & Madsen 10593* (AAU, QCA); *Alarcón 19558*
    (QCA); *Irvine 283* (F, QCA); *Neill & Palacios 6840* (QCA)
***Leersia hexandra* Sw.**
    Prov.: N; herb; *Lægaard 55800* (AAU)
***Leptochloa scabra* Nees**
    Prov.: N; herb; *Lægaard 51244* (AAU); *Pinkley 206* (GH)
***Leptochloa virgata* (L.) P. Beauv.**
    Prov.: N; herb; *Lægaard 51426* (AAU)
***Lithachne pauciflora* (Sw.) P. Beauv.**
    Prov.: N; herb; *Lægaard 55841* (AAU)
***Luziola subintegra* Swallen**
    Prov.: N; herb; *Azanza & Barfod 41195* (AAU

Poaceae   (cont.)

Olyra caudata Trin.
   Prov.: N, P, M-S; herb; *Balslev et al. 60569* (AAU); *H. Lugo 3555* (AAU, GB)
Olyra ecaudata Doell
   Prov.: N; herb; *Lægaard 52520* (AAU)
Olyra latifolia L.
   Prov.: N, P; herb; *Holm-Nielsen et al. 22186* (AAU); *Madison et al. 18* (QCA, SEL).   Reaches 800 m alt.
Olyra longifolia Kunth
   Prov.: N; herb; *Lægaard 51112* (AAU), *52536* (AAU)
Orthoclada laxa (L. C. Rich.) P. Beauv.
   Prov.: N, P; herb; *Øllgaard et al. 35478* (QCA); *Young 111* (QCA)
Oryza latifolia Desv.
   Prov.: N; herb; *Lægaard 55824* (AAU)
Oryza sativa L.
   Prov.: N; herb; *Balslev & Alarcón 2976* (QCA)
Panicum frondescens Meyer
   Prov.: N; herb; *Cerón 2032* (QAME n.v.)
Panicum hirsutum Sw.
   Prov.: P; herb; *Løjtnant & Molau 13467* (AAU, GB)
Panicum laxum Sw.
   Prov.: P, M-S; herb; *Løjtnant & Molau 13320* (AAU, GB, QCA); *Irvine 550* (QCA).   Reaches 1000 m alt.
Panicum pilosum Sw.
   Prov.: N, P; herb; *Holm-Nielsen & Jeppesen 1044* (AAU); *Neill & Palacios 6569* (QCA); *Irvine 551* (F, QCA).   Reaches 1050 m alt.
Panicum polygonatum Schrader
   Prov.: N, P; herb; *Balslev & Madsen 10591* (AAU); *Palacios et al. 137* (QCA); *Irvine 550* (F, QCA).   Reaches 1000 m alt.
Pariana campestris Aublet
   Prov.: N, P; herb; *Lægaard 41071* (AAU, QCA)
Pariana radiciflora Sagot ex Doell
   Prov.: N, P, M-S, Z-C; herb; *Vickers 64* (F); *Davis & Yost 946* (QCA); *Lugo 2575a* (GB).   Syn. *P. aurita* Swallen
Paspalum conjugatum Berg.
   Prov.: N, P; herb; *Løjtnant & Molau 13308* (AAU, QCA).   Reaches 1000 m alt.
Paspalum paniculatum L.
   Prov.: P; herb; *Løjtnant & Molau 11515* (AAU, GB, QCA)
Paspalum repens Berg.
   Prov.: N; herb; *Holm-Nielsen et al. 20009* (AAU)
Paspalum virgatum L.
   Prov.: N, M-S; herb; *Andrade 33019* (AAU); *Balslev 2290* (QCA); *Pinkley 328* (F).   Reaches 1000 m alt.
Paspalum sp.
   Prov.: N, P; herb; *Holm-Nielsen et al. 20010* (AAU); *Øllgaard et al. 35505* (AAU)
Pharus latifolius L.
   Prov.: N, P; herb; *Jaramillo & Coello 2828* (AAU, QCA); *Alarcón 33* (QCA); *Vickers 201* (F)
Pharus parvifolius Nash ssp. parvifolius
   Prov.: N; herb; *Lægaard 55807* (AAU)
Pharus virescens Doell
   Prov.: N, P; herb; *Harling & Andersson 16654* (GB), *16855* (QCA)

Poaceae (cont.)

***Piresia goeldii* Swallen**
Prov.: N, P; herb; *Lægaard 52524* (AAU)
***Piresia leptophylla* Soderstrom**
Prov.: N; herb; *Lægaard 52580* (AAU)
***Piresia sympodica* (Doell) Swallen**
Prov.: N; herb; *Lægaard 71259* (AAU)
***Saccharum officinarum* L.**
Cultivated in the area, not collected.
***Setaria vulpiseta* (Lam.) Roemer & Schultes**
Prov.: N; herb; *Davis & Yost 947* (QCA); *Harling et al. 7320* (GB)
***Zea mays* L.**
Prov.: N; herb; *Pinkley 547* (ECON)

Polygalaceae
J. F. Macbride, Fl. Peru 3(3), Publ. Field Mus. Nat. Hist., Bot. Ser. 13: 891–950. 1950. Identifications by B. Eriksen, GB.

***Monnina trichoptera* Diels**
Prov.: N; shrub; *Holm-Nielsen & Jeppesen 1035* (AAU, S). Reaches 1800 m alt.
***Polygala paniculata* L.**
Prov.: N, P; herb; *Øllgaard et al. 34996* (AAU); *Alarcón 69* (QCA); *Jaramillo & Coello 4580* (AAU, NY). Reaches 2800 m alt.
***Securidaca mollis* H.B.K.**
Prov.: N; vine; *Lawesson et al. 44281* (AAU)
***Securidaca* sp.**
Prov.: N; vine; *Holm-Nielsen et al. 21233* (AAU)

Polygonaceae
J. Brandbyge, Fl. Ecuador 38, 1989.

***Coccoloba acuminata* H.B.K.**
Prov.: N, tree; *Holm-Nielsen et al. 21526* (AAU)
***Coccoloba coronata* Jacq.**
Prov.: N, P; tree; *Brandbyge & Azanza 30406* (AAU); *Neill & Palacios 6645* (AAU, QCA)
***Coccoloba densifrons* C. Martius ex Meissner**
Prov.: N, M-S; tree; *Brandbyge & Azanza 30353* (AAU); *SEF 8839* (AAU, QCA); *Little et al. 752* (US); *Gentry et al. 21810* (MO, QCA)
***Coccoloba mollis* Casar.**
Prov.: N, M-S; tree; *Øllgaard et al. 57047* (AAU)
***Coccoloba obovata* H.B.K.**
Prov.: N; tree; *Neill 7308* (QAME n.v.)
***Coccoloba peruviana* Lindau**
Prov.: N, M-S; tree; *Brandbyge & Azanza 30392* (AAU); *Gentry 9729* (MO, QCA); *Foster 3883* (AAU, QCA)
***Coccoloba spruceana* Lindau**
Prov.: N; tree; *Neill 6030* (QAME n.v.); *SEF 10055* (AAU)
***Polygonum punctatum* Elliott**
Prov.: N, P; herb; *Brandbyge & Azanza 30078* (AAU)

Polygonaceae (cont.)

Triplaris americana L.
Prov.: N; tree; *Brandbyge et al. 33577* (AAU); *Irvine 725* (QCA)
Triplaris dugandii Brandbyge
Prov.: N, P, M-S; tree; *Brandbyge et al. 33304* (AAU); *SEF 10257* (AAU, QCA).
Reaches 1000 m alt. in Pastaza: *Neill et al. 6179* (AAU, QCA).
Triplaris weigeltiana (Reichb.) Kuntze
Prov.: N; tree; *Brandbyge et al. 33600* (AAU, QCA)

Pontederiaceae
C. N. Horn, Fl. Ecuador 29, 1987.

Eichhornia azurea (Sw.) Kunth
Prov.: N, P; herb; *Holm-Nielsen 20013* (AAU, QCA)
Eichhornia diversifolia (Vahl) Urban
Prov.: N; herb; *Holm-Nielsen et al. 19845* (AAU)
Eichhornia heterosperma E. J. Alexander
Prov.: N; herb; *Holm-Nielsen et al. 20058* (AAU, QCA)
Heteranthera reniformis Ruíz & Pavón
Prov.: N, P; herb; *Lægaard 51537* (AAU, QCA); *Lugo 2383* (AAU, GB)
Pontederia rotundifolia L. f.
Prov.: N, P; herb; *Holm-Nielsen et al. 20000* (AAU, GB, QCA)

Portulacaceae
J. F. Macbride, Fl. Peru 2(2), Publ. Field Mus. Nat. Hist., Bot. Ser. 13: 562–573. 1937.

Portulaca grandiflora Hook.
Prov.: N; herb; *Vickers 21* (F)
Portulaca oleracea L.
Prov.: N, P, M-S; herb; *Holm-Nielsen et al. 20023* (AAU); *Balslev & Santos Dea 2873* (QCA); *McElroy 235* (QCA); *Asdall 82–10* (QCA); *Vickers 34* (F)
Talinum triangulare (Jacq.) Willd.
Prov.: N; herb; *Davis & Yost 1060* (AAU, QCA)

Proteaceae
J. F. Macbride, Fl. Peru 2(2), Publ. Field Mus. Nat. Hist., Bot. Ser. 13: 367–375. 1937.

Panopsis rubescens (Pohl) Pittier
Prov.: N; shrub; *Brandbyge et al. 36155* (AAU); *Nowak 135* (QCA)
Panopsis sp.
Prov.: P; tree; *Øllgaard et al. 34919, 35021* (AAU)
Roupala montana Aublet
Prov.: N; tree; *Korning & Thomsen 47685* (AAU); *Øllgaard et al. 57196* (AAU)

Quiinaceae
J. F. Macbride, Fl. Peru 3A(2), Publ. Field Mus. Nat. Hist., Bot. Ser. 13: 717–726. 1956.

Lacunaria jenmani (Oliver) Ducke
Prov.: N; tree; *SEF 9228* (AAU, QCA); *Korning & Thomsen 58709* (AAU)
Quiina amazonica A. C. Smith
Prov.: N; tree; *Brandbyge et al. 30456* (AAU); *Palacios et al. 1000* (AAU)
Quiina florida Tul.
Prov.: N; tree; *Zaruma et al. 218* (QAME n.v.)
Quiina nitens J. F. Macbr.
Prov.: N; tree; *Cerón 2195* (QAME n.v.)

Rafflesiaceae
J. F. Macbride, Fl. Peru 2(2), Publ. Field Mus. Nat. Hist., Bot. Ser. 13: 443–444. 1937.

Apodanthes caseariae Poit.
Prov.: P; parasite on *Casearia* ; *Holm-Nielsen et al. 21997* (AAU, liquid coll.)

Ranunculaceae
J. F. Macbride, Fl. Peru 2(2), Publ. Field Mus. Nat. Hist., Bot. Ser. 13: 639–669. 1938.

Clematis sericea DC.
Prov.: N, P; vine; *Øllgaard et al. 34615* (AAU); *Lugo 2371* (AAU). Fide J. F. Macbride (Fl. Peru), this may be a variety of *C. dioica* L. (syn. *C. haenkeana* Presl).

Rapateaceae
J. F. Macbride, Fl. Peru 1(3), Publ. Field Mus. Nat. Hist., Bot. Ser. 13: 494–495. 1936.

Rapatea paludosa Aublet
Prov.: P; herb; *Jaramillo et al. 31342* (AAU, QCA)

Rhamnaceae
J. F. Macbride, Fl. Peru 3A(2), Publ. Field Mus. Nat. Hist., Bot. Ser. 13: 391–408. 1956.

Colubrina sp.
Prov.: N; tree; *Øllgaard et al. 57055* (AAU). Probably *C. glandulosa* Perkins or *C. elliptica* (Sw.) Briz. & Stern
Gouania colombiana Suess.
Prov.: N; liana; *Lugo 2558, 2571* (AAU, GB, QCA, S)

Rhamnaceae   (cont.)

Gouania frangulifolia (Schultes) Radlk.
> Prov.: N; shrub; *Holm-Nielsen & Jeppesen 1011* (AAU, S).   Collected at 600 m
> alt.   Syn. *Gouania adenophora* Pilger

Gouania lupuloides (L.) Urban
> Prov.: N, P, M-S; liana; *Løjtnant & Molau 13365* (AAU); *Lugo 1370* (QCA),
> 1329 (AAU).   Reaches 950 m alt.

Gouania polygama (Jacq.) Urban
> Prov.: N, P; liana; *Lugo 2936* (QCA); *Jaramillo et al. 30963* (AAU).   Reaches
> 900 m alt. in Pastaza: *Asplund 19416* (S)

Rhamnidium elaeocarpum Reiss.
> Prov.: N; tree; *Palacios 977* (QAME n.v.)

Zizyphus cf. cinnamomum Triana & Planchon
> Prov.: N; tree; *Korning & Thomsen 58662* (AAU)

Rosaceae

J. F. Macbride, Fl. Peru 2(3), Publ. Field Mus. Nat. Hist., Bot. Ser. 13:
1063–1119. 1938. Identifications by K. Romoleroux, QCA, 1991.

Prunus vana J. F. Macbr.
> Prov.: N, P; tree; *Holm-Nielsen et al. 22533* (AAU).   Reaches 1200 m alt. in
> Pastaza: *Neill et al. 5882* (AAU, QCA)

Rubiaceae

P. Standley *in* J. F. Macbride, Fl. Peru 6(1), Publ. Field Mus. Nat. Hist.,
Bot. Ser. 7: 179–251. 1931 and 13: 3–261. 1936. This listing checked by B.
Boom, Jan 1989.   Unfortunately, several *nomina nuda,* such as
*Coussarea flaviflora, Gonzalagunia villosa, Palicourea congesta, P.
stenostachya,* and *Psychotria flaviflora,* are being used widely.

Alibertia edulis (L. C. Rich.) A. Rich. ex DC.
> Prov.: N, P; shrub, tree; *Brandbyge et al. 33794* (AAU); *Neill et al. 6080* (AAU,
> QCA); *Davis & Yost 1046* (QCA)

Alibertia isernii (Standley) D. Simpson
> Prov.: N; shrub; *Foster 3837* (QCA)

Alibertia itayensis Standley
> Prov.: N; shrub; *Palacios 1022* (NY)

Alibertia macrantha Standley
> Prov.: N; shrub; *Foster 3673* (QCA)

Alibertia myrciifolia (Spruce ex K. Schum.) K. Schum.
> Prov.: N; tree; *Palacios et al. 289* (AAU, QCA)

Alibertia stenantha Standley
> Prov.: N, P; shrub, tree; *Lawesson et al. 44297* (AAU, QCA)

Amphidasya ambigua (Standley) Standley
> Prov.: N; shrub; *Øllgaard et al. 38989* (AAU)

Bathysa peruviana Krause
> Prov.: P; tree; *Holm-Nielsen et al. 22183* (AAU, NY); *Neill & Palacios 6756*
> (AAU, QCA, NY)

Rubiaceae　(cont.)

Bertiera guianensis Aublet
　　Prov.: N, P; shrub; *Holm-Nielsen et al. 22099* (AAU); *Cerón 1069* (QAME n.v.);
　　Irvine 337 (F, QCA)
Borojoa stipularis (Ducke) Cuatrec.
　　Prov.: N, P; tree; *Holm-Nielsen et al. 22551* (AAU); *Palacios & Neill 775* (NY)
Borreria laevis (Lam.) Griseb.
　　Prov.: N, P; herb; *Holm-Nielsen et al. 22231* (AAU)
Borreria ocymoides (Burm. f.) DC.
　　Prov.: N; herb; *Korning & Thomsen 47025* (AAU)
Bothriospora corymbosa (Benth.) Hook. f.
　　Prov.: N; shrub; *Harling et al. 7248* (GB)
Calycophyllum acreanum Ducke
　　Prov.: N; tree; *SEF 9243* (AAU, NY, QCA); *Davis & Yost 1041* (QCA)
Calycophyllum candissimum (Vahl) DC. aff.
　　Prov.: N; tree; *SEF 8915* (AAU); *Korning & Thomsen 47799* (AAU)
Calycophyllum spruceanum (Benth.) Hook. f. ex K. Schum.
　　Prov.: N, P; tree; *Holm-Nielsen et al. 21056* (AAU); *Neill et al. 6344* (AAU, NY);
　　Irvine 212 (F, QCA)
Capirona decorticans Spruce
　　Prov.: N, P; tree; *Brandbyge & Azanza 31008* (AAU); *Neill et al. 6385* (AAU,
　　QCA); *Irvine 527* (F, QCA)
Cephaelis elata Sw.
　　Prov.: P, M-S; tree; *Brandbyge & Azanza 31893* (AAU, QCA)
Cephaelis flaviflora (Krause) Standley
　　Prov.: N; *Neill 7071* (NY)
Cephaelis williamsii Standley
　　Prov.: N; shrub; *Neill et al. 6976* (AAU)
Chimarrhis glabriflora Ducke
　　Prov.: N, P; tree; *Brandbyge & Azanza 31615* (AAU); *Neill et al. 6220* (AAU,
　　QCA); *Irvine 204* (F, QCA)
Chomelia panamensis (Standley) Dwyer
　　Prov.: N; shrub; *Jaramillo & Coello 4511* (AAU)
Chomelia spinosa Jacq.
　　Prov.: N; tree; *SEF 10143* (AAU, NY, QCA)
Chomelia tenuiflora Benth.
　　Prov.: N; tree; *Irvine 788* (F)
Cinchona officinalis L.
　　Prov.: M-S; tree; *Palacios 571* (AAU).　Collected at 750 m alt.
Coccocypselum sp.
　　Prov.: P; shrub; *Løjtnant & Molau 13285* (AAU)
Coffea arabica L.
　　Prov.: N; shrub; *Balslev 4348* (QCA); *Balslev 4851* (MO)
Condaminea corymbosa (Ruíz & Pavón) DC.
　　Prov.: N, P; tree; *Øllgaard et al. 34667* (AAU).　Reaches 1050 m alt.
Cosmibuena grandiflora (Ruiz & Pavón) Rusby
　　Prov.: N; shrub; *Azanza & Barfod 41192, 41098* (AAU, QCA)
Coussarea brevicaulis Krause
　　Prov.: N, P; tree; *Lawesson et al. 39117* (AAU); *Davis & Yost 936* (QCA)
Coussarea cornifolia (Benth.) Benth. & Hook. f.
　　Prov.: N; shrub; *Brandbyge 42676* (AAU)
Coussarea longiflora Muell. Arg.
　　Prov.: P; shrub; *Neill & Palacios 6596* (AAU, QCA)

Rubiaceae   (cont.)

***Coussarea macrocalyx* Standley vel sp. aff.**
   Prov.: P; tree; *Øllgaard et al. 34792* (AAU)
***Coussarea paniculata* (Vahl) Standley**
   Prov.: N, P; shrub, tree; *Holm-Nielsen et al. 19946* (AAU); *Jaramillo & Coello 3505* (AAU)
***Coussarea tenuiflora* Standley**
   Prov.: N; tree; *Zaruma et al. 202* (AAU)
***Coutarea hexandra* (Jacq.) K. Schum.**
   Prov.: P; tree; *Palacios 3495* (QAME n.v.)
***Duroia duckei* Huber**
   Prov.: N; tree; *Lawesson et al. 43384* (AAU, QCA); *Foster 3600* (QCA)
***Duroia eriopila* L. f.**
   Prov.: N; shrub; *Luteyn et al. 8688* (AAU); *Palacios 1836* (QAME n.v.)
***Duroia hirsuta* (Poeppig & Endl.) K. Schum.**
   Prov.: N, P, M-S; tree; *Lawesson et al. 39738* (AAU); *Irvine 300* (QCA); *Davis & Yost 966* (QCA); *Little et al. 784* (US)
***Duroia petiolaris* Spruce ex K. Schum.**
   Prov.: N; tree; *Foster 3600* (QCA)
***Elaeagia* sp.**
   Prov.: P; tree; *Jaramillo et al. 30783A, 30929, 31163* (AAU)
***Exostema maynense* Poeppig & Endl.**
   Prov.: N; tree; *Luteyn et al. 9062* (AAU, QCA); *6664* (AAU)
***Faramea amplifolia* Standley**
   Prov.: N; tree; *Øllgaard et al. 39237* (AAU)
***Faramea axillaris* Standley**
   Prov.: N, P, M-S; shrub, tree; *Holm-Nielsen et al. 21329* (AAU); *Foster 3685* (QCA); *Irvine 814* (F, QCA)
***Faramea capillipes* Muell. Arg.**
   Prov.: N, P; shrub, tree; *Brandbyge & Azanza 30635* (AAU)
***Faramea eurycarpa* Donn. Smith**
   Prov.: P; tree; *Palacios 619* (QAME n.v.)
***Faramea glandulosa* Poeppig & Endl.**
   Prov.: N; tree; *Gentry 12448* (QCA)
***Faramea multiflora* A. Rich.**
   Prov.: N, P; treelet; *Øllgaard et al. 38881* (AAU); *Neill & Palacios 6676* (AAU, QCA).   Reaches 950 m alt. in Pastaza: *Jørgensen & Lægaard 56471* (AAU)
   Syn. *F. maynensis* Spruce ex Rusby; *F. salicifolia* Presl.
***Faramea occidentalis* (L.) A. Rich.**
   Prov.: N, P; shrub; *Holm-Nielsen et al. 27559* (AAU); *Cerón 575* (AAU)
***Faramea quinqueflora* Poeppig & Endl.**
   Prov.: N; shrub; *Irvine 1027* (F)
***Faramea rectinervia* Standley**
   Prov.: N; tree; *Øllgaard et al. 38839* (AAU)
***Faramea uniflora* Dwyer & Hayden**
   Prov.: M-S; shrub; *Brandbye & Azanza 31921* (AAU)
***Genipa americana* L.**
   Prov.: N, P; shrub, tree; *Vickers 223* (QCA)
***Genipa* cf. *curviflora* Dwyer**
   Prov.: P; tree; *Neill & Palacios 6820* (QCA)
***Genipa spruceana* Steyermark**
   Prov.: N; tree; *Holm-Nielsen et al. 21164* (AAU); *Foster 3593* (QCA)

Rubiaceae   (cont.)

Geophila cordifolia Miq.
  Prov.: N, P, M-S; herb; *Løjtnant & Molau 13552* (AAU); *Balslev & Santos Dea 2835* (QCA); *Foster 3695* (QCA). Reaches 1000 m alt.
Geophila gracilis (Ruíz & Pavón) DC.
  Prov.: N; herb; *Alarcón 58* (QCA); *Poulsen 78591* (AAU).   Often called *G. herbacea* (Jacq.) K. Schum.
Geophila macropoda (Ruíz & Pavón) DC.
  Prov.: N; herb; *Balslev et al. 60567* (AAU), *Neill 6428* (QAME n.v.)
Geophila repens (L.) I. M. Johnston
  Prov.: N, P; herb; *Holm-Nielsen et al. 19721* (AAU); *Alarcón 48* (QCA)
Gonzalagunia cornifolia (H.B.K.) Standley
  Prov.: N, P, M-S; tree; *Øllgaard et al. 39102* (AAU); *Neill & Palacios 6566* (QCA)
Gonzalagunia killipii Standley
  Prov.: N, P; shrub; *Jaramillo & Rivera 190* (AAU).   Reaches 1050 m alt. in Pastaza: *Øllgaard et al. 35551* (AAU)
Gonzalagunia pachystachya Standley
  Prov.: N, P; shrub; *Balslev & E. Madsen 10602* (AAU); *Jaramillo & Coello 3392* (QCA)
Gonzalagunia spicata (Lam.) Gómez
  Prov.: N, P, M-S; shrub; *Neill & Palacios 7119* (QCA); *Balslev et al. 62278* (AAU, QCA)
Guettarda acreana Krause
  Prov.: N; shrub; *Harling & Andersson 12009* (GB)
Guettarda crispiflora Vahl
  Prov.: P; shrub; *Lugo 2465, 4677* (AAU, GB, QCA).   Reaches 1100 m alt.
Guettarda sp. 1
  Prov.: N; tree; *Neill et al. 6285* (AAU, QCA)
Guettarda sp. 2
  Prov.: N, P; tree; *Brandbyge et al. 30318* (AAU)
Guettarda sp. 3
  Prov.: N, P; shrub; *Holm-Nielsen et al. 22155* (AAU)
Hamelia axillaris Sw.
  Prov.: N; shrub, tree; *Lawesson et al. 43492* (AAU); *Vickers 137* (QCA)
Hamelia patens Jacq.
  Prov.: N, P; shrub; *Øllgaard et al. 35139* (AAU); *Alarcón 19560* (QCA)
Hedyotis lancifolia K. Schum.
  Prov.: N; *Cerón 2035* (QAME n.v.).   Syn. *Oldenlandia lancifolia* (K. Schum.) DC.
Hillia illustris (Vell.) K. Schum.
  Prov.: N; shrub, tree; *Lawesson et al. 44421* (AAU)
Hillia parasitica Jacq.
  Prov.: N; epiphytic herb; *Oldeman et al. 38* (QCA)
Hippotis scarlatina Krause
  Prov.: P; shrub; *Løjtnant & Molau 13479* (AAU); *Lugo 3868* (AAU); *Jaramillo & Coello 3258* (AAU, QCA)
Isertia laevis (Triana) Boom
  Prov.: N, P; tree; *Brandbyge & Azanza 30368* (AAU).   Reaches 1300 m alt. in Pastaza: *Palacios et al. 181* (QCA)
Isertia pittieri (Standley) Standley
  Prov.: N; tree; *Cerón 2725* (QAME n.v.)

Rubiaceae (cont.)

***Isertia rosea* Spruce ex K. Schum.**
Prov.: N; shrub, tree; *Brandbyge et al. 36157* (AAU)
***Ixora killipii* Standley**
Prov.: N; shrub; *Jaramillo & Coello 4618* (AAU)
***Ixora sparsifolia* Krause**
Prov.: N, P; tree; *Holm-Nielsen et al. 21846* (AAU); *Luteyn et al. 9027* (QCA)
***Ixora ulei* Krause**
Prov.: N; tree; *Lawesson et al. 43474* (AAU, QCA)
***Kotchubaea sericantha* Standley**
Prov.: N, P, M-S; tree; *Korning & Thomsen 58740* (AAU)
***Ladenbergia* sp.**
Prov.: N; tree; *Oldeman & Arévalo 93* (QCA)
***Macrocnemum roseum* (Ruíz & Pavón) Wedd.**
Prov.: N; tree; *Palacios & Neill 905* (QAME n.v.)
***Macrocnemum sprucei* Rusby**
Prov.: N; tree; *Neill 7068* (QAME n.v.)
***Manettia calycosa* Griseb. vel sp. aff.**
Prov.: N; liana; *Palacios et al. 884* (AAU)
***Manettia divaricata* Wernh.**
Prov.: N; liana; *Lawesson et al. 39501* (AAU); *Neill et al. 6470* (AAU, QCA)
***Manettia pectinata* Sprague vel sp. aff.**
Prov.: N; *Cerón 1402* (QAME n.v.)
***Palicourea buntingii* Steyerm.**
Prov.: N; *Zaruma et al. 341* (QAME n.v.)
***Palicourea corymbifera* (Muell. Arg.) Standley**
Prov.: P; tree; *Øllgaard et al. 34551* (AAU)
***Palicourea crocea* (Sw.) Roemer & Schultes**
Prov.: N, P; shrub, treelet; *Brandbyge et al. 30547* (AAU); *Neill & Palacios 6670* (AAU, QCA). Syn. *P. stenoclada* (Muell. Arg.) Standley
***Palicourea guianensis* Aublet**
Prov.: N, M-S; tree; *Holm-Nielsen et al. 19658* (AAU); *Brandbyge & Azanza 32201* (AAU, QCA)
***Palicourea* cf. *huigrensis* Standley**
Prov.: N; shrub; *Jaramillo & Coello 3975* (AAU)
***Palicourea lagesii* K. Schum. ex Krause**
Prov.: N; shrub, tree; *Balslev 2322* (AAU); *Foster 3565* (QCA)
***Palicourea lasiantha* Krause**
Prov.: N, P; tree; *Holm-Nielsen 19342* (AAU); *Gentry 12437* (QCA)
***Palicourea nigricans* Krause**
Prov.: N; shrub; *Foster 3611* (QCA)
***Palicourea ovalifolia* (Rusby) Standley**
Prov.: P, M-S; tree; *Øllgaard et al. 34706* (AAU). Reaches 700 m alt.
***Palicourea punicea* (Ruíz & Pavón) DC.**
Prov.: N, P, M-S; tree; *Brandbyge & Azanza 30666* (AAU)
***Palicourea subspicata* Huber**
Prov.: N; shrub; *Lawesson et al. 39677* (AAU); *Foster 3619* (QCA)
***Pentagonia macrophylla* Benth.**
Prov.: N, P, M-S; tree; *Holm-Nielsen & Jeppesen 967* (AAU); *Korning & Thomsen 47168* (AAU). Reaches 1000 m alt.
***Pentagonia parvifolia* Steyermark**
Prov.: N; tree; *Davis & Yost 969* (QCA)

Rubiaceae   (cont.)

Pentagonia spathicalyx K. Schum.
Prov.: N; tree; *Foster 3585* (QCA); *Davis & Yost 971* (QCA)
Pentagonia subauriculata Standley
Prov.: N; shrub; *Foster 3846* (QCA)
Pentagonia williamsii Standley
Prov.: N; tree; *Vickers 95* (F)
Pentagonia sp.
Prov.: N; tree; *Korning & Thomsen 58690* (AAU)
Posoqueria latifolia (Rudge) Roemer & Schultes
Prov.: N; shrub; *Brandbyge et al. 33407* (AAU); *Gentry 12418* (QCA)
Posoqueria longiflora Aublet
Prov.: N; tree; *Lawesson et al. 44291* (AAU)
Posoqueria sp.
Prov.: N; tree; *Renner 69308* (AAU, QCA)
Psychotria acuminata Benth.
Prov.: N, M-S; shrub; *Brandbgye & Azanza 31934* (AAU, QCA); *Gentry 9763* (GB).   Reaches 700 m alt.
Psychotria alboviridula Krause
Prov.: N, P; shrub; *Balslev 2291* (AAU); *Jaramillo et al. 31529* (AAU); *Foster 3730* (QCA)
Psychotria cf. bahiensis DC.
Prov.: N; shrub; *Foster 3730* (QCA)
Psychotria brachybotrya Muell. Arg.
Prov.: N; shrub; *Foster 3607* (QCA)
Psychotria caerulea Ruíz & Pavón
Prov.: N, P, M-S; shrub; *Øllgaard et al. 34639* (AAU); *Løjtnant & Molau 13554* (AAU).   Reaches 1300 m alt.
Psychotria callithrix (Miq.) Steyermark
Prov.: P; shrub; *Øllgaard et al. 35335* (AAU)
Psychotria capitata Ruíz & Pavón
Prov.: P; tree; *Lugo 3936, 3944* (AAU, GB).   Reaches 700 m alt.
Psychotria carthaginensis Jacq.
Prov.: N, P; shrub; *Holm-Nielsen et al. 21380* (AAU); *Brandbyge & Azanza 31800* (AAU, QCA).   Syn. *P. alba* Ruíz & Pavón
Psychotria cincta Standley
Prov.: N, P; shrub, tree; *Holm-Nielsen et al. 20095* (AAU)
Psychotria cf. compta Standley
Prov.: N; shrub; *Brandbyge et al. 33708* (AAU)
Psychotria emetica L. f.
Prov.: N; shrub; *Balslev & Alarcón 2961* (QCA); *Foster 3841* (in QCA as *Cephaelis leucantha* (Krause) Standley)
Psychotria erecta (Aublet) Standley & Steyermark
Prov.: N, M-S; shrub; *Harling et al. 7644* (GB).   Reaches 800 m alt. in M-S: *MacBryde 171* (QCA)
Psychotria hebeclada DC.
Prov.: N; shrub; *Harling & Andersson 11979* (GB); *Lugo 2084* (AAU)
Psychotria hoffmannseggiana
(Willd. ex Roem. & Schultes) Muell.-Arg.
Prov.: N, P; shrub; *Holm-Nielsen et al. 20162* (AAU); *Palacios et al. 332* (AAU)
Psychotria juninensis Standley
Prov.: N, P; shrub; *Brandbyge & Azanza 31252* (AAU); *Jaramillo et al. 31726* (QCA)

Rubiaceae (cont.)

Psychotria loretensis Standley
Prov.: N, P, M-S; shrub; *Brandbyge et al. 33890* (AAU); *Foster 3638* (QCA)
Reaches 700 m alt.
Psychotria lupulina Benth.
Prov.: N, P; shrub; *Harling et al. 7227, 7548* (GB); *Palacios & Neill 711* (AAU)
Psychotria macrophylla Ruíz & Pavón
Prov.: N, P, M-S; shrub; *Brandbyge et al. 32564* (AAU)
Psychotria mapourioides DC.
Prov.: N; shrub; *Zaruma et al. 563* (QAME n.v.)
Psychotria marginata Sw.
Prov.: N; shrub; *Palacios et al. 308* (AAU, QCA)
Psychotria mathewsii Standley
Prov.: N; *Palacios 504* (AAU)
Psychotria micrantha H.B.K.
Prov.: P; shrub; *Neill & Palacios 6736* (AAU, QCA). Syn. *P. rufescens* Humb.
& Bonpl. ex Roemer & Schultes
Psychotria mima Standley
Prov.: N; shrub; *Palacios et al. 327* (AAU); *Irvine 766* (F)
Psychotria nautensis Standley
Prov.: N; shrub; *Cerón 844* (AAU)
Psychotria nervosa Sw.
Prov.: N; shrub, tree; *Brandbyge et al. 33346* (AAU, QCA)
Psychotria officinalis (Aublet) Räusch. ex Sandw.
Prov.: P; treelet; *Neill & Palacios 6729* (AAU)
Psychotria orchidearum Standley
Prov.: N; shrub; *Neill 7025* (QAME n.v.)
Psychotria pilosa Ruíz & Pavón
Prov.: P, M-S; shrub; *Brandbyge & Azanza 31933* (AAU, QCA); *Palacios et al.*
205 (AAU, QCA); *Croat 58904* (QCA)
Psychotria pithecobia Standley
Prov.: N; shrub; *Cerón 2692* (QAME n.v.)
Psychotria platypoda DC.
Prov.: N, P; shrub; *Holm-Nielsen et al. 21298* (AAU, QCA)
Psychotria poeppigiana Muell. Arg.
Prov.: N, P, M-S; shrub; *Brandbyge & Azanza 31073* (AAU, QCA). Reaches
1100 m alt. Syn. *Cephaelis tomentosa* (Aublet) Vahl
Psychotria racemosa (Aublet) Räusch.
Prov.: N, P; shrub; *Holm-Nielsen & Jeppesen 964* (AAU); *Alarcón 118* (QCA)
Psychotria remota Benth.
Prov.: N; shrub; *Cerón 3156* (QAME n.v.)
Psychotria rhodophylla Standley
Prov.: N; shrub; *Foster 3665* (QCA)
Psychotria cf. rosea (Benth.) Muell. Arg.
Prov.: N; shrub; *Luteyn et al. 9089* (AAU)
Psychotria siggersiana Standley
Prov.: N; shrub; *Cerón 2291* (QAME n.v.)
Psychotria stenostachya Standley
Prov.:N, P, M-S; shrub; *Holm-Nielsen et al. 19851* (AAU); *Irvine 504* (F, QCA)
Psychotria suerrensis Donn. Smith
Prov.: N, P; shrub; *Holm-Nielsen et al. 21386* (AAU)

Rubiaceae   (cont.)

***Psychotria tenuicaulis* Krause**
Prov.: N, P; shrub; *Luteyn et al. 9029* (AAU); *Neill & Palacios 6811* (AAU, QCA)

***Psychotria trichocephala* Poeppig & Endl.**
Prov.: N; tree; *Zaruma et al. 170* (QAME n.v.)

***Psychotria ulviformis* Steyermark**
Prov.: N; herb; *Poulsen 79627* (AAU)

***Psychotria viridis* Ruíz & Pavón**
Prov.: N, P; shrub, tree; *Neill & Palacios 6807* (AAU, QCA); *Pinkley 225* (ECON)

***Psychotria williamsii* Standley**
Prov.: N; shrub, tree; *Balslev 1593* (AAU, QCA)

***Randia armata* (Sw.) DC.**
Prov.: N, P, M-S; shrub, tree; *Lawesson et al. 39527* (AAU).   Syn. *R. spinosa* (Jacq.) Karst.

***Randia formosa* (Jacq.) K. Schum.**
Prov.: N; shrub; *Brandbyge & Azanza 30583* (AAU)

***Randia hondensis* Karst.**
Prov.: N; tree; *Lawesson et al. 39547* (AAU)

***Randia ruiziana* DC.**
Prov.: N, M-S; shrub, tree; *Lawesson et al. 43403* (AAU, QCA)

***Raritebe palicoureoides* Wernh.**
Prov.: N, P; tree; *Lugo 2146, 2202* (AAU, GB, QCA); *Brandbyge & Azanza 31040* (AAU, QCA)

***Remijia* sp.**
Prov.: N, P; shrub; *Holm-Nielsen et al. 22414* (AAU)

***Rondeletia* sp.**
Prov.: N, P; tree; *Øllgaard et al. 35172* (AAU)

***Rudgea* cf. *bracteata* Kirkbride**
Prov.: N; tree; *Korning & Thomsen 47090* (AAU)

***Rudgea cornifolia* (Roemer & Schultes) Standley**
Prov.: N; shrub, tree; *Lawesson et al. 43317* (AAU)

***Rudgea loretensis* Standley**
Prov.: N, P, M-S; shrub; *Lawesson et al. 43357* (AAU); *Croat 50336* (QCA)

***Rudgea poeppigii* K. Schum. ex Standley**
Prov.: N; shrub; *Foster 3663, 3743* (QCA)

***Rudgea retifolia* Standley**
Prov.: N; tree; *Lawesson et al. 39324* (AAU).   Syn. *R. cephalantha* Standley

***Rudgea sessiliflora* Standley**
Prov.: N, P; shrub; *Korning & Thomsen 47122* (AAU)

***Rudgea* sp .**
Prov.: N; tree; *SEF 8506, 8550, 9093* (AAU)

***Sabicea colombiana* Wernh.**
Prov.: N, P; tree, shrub, liana; *Brandbyge & Azanza 30065* (AAU); *Neill et al. 5857* (QCA)

***Sabicea villosa* Willd. ex Roemer & Schultes**
Prov.: N, P, M-S; shrub; *Holm-Nielsen et al. 21978* (AAU).   Reaches 1100 m alt. in Pastaza: *Neill et al. 5986* (QCA)

***Simira cordifolia* (Hook. f.) Steyermark**
Prov.: N, M-S; tree; *Luteyn et al. 8506* (QCA); *Little et al. 494* (US)

***Simira rubescens* (Benth.) Bremek. ex Steyermark**
Prov.: N, M-S; tree; *Neill et al. 6185* (AAU, QCA); *Davis & Yost 1007* (QCA); *Irvine 949* (F, QCA)

Rubiaceae (cont.)

Stachyarrhena sp.
> Prov.: N; tree; *Neill 8254* (QAME n.v.)

Tocoyena sp.
> Prov.: N; tree; *Pennington 12296* (MO n.v.)

Uncaria guianensis (Aublet) Gmel.
> Prov.: N; scandent shrub or liana; *Gentry et al. 21792* (QCA); *Brandbyge et al. 33572* (AAU, QCA)

Warscewiczia coccinea (Vahl) Klotzsch
> Prov.: N, P, M-S; shrub, tree; *Azanza & Barfod 41093* (AAU); *Neill 7145* (QCA); *Alarcón 19520* (QCA)

Warscewiczia cordata Spruce ex K. Schum.
> Prov.: N, M-S; tree; *Jaramillo & Coello 2200* (QCA); *Little et al. 579* (US)

Warscewiczia schwackei K. Schum.
> Prov.: N; tree; *Foster 3771* (QCA)

Wittmackanthus stanleyanus (Schomb.) Kuntze
> Prov.: N; tree; *Oldeman & Arévalo 94* (QCA). Syn. *Pallasia stanleyana* (Schomb.) Klotzsch

Rutaceae
J. F. Macbride, Fl. Peru 3(2), Publ. Field Mus. Nat. Hist., Bot. Ser. 13: 655–689. 1949. This listing checked by J. Kallunki, Mar 1989.

Amyris macrocarpa Gereau
> Prov.: N; shrub, tree; *Palacios 1382* (AAU, G, MO, NY, QUAME)

Angostura acuminata (Pilger) Albuq. vel sp. aff.
> Prov.: N; tree; *Zaruma et al. 527* (QAME n.v.)

Citrus aurantifolia (Christm.) Swingle
> Prov.: N; tree; *Pinkley 289* (ECON)

Citrus paradisii Macfad.
> Prov.: N; tree; *Vickers 145* (QCA)

Citrus reticulata Blanco
> Prov.: N; tree; *Vickers 149* (QCA); *Balslev & Irvine 4612* (AAU, QCA)

Citrus sinensis (L.) Osbeck
> Prov.: N; tree; *Vickers 148* (QCA); *Irvine 779* (F, QCA)

Dictyoloma peruviana Planchon
> Prov.: M-S; tree; *Palacios 1486* (NY n.v.). Collected at 800 m alt.

Ertela trifolia (L.) O. Ktze.
> Prov.: N, M-S; treelet; *Cazalet & Pennington 7768* (NY n.v.); *Holm-Nielsen et al. 21255* (AAU). Commonly filed as *Monnieria trifolia* Loef.

Erythrochiton trifoliatus Pilger
> Prov.: M-S; tree; *RBAE 166* (NY n.v.). Belongs in *Toxosiphon* (cf. Kallunki)

Esenbeckia amazonica Kaastra
> Prov.: N; tree; *Holm-Nielsen 19324* (AAU); *Neill 7492* (AAU)

Fagara culantrilo (H.B.K.) Schultes
> Prov.: N; tree; *Asplund 911* (S)

Pilocarpus peruvianus (J. F. Macbr.) Kaastra
> Prov.: N; tree; *Dwyer & Simmons 9756* (QCA)

Raputiarana subsigmoidea (Ducke) Emmerich vel sp. aff.
> Prov.: M-S; tree; *Brandbyge & Azanza 31990* (AAU)

Zanthoxylum cuiabense Engl.
> Prov.: N; tree; *Palacios 1513* (QAME n.v.)

Rutaceae (cont.)

***Zanthoxylum juniperinum* Poeppig & Endl. vel sp. aff.**
    Prov.: N, M-S; tree; *Brandbyge & Azanza 32860* (AAU); *Little et al. 399* (US)
***Zanthoxylum monophyllum* (Lam.) P. Wilson**
    Prov.: N; tree; *Palacios 2112* (QAME n.v.)
***Zanthoxylum procerum* Donn. Smith**
    Prov.: N; tree; *Neill et al. 6239* (AAU, QCA)
***Zanthoxylum* cf. *riedelianum* Engl.**
    Prov.: N; tree; *Holm-Nielsen et al. 19102A* (AAU); *Asplund 9132, 10249* (S)
***Zanthoxylum sobrevielae* D. Simpson**
    Prov.: N; tree; *Palacios 1824* (QAME n.v.)
***Zanthoxylum sprucei* Engl. aff.**
    Prov.: N; tree; *Palacios 1381* (QAME n.v.)
***Zanthoxylum weberbaueri* (K. Krause) J. F. Macbr.**
    Prov.: N; tree; *Palacios 1729* (QAME n.v.)

Sabiaceae
Identifications mostly by A. Gentry, MO.

***Meliosma glabrata* (Liebm.) Urban**
    Prov.: N; tree; *Korning & Thomsen 47552, 47780, 58675* (AAU). Possibly = *M. occidentalis* Cuatrec. or *M. herbertii* Rolfe
***Meliosma loretoyacuensis* Idrobo & Cuatrec.**
    Prov.: N; tree; *Palacios et al. 511* (AAU)
***Ophiocaryon heterophyllum* (Benth.) Urban**
    Prov.: N; tree; *Brandbyge et al. 36048* (AAU); *Jaramillo & Coello 3006* (AAU)
***Ophiocaryon manausense* (W. Rodr.) Barneby**
    Prov.: N; tree; *Brandbyge et al. 36228* (AAU); *Jaramillo 2721* (AAU, QCA)

Sapindaceae
J. F. Macbride, Fl. Peru 3A(2), Publ. Field Mus. Nat. Hist., Bot. Ser. 13: 291–391. 1956. This listing checked by P. Acevedo, US, January 1991.

***Allophylus divaricatus* Radlk.**
    Prov.: N; tree; *Holm-Nielsen 39845* (AAU); *Neill 7996* (MO, QAME n.v.)
***Allophylus excelsus* (Triana & Planchon) Radlk.**
    Prov.: N; tree; *Neill 6291* (MO, QAME n.v.)
***Allophylus floribundus* (Poeppig & Endl.) Radlk.**
    Prov.: N, P; tree; *Lugo 3208* (AAU, QCA); *Jaramillo et al. 31540* (AAU); *Brandbyge et al. 33580* (AAU); *Neill et al. 6885* (AAU, QCA); *Vickers 160* (F)
***Allophylus incanus* Radlk. vel sp. aff.**
    Prov.: N; tree; *Palacios 2415* (MO, QAME n.v.)
***Allophylus* cf. *leucoclados* Radlk.**
    Prov.: N; tree; *Lawesson et al. 43566* (AAU)
***Allophylus paniculatus* (Poeppig & Endl.) Radlk.**
    Prov.: N; tree; *Foster 3878* (QCA)
***Allophylus peruvianus* Radlk.**
    Prov.: N; tree; *Palacios 2284* (MO, QAME n.v.)

Sapindaceae (cont.)

***Allophylus pilosus* (J. F. Macbr.) A. Gentry**
Prov.: N; tree; *Palacios et al. 400* (AAU); *Brandbyge & Azanza 30110* (AAU)
***Allophylus punctatus* (Poeppig & Endl.) Radlk.**
Prov.: N; tree; *Palacios et al. 350* (AAU)
***Allophylus scrobiculatus* (Poeppig & Endl.) Radlk.**
Prov.: P; tree; *Neill & Palacios 6802* (AAU, QCA)
***Allophylus stenodictyus* Radlk. aff.**
Prov.: N; tree; *Palacios 2262* (MO, QAME n.v.)
***Cardiospermum grandiflorum* Sw.**
Prov.: N, P; liana; *Harling & Andersson 11845* (AAU, QCA)
***Cardiospermum halicacabum* L.**
Prov.: N, P, M-S; liana; *Lugo 937* (AAU); *Molau & Öhman 1578* (GB, QCA)
Syn. *C. microcarpum* H.B.K.
***Cupania cinerea* Poeppig & Endl.**
Prov.: N; tree; *Holm-Nielsen et al. 21423* (AAU); *Neill et al. 6248* (AAU, QCA)
***Cupania livida* (Radlk.) Croat**
Prov.: N; tree; *Palacios 2098; Neill 8341* (MO, QAME n.v.)
***Cupania scrobiculata* L. C. Rich.**
Prov.: N; tree; *SEF 10158* (AAU)
***Matayba* sp.**
Prov.: N; shrub or treelet; *Jaramillo 6887* (AAU); *Brandbyge et al. 33637* (AAU)
***Paullinia alata* (Ruíz & Pavón) G. Don**
Prov.:N, P, M-S; liana; *Holm-Nielsen & Jeppesen 851* (AAU, QCA)
***Paullinia bracteosa* Radlk.**
Prov.: N, P; liana; *Brandbyge & Azanza 30401* (AAU); *Vickers 67* (QCA)
***Paullinia castaneifolia* Radlk.**
Prov.: N; liana; *Brandbyge et al. 30494* (AAU)
***Paullinia clathrata* Radlk.**
Prov.: N; tree; *Neill 8263* (MO, QAME n.v.)
***Paullinia clavigera* Schlecht. vel sp. aff.**
Prov.: N; liana; *Lawesson et al. 43428* (AAU)
***Paullinia cuneata* Radlk.**
Prov.: N; tree; *Holm-Nielsen et al. 21226* (AAU); *Foster 3806* (AAU)
***Paullinia cupana* Kunth**
Prov.: N; tree; *Cerón 3192* (QAME n.v.)
***Paullinia dasystachya* Radlk. aff.**
Prov.: N; tree; *Brandbyge et al. 33661* (AAU)
***Paullinia erianthra* Benth. ex Radlk.**
Prov.: N; liana; *Neill et al. 6267* (AAU)
***Paullinia exalata* Radlk.**
Prov.: N; liana; *Jaramillo & Coello 2779* (AAU, QCA)
***Paullinia faginea* (Triana & Planchon) Radlk. vel sp. aff.**
Prov.:P; shrub; *Brandbyge & Azanza 31613* (AAU); *Foster 3880* (QCA)
***Paullinia fasciculata* Radlk.**
Prov.: N; liana; *Holm-Nielsen & Jeppesen 851* (AAU)
***Paullinia fimbriata* Radlk.**
Prov.: N; tree; *Marles 50* (QAME n.v.)
***Paullinia gigantea* Poeppig & Endl.**
Prov.: P; tree; *Rubio 88* (MO)
***Paullinia grandifolia* Benth. ex Radlk.**
Prov.: P; tree; *Øllgaard et al. 34834* (AAU)

Sapindaceae (cont.)

Paullinia nobilis Radlk. aff.
Prov.: P, M-S; liana or shrub; *Jaramillo & Coello 3292* (AAU)
Paullinia obovata (Ruíz & Pavón) Pers. aff.
Prov.: N, P; liana; *Gentry et al. 22103* (QCA); *Harling et al. 7491* (GB)
Paullinia paullinioides (Spruce) Radlk.
Prov.: N; tree; *Cerón & Hurtado 3994* (MO, QAME n.v.)
Paullinia pterocarpa Triana & Planchon
Prov.: N; tree; *Cerón 3174* (QAME n.v.); *Cerón & Hurtado 4259* (MO)
Paullinia pterophylla Triana & Planchon
Prov.: N; liana; *Gentry et al. 21795* (MO)
Paullinia rhizantha Poeppig & Endl.
Prov.: N; tree; *Cerón & Cerón 4600* (MO, QAME n.v.)
Paullinia rufescens Rich. ex Juss. vel sp. aff.
Prov.: N; tree; *Cerón & Gallo 5031* (MO, QAME n.v.)
Paullinia serjaniifolia Triana & Planchon
Prov.: N; tree; *Cerón 3076* (QAME n.v.)
Paullinia sphaerocarpa Rich. ex Juss.
Prov.: N, P; shrub; *Jaramillo & Coello 2921* (AAU); *Øllgaard et al. 35092* (AAU)
Paullinia tarapotensis Radlk.
Prov.: N; shrub or liana; *Holm-Nielsen et al. 20190* (AAU)
Paullinia tenuifolia Standley ex J. F. Macbr.
Prov.: N; liana; *Lawesson et al. 39523* (AAU, QCA); *Harling et al. 7751* (GB)
Paullinia trilatera Radlk.
Prov.: N; liana; *Holm-Nielsen et al. 21423* (AAU, S); *Foster 3562* (QCA, S)
Paullinia yoco Schultes & Killip
Prov.: N; liana; *Vickers 109* (F); *Pinkley 312, 428* (S)
Serjania altissima (Poeppig & Endl.) Radlk. aff.
Prov.: N; liana; *Cerón 2728* (QAME n.v.)
Serjania clematidea Triana & Planchon
Prov.: N;liana; *Dodson et al. 14925* (NY); *Grubb et al. 146* (NY)
Serjania communis Camb.
Prov.: P, M-S; liana; *Camp 1521* (NY); *Harling et al. 7052* (GB, MO)
Serjania didymadenia Radlk.
Prov.: N; liana; *Gentry 12470* (GB, MO)
Serjania glabrata Kunth
Prov.: N; liana; *H. Lugo 2071* (GB)
Serjania grandifolia Sagot
Prov.: N; liana; *Palacios et al. 3571* (MO, QAME n.v.)
Serjania inflata Poeppig & Endl.
Prov.: N; liana; *Marles 50* (QAME n.v.)
Serjania leptocarpa Radlk.
Prov.: N; liana; *Mexía 7183* (F, NY); *Palacios & Neill 676* (NY)
Serjania membranacea Splitgerber
Prov.: N; liana; *Neill et al. 6287*(AAU, MO, NY, QAME n.v.)
Serjania mucronulata Radlk.
Prov.: N; liana; *Neill et al. 6900* (NY, QAME n.v.)
Serjania rhombea Radlk.
Prov.: N; liana; *Cerón 1655* (QAME n.v.).   Reaches 800 m alt. in M-S: *Baker et al. 6296* (NY)

Sapindaceae   (cont.)

Serjania rubicaulis Benth. ex Radlk.
Prov.: N, P, M-S; liana; *Bennett 3434* (NY); *Cerón 1687* (QAME n.v.)
Serjania rufa Radlk.
Prov.: N, P; liana; *H. Lugo 2232* (GB, MO); *Øllgaard et al. 35151* (AAU)
Serjania schunkei Acevedo-Rdgz.
Prov.: N; liana; *Cerón 7372* (MO, QAME n.v.)
Serjania trirostris Radlk.
Prov.: N; liana; *H. Lugo 2232* (GB)
Talisia pachycarpa Radlk.
Prov.: N; tree; *Palacios 2182* (QAME n.v.)
Talisia peruviana Standley
Prov.: N, P; shrub; *Lawesson et al. 39586* (AAU, S); *Brandbyge et al. 32959*
(AAU, S); *Jaramillo et al. 31134* (AAU, S); *Neill 7604* (QAME n.v.)
Thinouia obliqua (Ruiz & Pavón) Radlk.
Prov.: N; tree; *Cerón 3657* (MO, QAME n.v.)
Toulicia reticulata Radlk.
Prov.: M-S; tree; *Pennington 10783* (QCA). Collected at 700 m alt.

Sapotaceae
T. D. Pennington, Fl. Neotropica, 52. 1990.

Chrysophyllum amazonicum Pennington
Prov.: N; tree; *Chaguaro 26* (QCA)
Chrysophyllum argenteum Jacq.
Prov.: N, M-S; tree; *Øllgaard et al. 30399* (AAU); *Neill 7075* (QAME n.v.);
Pennington 10645 (K, NY, QCA); *Little et al. 487* (COL)
Chrysophyllum cuneifolium (Rudge) A. DC.
Prov.: N; tree; *Korning & Thomsen 47196* (AAU)
Chrysophyllum manaosense (Aubrev.) Pennington
Prov.: N; tree; *Palacios 857* (QAME n.v.); *Flores 45* (QCA)
Chrysophyllum pomiferum (Eyma) Pennington
Prov.: N; tree; *SEF 9122* (AAU); *Palacios 1852* (QAME n.v.)
Chrysophyllum sanguinolentum (Pierre) Baehni
Prov.: P, M-S; tree; *Neill 8802* (QAME n.v.); *Little et al. 794* (COL, US)
Chrysophyllum venezuelanense (Pierre) Pennington
Prov.: N, M-S; tree; *Holm-Nielsen 19242* (AAU); *Pennington 10621* (K, NY,
QCA); *Neill et al. 6522* (QCA)
Diploon cuspidatum (Hoehne) Cronquist
Prov.: N; tree; *Neill et al. 8862* (QAME n.v.)
Ecclinusa guianensis Eyma
Prov.: N; tree; *Palacios 3058* (QAME n.v.)
Ecclinusa lanceolata (C. Martius & Eichler) Pierre
Prov.: N; tree; *Neill et al. 7854* (QAME n.v.)
Manilkara bidentata (A. DC.) Chev.
Prov.: N; tree; *Alarcón 20* (QCA); *Davis & Yost 1000* (F, QCA)
Micropholis brochidodroma Pennington
Prov.: P; tree; *Palacios 736* (QAME n.v.)
Micropholis egensis (A. DC.) Pierre
Prov.: N; tree; *SEF 8874* (AAU, NY, QCA). Syn. *M. ulei* (Krause) Eyma

Sapotaceae (cont.)

***Micropholis guyanensis* (A. DC.) Pierre**
Prov.: P, M-S; tree; *Little et al. 526* (COL); *Neill et al. 8906* (QAME n.v.)
***Micropholis melinoniana* Pierre**
Prov.: N; tree; *Oldeman & Arévalo 33* (MO, QCA)
***Micropholis sanctae-rosae* (Baehni) Pennington**
Prov.: N; tree; *Korning & Thomsen 47815* (AAU)
***Micropholis venulosa* (C. Martius & Eichl.) Pierre**
Prov.: N, M-S; tree; *Holm-Nielsen & Jeppesen 782* (AAU); *Chaguro 1* (QCA); *Irvine 888* (F, QCA); *Neill 7329* (QAME n.v.)
***Pouteria baehniana* Monach.**
Prov.: N; tree; *SEF 9175* (AAU, K, NY, QCA);
***Pouteria bangii* (Rusby) Pennington**
Prov.: N; tree; *Palacios 1252* (QAME n.v.)
***Pouteria bilocularis* (Winkler) Baehni**
Prov.: N, M-S; tree; *Holm-Nielsen & Jeppesen 898* (AAU)
***Pouteria caimito* (Ruiz & Pavón) Radlk.**
Prov.: N; tree; *Jaramillo & Coello 4209* (AAU, QCA); *Irvine 159* (F, QCA); *Pinkley 151* (ECON, S); *Alarcón 137* (QCA); *Vickers 48* (F); *Foster 3862* (QCA)
***Pouteria durlandii* (Standley) Baehni**
Prov.: N; tree; *SEF 8939, 8951* (AAU, K, QCA)
***Pouteria ephedrantha* (A. C. Smith) Pennington**
Prov.: N; tree; *Palacios 914* (QAME n.v.)
***Pouteria glomerata* (Miq.) Radlk.**
Prov.: N; tree; *Nowak 80* (QCA); *Lawesson et al. 44302* (AAU, QCA); *Irvine 315* (F, QCA)
***Pouteria hispida* Eyma**
Prov.: N; tree; *Palacios 956* (QAME n.v.)
***Pouteria lucumifolia* (Reiss. ex Max.) Pennington**
Prov.: N; tree; *Cerón 1039* (QAME n.v.). More likely this is *P. lucuma* (Ruiz & Pavón) Kuntze
***Pouteria multiflora* (A. DC.) Eyma**
Prov.: N; tree; *SEF 8921* (AAU, K, NY, QCA); *Oldeman & Arévalo 51* (QCA); *Irvine 695* (F, QCA)
***Pouteria nudipetala* Pennington aff.**
Prov.: N; tree; *Palacios 2360* (QAME n.v.)
***Pouteria oblanceolata* Pires**
Prov.: N; tree; *Neill et al. 7818* (QAME n.v.)
***Pouteria platyphylla* (A. C. Smith) Baehni**
Prov.: N; tree; *Korning & Thomsen 47616* (AAU); *Palacios 887* (QAME n.v.)
***Pouteria pubescens* (Aubrev. & Pellegr.) Pennington**
Prov.: N; tree; *Palacios 513* (QAME n.v.)
***Pouteria reticulata* (Engl.) Eyma**
Prov.: N, M-S; tree; *Brandbyge & Azanza 32267* (AAU)
***Pouteria rostrata* (Huber) Baehni**
Prov.: N; tree; *Korning & Thomsen 47808* (AAU); *SEF 8588* (AAU, K, NY, QCA)
***Pouteria sclerocarpa* (Pittier) Cronquist**
Prov.: N; tree; *Oldeman & Arévalo 23* (MO, QCA)
***Pouteria torta* (C. Martius) Radlk.**
Prov.: N, P, M-S; tree; *Pennington & Tenorio 10784* (K, QCA); *Brandbyge et al. 36197* (AAU); *SEF 8910* (AAU). Also collected above 600 m alt.
***Pouteria trilocularis* Cronquist**
Prov.: N; tree; *SEF 10086* (AAU, K, NY, QCA)

Sapotaceae (cont.)

Sarcaulus brasiliensis (A. DC.) Eyma
 Prov.: N; tree; *SEF 10226* (AAU, K, NY, QCA); *Palacios 302* (QAME n.v.)
Sarcaulus oblatus Pennington
 Prov.: M-S; tree; *Pennington & Tenorio 10768* (K, NY, QCA). Expected below
 600 m alt.

Scrophulariaceae
N. N. Holmgren and U. Molau, Fl. Ecuador 21, 1984.

Lindernia crustacea (L.) F. Muell.
 Prov.: N, P, M-S; herb; *Holm-Nielsen & Jeppesen 938* (AAU)
Mecardonia procumbens (Mill.) Small
 Prov.: N; herb; *Fagerlind & Wibom 2269* (S); *Holm-Nielsen et al. 19828* (AAU)
Scoparia dulcis L.
 Prov.: N, P, M-S; herb; *Balslev 2811* (QCA); *Løjtnant & Molau 13594* (AAU);
 Irvine 549 (F, QCA). Reaches 1100 m alt.
Stemodia angulata Oerst.
 Prov.: N, P, M-S; herb; *Løjtnant & Molau 13424* (AAU, GB, QCA). Reaches 900
 m alt.
Stemodia verticillata (Mill.) Hassl.
 Prov.: N, P; herb; *Løjtnant & Molau 13411* (AAU, GB). Reaches 1100 m alt.
Torenia thouarsii (Cham. & Schlecht.) Kuntze
 Prov.: N, P, M-S; herb; *Løjtnant & Molau 13324* (AAU). Reaches 1100 m alt. in
 Pastaza: *Asplund 9052* (S)

Simaroubaceae
J. F. Macbride, Fl. Peru 3(2), Publ. Field Mus. Nat. Hist., Bot. Ser. 13:
689–703. 1949. This listing checked by W. Thomas, Jan 1989.

Picramnia latifolia Tul.
 Prov.: N, M-S; tree; *Gentry et al. 21813* (QCA); *Luteyn et al. 9018* (QCA)
 Syn. *P.macrostachys* Klotzsch ex Engl.
Picramnia magnifolia J. F. Macbr.
 Prov.: N, P, M-S; tree; *Brandbyge & Azanza 31835* (AAU). Reaches slightly
 higher altitudes.
Picramnia spruceana Engl.
 Prov.: N, P, M-S; tree; *Palacios 753* (QAME n.v.); *Davis & Yost 1012* (QCA);
 Vickers 233 (F). Syn. *Picramnia martiniana* J. F. Macbr.
Picrolemma sprucei Hook. f.
 Prov.: N; shrub; *Palacios & Neill 938* (QAME n.v.)
Simaba cedron Planch.
 Expected from eastern Ecuador.
Simaba guianensis Aublet
 Prov.: N; tree; *SEF 8710* (AAU); *Korning & Thomsen 47666* (AAU)
 Syn. *Quassia cuspidata* (Spruce ex Engl.) Nooteboom

Simaroubaceae   (cont.)

***Simaba orinocensis* H.B.K.**
    Prov.: N; tree; *Lawesson et al. 44237* (AAU, QCA), *43397* (NY)
    Syn. *S. multiflora* Juss.
***Simaba polyphylla* (Caval.) Thomas**
    Prov.: N; tree; *Korning & Thomsen 47809* (AAU)
***Simarouba amara* Aublet**
    Prov.: N; tree; *SEF 10234* (AAU, NY, QCA); *Pennington 10644* (QCA)

Smilacaceae

***Smilax* sp.**
    Prov.: N, P, M-S; liana; *Lawesson et al. 43410* (AAU); *Irvine 899* (QCA);
    Alarcón 87 (QCA)

Solanaceae
J. F. Macbride, Fl. Peru 5B(1), Publ. Field Mus. Nat. Hist., Bot. Ser. 13:
3–267. 1962. *Solanum* by Correll *in* J. F. Macbride, Fl. Peru 5B(2),
Publ. Field Mus. Nat. Hist., Bot. Ser. 13: 271–458. 1967. M. D. Whalen et
al., Gentes Herb. 12: 41–129. 1981. Identifications mostly by M. Nee, NY.

***Acnistus arborescens* (L.) Schlecht.**
    Prov.: P, M-S; shrub; *McElroy 192* (QCA).   Reaches 800 m alt. in M-S: *Holm-
    Nielsen et al. 20593* (AAU)
***Brugmansia arborea* (L.) Lagerheim**
    Prov.: N; shrub; *Alarcón 19* (QCA); *Balslev & Santos Dea 2887* (QCA)
***Brugmansia sanguinea* (Ruíz & Pavón) D. Don**
    Prov.: N; shrub; *Villegas & Meneses 18* (QCA)
***Brugmansia suaveolens* (Humb. & Bonpl. ex Willd.) Bercht. & Presl**
    Prov.: N, P; shrub; *Brandbyge & Azanza 32285* (AAU, QCA); *Pinkley 76* (S);
    Irvine 698 (F, QCA)
***Brugmansia × insignis* (Barb. Rodr.) Lockwood ex Davis**
    Prov.: N; shrub; *Lawesson et al. 39722* (AAU); *Vickers 19* (F); *Davis & Yost
    1054* (QCA)
***Brunfelsia chiricaspi* Plowman**
    Prov.: N; shrub; *Lawesson et al. 39491* (AAU); *Alarcón 19501* (QCA); *Pinkley
    420* (S); *Harling et al. 19785* (QCA)
***Brunfelsia grandiflora* D. Don**
    Prov.: N, P; shrub; *Brandbyge & Azanza 30844* (AAU); *Davis & Yost 1062*
    (QCA); *Vickers 190* (QCA); *Alarcón 12* (QCA); *Irvine 1079* (F, QCA)
***Capsicum annuum* L.**
    Prov.: N, P, M-S; shrub; *Alarcón 102* (QCA); *Vickers 227* (F); *Asdall 82–59*
    (QCA)
***Capsicum chinense* Jacq.**
    Prov.: N; shrub; *Lawesson et al. 39639* (AAU); *Balslev & Irvine 4598* (AAU);
    Vickers 115 (F); *Davis & Yost 993* (QCA); *Pinkley 259* (S)
***Capsicum frutescens* L.**
    Prov.: N; shrub; *Balslev & Irvine 4599* (AAU); *Vickers 208, 226* (QCA)

Solanaceae (cont.)

Cestrum megalophyllum Dunal
Prov.: N, P; shrub; *Holm-Nielsen et al. 21903* (AAU); *Lawesson et al. 39750* (AAU, QCA)

Cestrum racemosum Ruíz & Pavón
Prov.: N, P; tree; *Holm-Nielsen et al. 19149* (AAU, QCA); *Irvine 146* (F, QCA)

Cestrum reflexum Sendtner
Prov.: P; shrub; *Brandbyge & Azanza 31609* (AAU, QCA)

Cestrum silvaticum Francey
Prov.: N; *Zaruma et al. 198* (AAU); *Balslev 2308* (AAU); *Irvine 628* (F, QCA)

Cestrum strigillatum Ruiz & Pavón
Prov.: N, M-S; tree; *Zaruma et al. 198* (AAU). Reaches 850 m alt. in M-S: *Holm-Nielsen et al. 20547* (AAU)

Cuatresia sp.
Prov.: N; shrub; *Luteyn et al. 8678* (AAU)

Cyphomandra crassifolia (Ortega) Kuntze
Prov.: N; tree; *Knapp & Mallet 6184* (QCA). Syn. *C. betacea* (Cav.) Sendt.

Cyphomandra endopogon Bitter
Prov.: N, P, M-S; shrub; *Holm-Nielsen et al. 21721* (AAU); *Løjtnant & Molau 14548* (AAU)

Cyphomandra fragilis Bohs
Prov.: N; shrub; *Øllgaard et al. 39210* (AAU); *Palacios 2233* (QAME n.v.)

Cyphomandra hartwegii (Miers) Walp.
Prov.: N, P; shrub; *Brandbyge et al. 33465* (AAU); *Vickers 98, 196* (F); *Palacios et al.264* (AAU)

Cyphomandra pilosa Bohs
Prov.: N, P, M-S; shrub; *Gentry 12517* (MO); *Holm-Nielsen et al. 19625* (AAU); *Irvine 149* (QCA)

Cyphomandra stellata Bohs
Prov.: N; tree; *Holm-Nielsen et al. 19668* (AAU)

Juanulloa ferruginea Cuatrec.
Prov.: N; tree; *Lawesson et al. 44289* (AAU)

Juanulloa ochracea Cuatrec.
Prov.: N, P, M-S; shrub; *Lawesson et al. 43466* (AAU, QCA)

Larnax peruviana (Zahlbr.) Hunz.
Prov.: P, M-S; herb; *Øllgaard et al. 35468* (AAU)

Lycianthes acutifolia (Ruíz & Pavón) Bitter
Prov.: N; herb; *Jaramillo & Coello 3954* (AAU)

Lycianthes amatitlanensis (Coulter & Donn. Smith) Bitter
Prov.: N, P; shrub; *Øllgaard et al. 35225* (AAU)

Lycianthes cf. cyathocalyx (Van Heurck & Muell. Arg.) Bitter
Prov.: N, P; shrub; *Andrade 33162* (AAU, QCA)

Lycianthes medusocalyx Bitter
Prov.: N, P; shrub; *Jaramillo & Coello 2632* (QCA); *3287* (AAU)

Lycianthes pauciflora (Vahl) Bitter
Prov.: N, P, M-S; climber, shrub, treelet; *Brandbyge et al. 32804* (AAU, QCA); *Zaruma et al. 158* (AAU). Reaches 1600 m alt.

Lycianthes sprucei (Van Heurck & Muell. Arg.) Bitter
Prov.: N; tree; *Holm-Nielsen et al. 21650* (AAU)

Lycianthes sp.
Prov.: N; shrub; *Jaramillo & Coello 4407, 4490* (AAU, QCA)

Lycopersicum esculentum Mill.
Prov.: N, P, M-S; shrub; *Balslev 4877* (QCA); *Vickers 197* (F)

Solanaceae   (cont.)

Markea cf. **ulei (Damm.) Hunz.**
  Prov.: M-S; *Cerón 193* (QAME n.v.)
Nicotiana tabacum L.
  Prov.: N; shrub; *Alarcón 102a* (QCA); *Vickers 5* (F); *Irvine 1070* (F, QCA)
Physalis angulata L.
  Prov.: N; shrub; *Brandbyge et al. 30277* (AAU); *Davis & Yost 1995* (QCA);
  Pinkley 549 (ECON); *Vickers 101* (F); *Irvine 219* (F, QCA)
Physalis peruviana L.
  Prov.: N; shrub; *Villegas & Meneses 28* (QCA)
Physalis pubescens L.
  Prov.: N; shrub; *Pinkley 194, 548* (ECON); *Irvine 220* (F, QCA)
Solanum acuminatum Ruíz & Pavón
  Prov.: N; shrub; *Knapp & Mallet 6188* (QCA).   Reaches 1400 m alt.
Solanum anceps Ruiz & Pavón
  Prov.: P, M-S; herb or shrub; *Brandbyge & Azanza 31783* (AAU, QCA)
Solanum anisophyllum Van Heurck & Muell. Arg.
  Prov.: N, P, M-S; shrub; *Luteyn et al. 8657* (AAU); *Knapp & Mallet 6292*
  (QCA).   Reaches 950 m alt.
Solanum appressum Roe
  Prov.: N; shrub; *Andrade 33062* (AAU); *Irvine 224* (F, QCA)
Solanum asperolanatum Ruiz & Pavón
  Prov.: N; treelet; *Holm-Nielsen et al. 26736* (AAU)
Solanum aturense Dunal
  Prov.: N, P; shrub; *Brandbyge & Azanza 33229* (AAU, QCA)
Solanum barbeyanum Huber
  Prov.: N, P; shrub or climber; *Brandbyge & Azanza 31788* (AAU, QCA)
Solanum candidum Lindl.
  Prov.: N; shrub; *Vickers 13* (F); *Pinkley 448* (ECON)
  Syn. *S. tequilense* A. Gray
Solanum diffusum Ruíz & Pavón
  Prov.: N; vine; *Vickers 143* (QCA); *Balslev & Alarcón 2950* (QCA)
Solanum grandiflorum Ruiz & Pavón
  Prov.: N; tree; *Brandbyge et al. 30457* (AAU); *Øllgaard et al. 57053* (AAU, QCA)
Solanum cf. **hypermegethes Werdelin**
  Prov.: N; tree; *Øllgaard et al. 57102* (AAU); *Vickers 110* (F).   Distributed as *S.*
  cf. *kioniotrichum* Bitter ex J. F. Macbr.
Solanum cf. **hypocalycosarcum Bitter**
  Prov.: N; shrub; *Brandbyge & Azanza 32890* (AAU)
Solanum lepidotum Dunal
  Prov.: N; shrub; *Brandbyge & al. 33319* (AAU, QCA); *Vickers 232* (QCA);
  Irvine 601 (F, QCA).   Syn. *S. argenteum* Dunal ex Poir.
Solanum leptopodum Van Heurck & Muell. Arg.
  Prov.: N; shrub; *Holm-Nielsen et al. 33319* (AAU, QCA); *Vickers 232* (F);
  Irvine 1114 (F, QCA); *Balslev 2386* (AAU)
Solanum leucopogon Huber
  Prov.: N, P; shrub; *Brandbyge & Azanza 31773* (AAU, QCA)
Solanum miquelii Morton
  Prov.: N; shrub; *Balslev & E. Madsen 10579* (QCA)

Solanaceae (cont.)

***Solanum mite* Ruiz & Pavón**
Prov.: N, P; shrub; *Jaramillo et al. 31719* (AAU); *MacBryde & Dwyer 1367* (QCA)

***Solanum monadelphum* Van Heurck & Muell. Arg.**
Prov.: N; shrub; *Balslev & Alarcón 2943* (QCA)

***Solanum nemorense* Dunal**
Prov.: P; shrub; *Jaramillo et al. 31550* (AAU)

***Solanum oppositifolium* Rúiz & Pavón**
Prov.: N; shrub; *Jaramillo & Coello 4282* (AAU)

***Solanum pectinatum* Dunal**
Prov.: N, M-S; shrub; *Brandbyge & Azanza 32239* (AAU, QCA); *Davis & Yost 930* (QCA); *Pinkley 35* (ECON); *Irvine 1060* (F, QCA)

***Solanum pensile* Sendtner**
Prov.: N, P; shrub; *Holm-Nielsen & Jeppesen 821* (AAU); *Palacios et al. 26* (AAU, QCA)

***Solanum rugosum* Dunal**
Prov.: N, P; tree; *Holm-Nielsen et al. 22190* (AAU)

***Solanum schlechtendalianum* Walp.**
Prov.: N; *Holm-Nielsen et al. 19641* (AAU); *Miller 2245* (QAME n.v.)

***Solanum sessile* Rúiz & Pavón**
Prov.: N; shrub, tree; *Holm-Nielsen 19147* (AAU, QCA); *Irvine 957* (F, QCA)

***Solanum sessiliflorum* Dunal**
Prov.: N; shrub; *Holm-Nielsen et al. 21553* (AAU); *Davis & Yost 918* (QCA); *Vickers 411* (F); *Balslev & Irvine 4620* (AAU, QCA); *Pinkley 334* (ECON)

***Solanum stramonifolium* Jacq.**
Prov.: N; shrub; *Brandbyge & Azanza 32825* (AAU); *Alarcón 129* (QCA); *Balslev 4893* (QCA); *Vickers 14* (F); *Pinkley 35* (ECON); *Irvine 777* (F, QCA)

***Solanum supranitidum* Bitter**
Prov.: M-S; shrub; *Holm-Nielsen et al. 26078* (AAU); *Irvine 473* (F, QCA)

***Solanum ternatum* Ruíz & Pavón**
Prov.: P; treelet; *Zaruma et al. 21A* (AAU)

***Solanum thelopodium* Sendter**
Prov.: N, P; shrub; *Holm-Nielsen et al. 19867* (AAU, QCA); *Foster 3843* (QCA)

***Solanum* cf. *xanthophaem* Bitter**
Prov.: N, M-S; shrub; *Foster 3842* (QCA); *Brandbyge & Azanza 32330* (AAU, QCA); *Lawesson et al. 39507* (AAU, QCA)

***Trianaea* cf. *speciosa* (Drake del Cast.) Soler.**
Prov.: P; tree; *Jaramillo et al. 31745* (AAU, QCA)

***Witheringia solanacea* L' Hér.**
Prov.: N, P; shrub; *Holm-Nielsen et al. 20273* (AAU, QCA); *Irvine 362* (QCA)
Reaches 1100 m alt.

Staphyleaceae
J. F. Macbride, Fl. Peru 3A(1), Publ. Field. Mus. Nat. Hist., Bot. Ser. 13: 233–235. 1951.

***Huertea glandulosa* Ruíz & Pavón**
Prov.: N; tree; *SEF 10360* (AAU); *Bravo 294* (QCA); *Neill 7427* (QAME n.v.)

***Turpinia occidentalis* (Sw.) G. Don**
Prov.: N; tree; *Irvine 353* (F, QCA)

Sterculiaceae
J. F. Macbride, Fl. Peru 3A(2), Publ. Field Mus. Nat. Hist., Bot. Ser. 13: 622–667. 1956. All *Sterculia* identifications by E. L. Taylor, GH, 1989.

***Byttneria aculeata* (Jacq.) Jacq.**
   Prov.: P; liana; *Jaramillo & Coello 3232* (AAU)
***Byttneria ancistrodonta* Mildbr.**
   Prov.: N; liana; *Holm-Nielsen et al. 21227* (AAU); *Lawesson et al. 43404* (AAU)
***Byttneria aurantiaca* Mildbr.**
   Prov.: P; climbing shrub; *Øllgaard et al. 34999* (AAU)
***Guazuma crinita* C. Martius**
   Prov.: N; tree; *Jaramillo & Coello 4145* (AAU, S); *Irvine 404* (F, QCA)
***Guazuma ulmifolia* Lam.**
   Prov.: N; tree; *Palacios 2017* (QAME n.v.)
***Herrania balaensis* Preuss**
   Prov.: N; tree; *Vickers 94* (F); *Pinkley 574* (ECON)
***Herrania cuatrecasana* García-Barriga**
   Prov.: N; tree; *Korning & Thomsen 47130* (AAU); *Pinkley 535* (S)
***Herrania dugandii* García-Barriga**
   Prov.: N; tree; *Pinkley 242* (S)
***Herrania nitida* (Poeppig & Endl.) Schultes**
   Prov.: N, P; tree; *Davis & Yost 1030* (QCA); *Balslev & Irvine 4615* (AAU, QCA)
***Melochia lupulina* Sw.**
   Prov.: N, M-S; shrub; *Holm-Nielsen et al. 19834* (AAU, S).   Reaches 850 m alt.
***Sterculia apeibophylla* Ducke**
   Prov.: N; tree; *Balslev 60522* (AAU); *Irvine 1633* (F n.v.); *Oldeman & Arevalo 45* (QCA); *Palacios et al. 508* (GH n.v.); *SEF 8950* (AAU, GH)
***Sterculia apetala* (Jacq.) Karsten**
   Prov.: N, M-S; tree; *Palacios et al. 794* (GH n.v.); *Palacios & Neill 935* (GH n.v.); *SEF 10213* (AAU, GH); *Little et al. 592* (COL n.v.)
***Sterculia colombiana* Sprague**
   Prov.: N; tree; *Oldeman et al. 39* (QCA); *SEF 9262* (AAU, NY)
***Sterculia corrugata* Little**
   Prov.: N; tree; *Neill et al. 7350* (GH n.v.)
***Sterculia guapayensis* Cuatrec.**
   Prov.: N; tree; *SEF 10112, 10300* (AAU, GH, NY, QCA)
***Sterculia tessmannii* Mildbr.**
   Prov.: N, P; tree; *Cerón 366* (GH n.v.); *Miller et al. 2424* (GH n.v.); *Palacios et al. 882* (GH n.v.); *SEF 8545, 8560, 8562, 8837* (AAU)
***Sterculia* sp.**
   Prov.: N; tree; *Cerón 2477* (GH); *Neill et al. 6897* (GH n.v.); *Neill et al. 7331* (GH n.v.); *Palacios et al. 826* (GH n.v.)
***Theobroma bicolor* Humb. & Bonpl.**
   Prov.: N; tree; *Fagerlind & Wibom 2371* (S); *Irvine 436* (QCA); *Balslev 4898* (QCA); *Pinkley 94* (ECON); *Neill 6939* (QAME n.v.).   Reaches 700 m alt. in Napo: *Asplund 10271* (S)
***Theobroma cacao* L.**
   Prov.: N; tree; *Lawesson et al. 39362* (AAU, QCA); *Irvine 418* (QCA)
***Theobroma speciosum* Willd. ex Sprengel**
   Prov.: N, P; tree; *Korning & Thomsen 58691* (AAU); *Neill 7149* (AAU, QCA); *Oldeman & Arévalo 91* (QCA); *Davis & Yost 927* (QCA); *Irvine 1066* (F, QCA)

Sterculiaceae (cont.)

Theobroma subincanum C. Martius
Prov.: N, P; tree; *Øllgaard et al.* 39000 (AAU); *Foster 3758* (AAU, QCA); *Irvine 568* (QCA); *Neill 7172* (QCA)

Styracaceae
J. F. Macbride, Fl. Peru 5(1), Publ. Field Mus. Nat. Hist., Bot. Ser. 13: 225–235. 1959.

Styrax schultzei Perkins aff.
Prov.: P; tree; *Jaramillo et al. 31312* (AAU)
Styrax tessmannii Perkins
Prov.: N; tree; *Lawesson et al. 44293* (AAU, QCA); *SEF 9121* (AAU, QCA)

Symplocaceae
J. F. Macbride, Fl. Peru 5(1), Publ. Field Mus. Nat. Hist., Bot. Ser. 13: 214–225. 1959.

Symplocos matthewsii A. DC.
Prov.: N; tree; *Neill et al. 6360* (QCA)

Theaceae
J. F. Macbride, Fl. Peru 3A(2), Publ. Field Mus. Nat. Hist., Bot. Ser. 13: 726–741. 1956.

Laplacea fruticosa (Schrader) Kobuski
Prov.: N; tree; *SEF 9215* (AAU, QCA)

Theophrastaceae
B. Ståhl, Fl. Ecuador 39, 1990.

Clavija harlingii Ståhl
Prov.: N, P, M-S; shrub; *Harling & Andersson 11905* (GB); *Brandbyge & Azanza 31279* (AAU); *Balslev 2345* (QCA); *Madison et al. 5311* (QCA, SEL)
Clavija ornata D. Don
Prov.: N; shrub; *Bravo & Gomes 9* (QCA); *Andrade 33021* (AAU); *Holm-Nielsen et al. 21410* (AAU). Syn. *C. longifolia* (Jacq.) Mez
Clavija procera Ståhl
Prov.: N; shrub; *Øllgaard et al. 38996* (AAU)
Clavija venosa Ståhl
Prov.: N, P, M-S; shrub; *Jaramillo et al. 31713* (AAU); *Brandbyge & Azanza 31837* (AAU)
Clavija weberbaueri Mez
Prov.:N, P; shrub, tree; *Lawesson et al. 39558* (AAU, QCA); *Balslev & Santos Dea 2882* (QCA); *Neill & Palacios 6684* (QCA). Syn. *C. hookeri* A. DC.

Thymelaeaceae

J. F. Macbride, Fl. Peru 4(1), Publ. Field Mus. Nat. Hist., Bot. Ser. 13: 203–206. 1941. One of the mentioned species probably is *S. daphnoides* Mart. & Zucc., the other *S. peruvianus* Standley.

Schoenobiblus sp. 1
Prov.: N, P; shrub; *Brandbyge et al. 32613* (AAU); *Holm-Nielsen et al. 22270, 22573* (AAU)

Schoenobiblus sp. 2
Prov.: N, P; shrub; *Brandbyge & Azanza 31786* (AAU); *Pinkley 565* (S)

Tiliaceae

J. F. Macbride, Fl. Peru 3A(2), Publ. Field Mus. Nat. Hist., Bot. Ser. 13: 413–442. 1956.

Apeiba membranacea Spruce ex Benth.
Prov.: N, P, M-S; tree; *Holm-Nielsen et al. 21424* (AAU); *Pennington 10764* (QCA); *Neill et al. 6320* (QCA); *Irvine 454* (F, QCA). Reaches 700 m alt.

Apeiba tibourbou Aublet
Prov.: N; tree; *Brandbyge et al. 30297* (AAU); *Jaramillo & Coello 3342* (QCA); *Irvine 580* (F, QCA)

Heliocarpus americanus (L.) H.B.K.
spp. popayanensis (H.B.K.) Meijer
Prov.: N, P; tree; *Øllgaard et al. 34623* (AAU); *Neill et al. 6868* (QCA); *Alarcón 19372* (QCA); *Asplund 9202* (S); *Irvine 524* (F, QCA). Reaches 1700 m alt.

Mollia lepidota Spruce ex Benth.
Prov.: N; tree; *Korning & Thomsen 47787* (AAU); *Neill et al. 6887* (AAU, QCA)

Trichospermum mexicanum (DC.) Baillon aff.
Prov.: N, P; tree; *Brandbyge et al. 33645* (AAU, QCA)

Triumfetta sp.
Prov.: N; shrub; *Navarrete 33* (QCA)

Ulmaceae

J. F. Macbride, Fl. Peru 2(2), Publ. Field Mus. Nat. Hist., Bot. Ser. 13: 268–274. 1937.

Ampelocera longissima Todzia
Prov.: N; tree; *SEF 8616* (AAU, QCA); *Pennington 10596* (QCA); *Palacios 519* (QAME n.v.)

Celtis iguana (Jacq.) Sargent
Prov.: N; tree; *Brandbyge & Azanza 30002* (AAU, QCA)

Celtis schippii Standley
Prov.: N; tree; *Brandbyge et al. 33254* (AAU); *Pennington 10642* (QCA); *Irvine 874* (F, QCA). Syn. *Sparrea schippii* (Standley) Hunziker & Dottori

Trema integerrima (Beurl.) Standley
Prov.: N, M-S; shrub; *Zaruma 103* (QAME n.v.); *Little et al. 334* (US)

Trema micrantha (L.) Blume
Prov.: N, P, M-S; tree; *Holm-Nielsen et al. 21614* (AAU); *Irvine 156* (QCA); *Vickers 117* (F)

Urticaceae

E. P. Killip *in* J. F. Macbride, Fl. Peru 2(2), Publ. Field Mus. Nat. Hist., Bot. Ser. 13: 331–367. 1937.

Boehmeria caudata Sw.
Prov.: N; tree; *Cerón 2532* (QAME n.v.)
Boehmeria pavonii Wedd.
Prov.: N; shrub; *Cerón 2665* (QAME n.v.)
Myriocarpa stipitata Benth.
Prov.: N; tree; *Zarucchi 8–78* (MO n.v.)
Pilea galowayana Killip
Prov.: N; shrub; *Cerón 3262* (QAME n.v.)
Pilea hitchcockii Killip
Prov.: N; shrub; *Palacios 1579* (QAME n.v.)
Pilea hydrocotyliflora Killip aff.
Prov.: N; herb; *Vickers 87, 169* (F)
Pilea imparifolia Wedd.
Prov.: N, P, M-S; epiphytic herb; *Fagerlind & Wibom 2226* (S); *Løjtnant & Molau 13431* (QCA); *Foster 3810* (QCA); *Asdall 82–36* (QCA)
Pilea pubescens Liebm.
Prov.: N; herb; *Oldeman & Arévalo 112* (QCA)
Pilea schimpfii Diels vel sp. aff.
Prov.: N; shrub; *Cerón 2852* (QAME n.v.)
Pouzolzia sp.
Prov.: P; shrub; *Løjtnant & Molau 13246* (QCA)
Urera baccifera (L.) Gaudich.
Prov.: N; tree; *Balslev 2798* (QCA); *Davis & Yost 956* (QCA); *Korning & Thomsen 58658* (AAU)
Urera caracasana (Jacq.) Griseb.
Prov.: N, P, M-S; t; *Holm-Nielsen & Jeppesen 955* (AAU, QCA); *Irvine 523* (QCA); *Vickers 162* (F); *Little et al. 478* (US). Reaches 2000 m alt.
Urera eggersii Hieron.
Prov.: N; shrub; *Cerón 1082* (QAME n.v.)
Urera laciniata (Goudot) Wedd.
Prov.: N; shrub; *Alarcón 19373* (QCA); *Balslev & Santos Dea 2812* (QCA); *Pinkley 171* (S); *Vickers 165* (QCA)

Verbenaceae

J. F. Macbride, Fl. Peru 5(2), Publ. Field Mus. Nat. Hist., Bot. Ser. 13: 609–71. 1960.

Aegiphila boliviana Moldenke
Prov.: N; tree; *Palacios 909* (QAME n.v.)
Aegiphila haughtii Moldenke aff.
Prov.: N; tree; *Neill et al. 6857* (QCA); *SEF 10127* (AAU, QCA)
Aegiphila integrifolia (Jacq.) B. D. Jacks.
Prov.: N, P; tree; *Asplund 8868* (S); *Løjtnant & Molau 13356* (AAU); *Zaruma 279* (QAME n.v.)
Aegiphila sp.
Prov.: N, P; shrub *Jaramillo & Coello 3434* (AAU). Possibly = *A. panamensis* Moldenke

Verbenaceae   (cont.)

***Citharexylum macrophyllum* Poir.**
Prov.: N; tree; *Gentry 9810* (GB)

***Citharexylum poeppigii* Walp.**
Prov.: N, P; herb; *Løjtnant & Molau 13592* (AAU); *Neill & Palacios 7126* (QCA)

***Citharexylum subflavescens* Blake**
Prov.: N; tree; *Arévalo & Lara 5* (QCA)

***Clerodendron tessmannii* Moldenke**
Prov.: M-S; tree; *Cerón 92* (QAME n.v.)

***Cornutia odorata* (Poeppig & Endl.) Poeppig ex Schauer**
Prov.: N; tree; *Harling & Asplund 11708* (GB)

***Gmelina arborea* Roxb.**
Prov.: N; tree; *Palacios et al. 816* (AAU)

***Lantana armata* Schauer**
Prov.: N, M-S; shrub; *Andrade 33003* (AAU, QCA), *Asdall 82–20* (QCA); *Balslev & Alarcón 3073* (QCA)

***Lantana camara* L.**
Prov.: N, P, M-S; herb; *Lawesson et al. 39764* (AAU, QCA)

***Lantana pastazensis* Moldenke**
Prov.: P; herb; *Løjtnant & Molau 13421* (AAU)

***Lippia alba* (Mill.) N. E. Brown**
Prov.: N; tree; *Irvine 675* (F, QCA)

***Petrea maynensis* Huber**
Prov.: P; tree; *Holm-Nielsen et al. 22457* (AAU)

***Stachytarpheta cayennensis* (L. C. Rich.) Vahl**
Prov.: N, P; shrub; *Irvine 771* (QCA); *Jaramillo & Coello 4505* (AAU), *4506* (QCA). Reaches 1000 m alt. in Pastaza: *Asplund 19089* (S)

***Tectona grandis* L.f.**
Prov.: N; tree; *Jaramillo & Rivera 126* (AAU, QCA)

***Verbena litoralis* H.B.K.**
Prov.: N; tree; *Brandbyge & Azanza 32866* (AAU); *Marles 98* (QAME n.v.)

***Vitex cymosa* Bert. ex Sprengel**
Prov.: N; tree; *Palacios 978* (QAME n.v.)

***Vitex* cf. *gigantea* H.B.K.**
Prov.: N; tree; *Korning & Thomsen 47784* (AAU)

***Vitex orinocensis* H.B.K.**
Prov.: N; treelet; *Brandbyge & Azanza 30573* (AAU)

***Vitex schunkei* Moldenke**
Prov.: N; tree; *SEF 8877* (AAU, QCA)

Violaceae
W. H. A. Hekking, Fl. Neotropica 46, 1988.

***Corynostylis arborea* (L.) S. F. Blake**
Prov.: N; shrub; *Lawesson et al. 44234* (AAU); *Foster 3589* (QCA, S)

***Gloeospermum equatoriense* Hekking**
Prov.: N; treelet; *Brandbyge & Azanza 32808* (AAU, QCA)

***Gloeospermum longifolium* Hekking**
Prov.: N; treelet; *Dwyer & MacBryde 9788* (MO)

***Gloeospermum* cf. *sclerophyllum* Cuatrec.**
Prov.: N; treelet; *Zaruma 407* (QAME n.v.)

Violaceae   (cont.)

***Gloeospermum* cf. *sphaerocarpum* Triana & Planchon**
Prov.: N; tree, shrub; *MacBryde & Dwyer 1432* (QCA)
***Leonia crassa* Sm. & Fernández**
Prov.: P; tree; *Balslev 2336* (QCA); *Balslev & Madsen 10647* (AAU)
***Leonia cymosa* C. Martius**
Prov.: N, P, M-S; tree; *Holm-Nielsen et al. 20116* (AAU); *Foster 3651* (S)
***Leonia glycycarpa* Ruíz & Pavón**
Prov.: N, P, M-S; tree; *Holm-Nielsen et al. 19896* (AAU, QCA); *Irvine 349* (F, QCA)
***Orthion* sp.**
Prov.: N; tree; *SEF 8618* (AAU, QCA)
***Rinorea apiculata* Hekking**
Prov.: N; treelet; *Jaramillo & Coello 2598* (AAU, QCA); *Neill et al. 6849* (QCA)
***Rinorea lindeniana* (Tul.) Kuntze**
Prov.: N, P, M-S; tree; *Øllgaard et al. 38901* (AAU); *Neill & Palacios 6749* (QCA); *Little et al. 786* (US), *Foster 3710* (AAU)
***Rinorea macrocarpa* (C. Martius ex Eichler) O. Kuntze**
Prov.: P; shrub; *McElroy 300* (QCA)
***Rinorea multivenosa* Hekking**
Prov.: N; tree; *Jaramillo & Coello 4289* (QCA)
***Rinorea pubiflora* (Benth.) Sprague & Sandw.**
Prov.: N; tree; *SEF 10410* (AAU, QCA)
***Rinorea viridifolia* Rusby**
Prov.: N; shrub, tree; *Jaramillo & Coello 4479* (AAU, QCA); *Foster 3683* (AAU, F, QCA); *Vickers 217* (F); *Neill & Palacios 6573* (QCA)

Viscaceae
J. Kuijt, Fl. Ecuador 24, 1986.

***Dendrophthora obliqua* (Presl) Wiens**
Prov.: N, P; epiphytic herb; *Holm-Nielsen et al. 26535* (AAU); *Davis 498* (S)
Reaches 1000 m alt. in Pastaza: *Harling 3444* (GB, S)
***Phoradendron acinacifolium* C. Martius ex Eichler**
Prov.: N; epiphytic herb; *Lawesson et al. 44242* (AAU, QCA)
***Phoradendron crassifolium* (DC.) Eichler**
Prov.: N, P; epiphytic herb; *Jaramillo & Coello 4441* (AAU, QCA); *Alarcón 80* (QCA).   Reaches 1000 m alt.
***Phoradendron laxiflorum* Ule**
Prov.: P; epiphytic herb; *Holm-Nielsen et al. 22172* (AAU).   Reaches 1050 m alt. in P: *Harling 3820* (S)
***Phoradendron piperoides* (H.B.K.) Trel.**
Prov.: N, P, M-S; epiphytic herb; *Holm-Nielsen & Jeppesen 817* (AAU, S); *Løjtnant & Molau 13525* (AAU); *Neill et al. 6225* (QCA)
***Phoradendron robustissimum* Eichler**
Prov.: N; epiphytic herb; *Holm-Nielsen et al. 20044* (AAU)

Vitaceae

J. F. Macbride, Fl. Peru 3A(2), Publ. Field. Mus. Nat. Hist., Bot. Ser. 13: 408–413. 1956.

Cissus erosa L. C. Rich.
Prov.: N, P; vine; *Balslev & E. Madsen 10581* (AAU, QCA)

Cissus pseudosicyoides Croat
Prov.: N; vine; *Gentry 12549* (S)

Cissus rhombifolia Vahl
Prov.: N; vine; *Balslev & E. Madsen 10590* (AAU, QCA, S)

Cissus sicyoides L.
Prov.: N, P, M-S; vine; *Holm-Nielsen & Jeppesen 724* (AAU)

Cissus ulmifolia (Baker) Planchon vel sp. aff.
Prov.: N, P; vine; *Gentry 12490* (QCA); *Neill 6734* (QAME n.v.)

Vochysiaceae

J. F. Macbride, Fl. Peru 3(3), Publ. Field Mus. Nat. Hist., Bot. Ser. 13: 872–891. 1950.

Erisma uncinatum Warm.
Prov.: N; tree; *SEF 9001* (AAU, QCA)

Qualea sp.
Prov.: P; tree; *Brandbyge & Azanza 31483* (AAU).　　Possibly *Q. paraensis* Ducke

Qualea sp.
Prov.: N; tree; *Korning & Thomsen 47823* (AAU)

Vochysia biloba Ducke
Prov.: N; tree; *Palacios 1762* (QAME n.v.)

Vochysia bracelinii Standley
Prov.: N; tree; *Neill 7109* (AAU)

Vochysia gardneri Warm.
Prov.: M-S; tree; *Little et al. 760* (US)

Vochysia grandis C. Martius
Prov.: N; tree; *Korning & Thomsen 58623, 47441* (AAU)

Vochysia guianensis Aublet
Prov.: M-S; tree; *Little et al. 699* (US)

Zingiberaceae (excl. Costaceae)

P. J. M. Maas, Fl. Ecuador 6, 1976; this listing checked by P. Maas, Jan 1989.

Curcuma longa L.
Prov.: N; herb; *Brandbyge & Azanza 32810* (AAU); *Vickers 103, 173* (QCA)

Hedychium coronarium Koenig
Prov.: N; herb; *Holm-Nielsen et al. 19134* (AAU)

Renealmia alpinia (Rottb.) Maas
Prov.: N, P, M-S; herb; *Holm-Nielsen et al. 21026* (AAU); *MacBryde & Dwyer 1459* (QCA); *Pinkley 8* (ECON).　Reaches 900 m alt. in M-S: *Harling & Andersson 12888* (GB)

Zingiberaceae   (cont.)

Renealmia asplundii Maas
Prov.: N, M-S; herb; *Holm-Nielsen et al. 21474* (AAU); *Davis & Yost 933* (QCA); *Pinkley 83* (ECON); *Cazalet & Pennington 7800* (US)

Renealmia breviscapa Poeppig & Endl.
Prov.: N, P, M-S; herb; *Holm-Nielsen et al. 21490* (AAU); *Alarcón 19389* (QCA); *Asdall 82–38* (QCA); *Pinkley s.n.* (ECON); *Irvine 859* (F, QCA)

Renealmia cernua (Sw. ex Roem. & Schultes) J. F. Macbr.
Prov.: N, M-S; herb; *Holm-Nielsen et al. 20453* (AAU); *Jaramillo 100* (QCA); *Camp E-896* (US).   Reaches slightly higher altitudes.

Renealmia monosperma Miq.
Prov.: N, M-S; herb; *Holm-Nielsen et al. 21301* (AAU); *Foster 3694* (QCA)

Renealmia nicolaioides Loes.
Prov.: N, P; herb; *Løjtnant & Molau 1335* (AAU); *MacBryde & Dwyer 1460* (QCA); *Vickers 209* (F).   Reaches 1600 m alt.

Renealmia puberula Steyerm.
Prov.: N; herb; *Holm-Nielsen et al. 26439* (AAU)

Renealmia thyrsoidea (Ruíz & Pavón) Poeppig & Endl.
spp. *thyrsoidea*
Prov.: N, P, M-S; herb; *Brandbyge et al. 32690* (AAU); *Davis & Yost 934* (QCA); *Alarcón 60* (QCA); *Vickers 44* (FLAS); *Balslev 2803* (QCA), *4849* (AAU)
Reaches 1500 m alt. in M-S: *Harling & Andersson 12792* (GB)

Zingiber officinale Roscoe
Prov.: N, P, M-S; herb; *Brandbyge & Azanza 32829* (AAU); *Balslev & Irvine 4613* (QCA); *Asdall 82–07* (QCA); *Alarcón 18* (QCA); *Vickers 28* (QCA); *Pinkley 201* (ECON)

9. INDEX TO SCIENTIFIC NAMES

In this index we list all latin names of families, genera, and species included in the previous chapter of this book with reference to the page(s) where they are mentioned. Names marked with an * are those mentioned as synonyms or in the notes, for instance as uncertain or misused names.